# LABORATORY
# FRACTIONAL
# DISTILLATION

THE MACMILLAN COMPANY
NEW YORK · BOSTON · CHICAGO
DALLAS · ATLANTA · SAN FRANCISCO

MACMILLAN AND CO., LIMITED
LONDON · BOMBAY · CALCUTTA
MADRAS · MELBOURNE

THE MACMILLAN COMPANY
OF CANADA, LIMITED
TORONTO

*Thomas P. Carney*

# LABORATORY

# FRACTIONAL

# DISTILLATION

THE MACMILLAN COMPANY
*NEW YORK: 1949*

27883

COPYRIGHT, 1949, BY THE MACMILLAN COMPANY

*All rights reserved—no part of this book may be reproduced in any form without permission in writing from the publisher, except by a reviewer who wishes to quote brief passages in connection with a review written for inclusion in magazine or newspaper.*

PRINTED IN THE UNITED STATES OF AMERICA

MAR 21 1952 AT 5.28

# *Preface*

The fundamental purpose of this book is to bring to the research worker and student a practical working knowledge of the art of fractional distillation.

In the past two decades progress in distillation has been so rapid and so extensive that the research worker has not been able to keep himself as well informed as he might wish to be. The voluminous, uncorrelated publications on distillation have served also to obscure fundamental principles in many cases. No book has been published which describes the modern laboratory distillation apparatus and its operation in detail.

Fractional distillation, when properly utilized, can be an invaluable tool to any research man concerning himself with the investigation of either liquids, solids, or gases. Materials boiling at $-100$ C and at 350 C can be distilled with almost the same ease as can water. Laboratory fractional distillation, as discussed in this book, will be considered as being applied to

1. Preparation of pure compounds
2. Analyses of complex mixtures
3. Preliminary studies on distillation theories and processes

However, this tool is not the universal solution to purification problems. This book also attempts to point out the limitations of various methods of distillation.

The author has tried to discuss the equipment mentioned from a practical point of view, that is, considering ease of construction and operation, first cost and upkeep, and generality of use. Data are given for various columns so that the reader may judge for himself what equipment will best fit his needs. Discussion of all accessory equipment necessary for testing and operating columns at any given temperature and pressure is also included.

In addition, descriptions of the techniques and equipment used in extractive, azeotropic, and molecular distillations are included. The use of these special types of distillation is becoming more commonplace in the laboratory. With these techniques it is possible to separate materials which cannot be separated by ordinary fractional distillation.

With the hope, then, that a better understanding of the uses, potentialities, and limitations of fractional distillation will result for the student and for the research man, both in the laboratory and in the plant, this book is written.

# ACKNOWLEDGMENT

*I wish to acknowledge the help and suggestions of Dr. F. D. Rossini of the U. S. Bureau of Standards, Dr. Homer J. Hall of the Standard Oil Development Company, and Dr. Donald F. Othmer of the Polytechnic Institute of Brooklyn, who read the manuscript for this work during various stages of its preparation.*

*I am particularly grateful to Mr. James B. Davis of the University of Wisconsin for the construction of many pieces of the glass equipment described in this book, and for his suggestions concerning some of the working drawings.*

THOMAS P. CARNEY

*Head, Organic Chemical*
*Research Department*
*Eli Lilly and Company*
*Indianapolis, Ind.*

# Contents

# I

# *Theory*

SMALL DISTILLATION is the separation of the components of a mixture by partial vaporization of the mixture, and separate recovery of the vapor and residue. Fractional distillation consists of a continuous series of vaporizations and condensations in the same still or column, the final enriched vapor being removed at the top of the column. Dephlegmation is the corresponding term applied to partial condensation, when the vaporized material is cooled to such a point that only the higher boiling materials are condensed, leaving the vapor, further enriched in the lower boiling component, to be recovered separately.

Theoretically, any two liquids which have different vapor pressures at a given temperature, or different boiling points at a given pressure, can be separated by fractional distillation. By a consideration of the vapor pressure or boiling points, the vapor composition, and the liquid composition, possible methods of separating the components can be predicted.

In any system, an equilibrium exists between a liquid or mixture of liquids and the vapor above it. When distillation takes place, this vapor is removed from the system and condensed as distillate. Therefore, the more this vapor can be enriched with respect to one component, the greater will be the efficiency of the fractionation obtained.

The composition of the vapor above a mixture of mutually soluble liquids depends to a large extent on the relative amounts of the components making up the mixture. If we assume a mixture of two such liquids, we find that the vapor pressure of each is reduced by the presence of the other, and therefore the total vapor pressure of the mixture is less than the sum of the vapor pressures of the two pure components. For ideal systems, that is, systems in which there is no molecular association or other complicating factors, the composition of the vapor can be predicted by Raoult's law, which states that the partial pressure of one component of a solution is equal to the product of the vapor pressure of that component in the pure state and its mole fraction in the solution.

Let us use for the purpose of illustration a solution of toluene and benzene. Any pair of liquids differing in vapor pressure may be selected and analyzed like benzene-toluene.

The boiling points of mixtures of benzene and toluene in all proportions have been determined at a pressure of 750 mm, as well as the vapor composition in equilibrium with the specified mixture at the boiling point. Now, if the boiling points are plotted against liquid composition and vapor composition, Figure 1 is obtained,

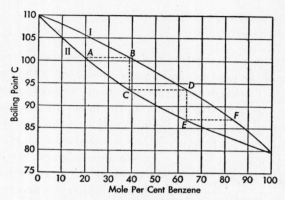

**Figure 1.** Benzene-Toluene Equilibrium Diagram

where I is the vapor composition curve and II is the boiling point curve. A horizontal line drawn from a point on the boiling point line to the vapor composition line will give the composition of the vapor existing above a specified mixture of benzene-toluene at its boiling point. It at once becomes apparent that the vapor above a given mixture contains a higher percentage of one component and less of the second component than did the mixture from which it came. For example, if a mixture of 20 mole per cent benzene and 80 per cent toluene is heated, it will start to boil at 101 C, or at point $A$. The first vapor, therefore, will consist not of the original 80-20 per cent mixture, but of a 61-39 per cent mixture determined on curve I, or at point $B$. Now, if vapor of this composition is removed from the system and condensed, a certain degree of fractionation has been obtained. When this vapor $B$ is condensed, it will have the composition of liquid $C$. If, now, the liquid $C$ is heated as before, it will boil at temperature $C$, giving vapor of composition $D$, which in turn may be condensed and heated at $E$, producing enrichment to $F$. This boiling, separation, condensation, and reboiling with enrichment from each operation may be continued until pure benzene is obtained.

The relative weights of vapor and solution may be determined as follows from Figure 2. Suppose a solution of original composition $C$ be fractionated until the residue consists of material of composition $A$ and the vapor consists of composition $B$. If the weight of the original material is $W$, then

$$W = A + B \tag{1}$$

If the weight of the residue is $a$ and that of the vapor is $b$, then

$$WC = Aa + Bb \tag{2}$$

$$\frac{A}{B} = \frac{b - C}{C - a} \tag{3}$$

By reference to the figure, it is seen that the ratio of the weight of the residue to that of the vapor is $XB/XA$. Therefore the proportion of the total is given by $XB/AB$ for the residue, and $XA/AB$ for the vapor.

This, then, is the basis of all fractionation: the vaporization of a liquid to vapor richer in one component and poorer in others, removal of the vapor from the system, and condensation.

Originally, fractionation was carried out as outlined above. The starting material was charged to the still, the distillate cut into fractions, and these

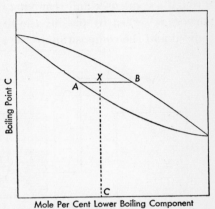

Figure 2. Relative Weights of Vapor and Liquid in Equilibrium

were redistilled, being themselves then divided into other fractions. This process was repeated until either the desired separation was effected or the volume of the fractions became so small as to make their distillation impractical. This process, however, is impractical both from the point of time consumed and heat lost. For example, in Figure 1, if we distill a liquid of composition $A$, we obtain a vapor $B$. Now $B$ is condensed, giving liquid $C$, which is again placed in a still and vaporized, giving vapor $D$, which condenses to $E$, which is again separately distilled. In this process, we have used three separate vaporizations and condensations, and have recovered heat from none of them.

The next step in the development of our process becomes obvious. If, instead of three separate and distinct stills, we have three stills in series, the con-

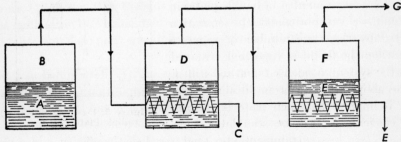

Figure 3. Development of Bubble Plate Column

denser of the first serving as the heating coil of the second, and the condenser of the second heating the liquid of the third, we conserve the heat of the condensation in the first two condensers.

It is also obvious that the composition of vapor from one still is the same as the charged liquid for the next. Therefore, instead of passing the vapor $B$ through a condenser and removing it from the system as liquid $C$, the same purpose is served by passing the live vapors into the liquid $C$. The heat is utilized and the composition of the still is the same.

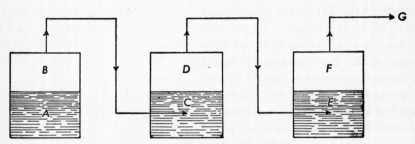

**Figure 4.** Development of Bubble Plate Column

This process requires the use of three separate stills. If some method could be devised for carrying out the necessary vaporizations and condensations in the same vessel, a further convenience could be obtained. This is accomplished in a bubble plate tower which does the work of our three stills in one combined unit.

The vapors $B$ from the liquid $A$ pass up through the layer of liquid $C$ on the plate above. The vapors lose their heat of condensation, condensing to liquid $C$. The heat given up vaporizes the lower boiling components of liquid $C$, giving $D$, which passes through liquid $E$, and the process is repeated. Thus, by using $n$ number of bubble plates in a column, we can approximate the separation effected by the same number of separate stills when the liquid is vaporized, removed from the system, condensed, and redistilled.

The above example is an idealized one, since it implies that each plate is 100 per cent efficient. As will be seen later, such

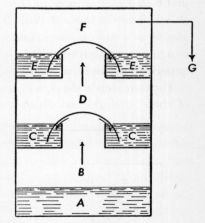

**Figure 5.** Development of Bubble Plate Column

factors as heat loss, entrainment, etc., tend to reduce the efficiency of a plate,

However, as the $\alpha$ increases, the boiling range of the system under study also increases, so that the error remains almost constant. For example, the theoretical plates calculated between the minimum and maximum values of $\alpha$ for a range of about 100 plates vary by only about 4 or 5 plates, depending on the formula used for calculation (see Chapter IV).

**Activity Coefficient.** The activity coefficient $\gamma$ is used to express the deviation from ideality. The activity $a$ is the relative fugacity, or the ratio between the fugacity of a substance in solution and its fugacity in the pure state, where the fugacity is an ideal vapor pressure, identical with the partial pressure $p$ under conditions governed by the perfect gas laws. The activity coefficient $\gamma$ is then defined as the activity divided by the mole fraction, or

$$\gamma_1 = \frac{a_1}{x_1}, \text{ and } \gamma_2 = \frac{a_2}{x_2} \tag{5}$$

If the components obey the perfect gas laws, then the fugacity and the partial pressure are identical, so that

$$\gamma_1 = \frac{p}{P_1 x_1} = \frac{P y_1}{P_1 x_1}, \text{ etc.} \tag{6}$$

where $P_1$ is the vapor pressure of the pure component and $P$ is the total pressure. If equation (6) is rearranged to give

$$y_1 = \frac{\gamma_1 P_1 x_1}{P}, \text{ and } y_2 = \frac{\gamma_2 P_2 x_2}{P} \tag{7}$$

and if these values are substituted in equation (4), the relationship between the relative volatility and the activity coefficient is given by

$$\alpha = \frac{\gamma_1 P_1}{\gamma_2 P_2} \tag{8}$$

Again, if the system is ideal, $\gamma_1 / \gamma_2 = 1$, and $\alpha$ is the ratio of the vapor pressures.

**Methods of Distillation.** There are two general methods of distillation: continuous, and discontinuous or batch.

In continuous distillation, the preheated material to be fractionated is admitted to the column at a point near the middle of the column. The lower boiling materials are taken off at the head of the column, while the higher boiling fractions are removed at the bottom. The rate of feed and the temperature are so adjusted that volume of feed is equal to the total volume of takeoff from the head and bottom, and conditions at any given point in the system will be constant during the period of distillation.

In batch distillation, on the other hand, a definite amount of material is charged to the still pot at the bottom and distilled to dryness, material being taken off only at the top. In this type of distillation, therefore, conditions throughout the system are continually changing as more volatile distillate is taken off and less volatile material moves up the column from plate to plate. However, if we operate a batch still on total reflux, that is, return to the system as reflux all the material condensing at the head without removing any as product, we then have constant conditions throughout the system, and this method of distillation can be analyzed like continuous distillation.

# *Mathematical Treatment*

THE PURPOSE of a mathematical analysis of the process of distillation through a column is: first of all, to determine the conditions existing at any place within the column at a given time; second, knowing the above conditions, to be able to predict the results that will be obtained by any given column when operating on a given charged mixture; and third, to be able to predict the operating conditions that will give optimum separation of the mixture.

*Sorel Method.* Sorel[1] developed the first mathematical theory of the rectifying column for binary mixtures. He studied each plate in a column separately, assuming equilibrium at each plate. When equilibrium is assumed, the method may be applied successively from plate to plate in the column. Sorel considered a system of two liquids in a column operating continuously.

The following nomenclature will be used in explaining Sorel's derivation:

$x$ = mole fraction of more volatile in liquid
$y$ = mole fraction of more volatile in vapor
$D$ = moles of distillate withdrawn as overhead per unit time
$x_D$ = mole fraction of more volatile component in distillate
$O$ = total moles overflow from one plate to next per unit time
$V$ = total moles vapor passing from one plate to next per unit time
$W$ = moles residue per unit time
$n$ = number of plate under consideration, counting from feed
$m$ = number of plate under consideration, counting from still
$H$ = enthalpy, or heat content of vapor
$h$ = enthalpy, or heat content of liquid

Subscripts:

$f$ = feed plate
$R$ = reflux
$t$ = top plate

If we take a section in a column between the $n$th and the $(n+1)$th plate and consider a material balance in that section, we find the only material entering the section is the vapor from the plate below, $V_n$, while leaving the section is the distillate $D$ and the overflow from the $(n+1)$th plate, $(O_n + 1)$. Therefore,

$$V_n = O_n + 1 + D \tag{1}$$

A material balance on the more volatile component on the plate gives

$$V_n y_n = O_{n+1}\, x_{n+1} + D x_D \tag{2}$$

or
$$y_n = \frac{O_{n+1}}{V_n} x_{n+1} + \frac{D}{V_n} x_D \tag{2a}$$

$$y_n = \frac{O_{n+1}}{O_{n+1} + D} x_{n+1} + \frac{D}{O_{n+1} + D} x_D \tag{2b}$$

since we can find the moles of more volatile component by multiplying the total moles of vapor from the $n$th plate by the mole fraction of this compound.

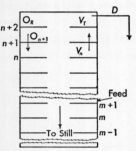

Since equilibrium is assumed, the above is true for the top plate and the condenser. The distillate from the top plate may be analyzed and considered to be the same composition as the vapor above the top plate. By applying the same reasoning to each plate in the column it is possible to calculate the distillate, the reflux, and the residue. However, we do not know the composition of the vapor above plates in the column other than the top plate. To obtain the moles of overflow from, and the vapor to a plate, Sorel employed heat balances. There must be no overall heat change in a plate. Therefore

**Figure 8.** Development of Sorel Theory

$$O_R h_R + V_{t-1} H_{t-1} = V_t H_t + O_t h_t + \text{losses} \tag{3}$$

If $H$ is known, equations (1) and (3) can be solved simultaneously to give $V_{t-1}$ and $O_t$. Substituting these values in equation (2a), we get $y_{t-1}$. The value of $H$ is assumed for $H_{t-1}$, and is then checked for accuracy after $x_{t-1}$ is calculated from $y_{t-1}$ and vapor-liquid equilibrium data.

The above may also be used below the feed plate to give

$$y_m = \frac{O_{m+1}\, x_{m+1}}{V_m} - \frac{W x_w}{V_m} = \tag{4}$$

$$\frac{O_{m+1}\, x_{m+1}}{O_{m+1} - W} - \frac{W x_w}{O_{m+1} - W} \tag{4a}$$

To simplify the above equations four assumptions are made, which generally do not introduce appreciable error. The assumptions are: the moles of overflow are equal to the moles of vapor ascending the column, operation of the column is continuous, it is adiabatic, and there is no heat of mixing. Based on these assumptions the relation between $y_n$ and $x_{n+1}$ in equation (2a) becomes a straight line with the slope equal to $O/V$, since $O_{n+1}$ and $V_n$ are constant in the section above the feed plate. Likewise, $y_m$ is a straight line in $x_{m+1}$. Normally, certain conditions such as composition of distillate, composition of residue, composition of feed, and quantity of feed are also defined before the solution of a problem is started. Knowing these and the above equations, the relation between $y_n$ and $x_{n+1}$, and $y_m$ and $x_{m+1}$ is completely defined.

**McCabe-Thiele Method.**  Sorel's method is sound, but it is based on an algebraic analysis of equilibrium conditions existing between one plate and the plate above or below it. Therefore, if, for example, we know the conditions existing at the top plate and desire to know the conditions 20 plates below the top, it is necessary to substitute 20 different times in the required equation.

Many workers have modified Sorel's method of determining plates and predicting necessary conditions for column design. McCabe and Thiele[2] developed a graphical method for doing what Sorel and others did by the tedious algebraic analytical procedure.

When the usual simplifying assumptions (page 12) are applied to Sorel's method, the relation between $y_n$ and $x_{n+1}$ is a straight line defined by the equation

$$y_n = \frac{O_{n+1}}{V_n} x_{n+1} + \frac{D}{V_n} x_D \qquad (2a)$$

This line, with slope $O_{n+1}/V_n$, crosses the $y = x$ diagonal at $y_n = x_{n+1} = x_D$. If the column is being operated continuously, and if the charge is being admitted somewhere above the bottom of the column, a similar line for conditions below the feed can be predicted from the equation

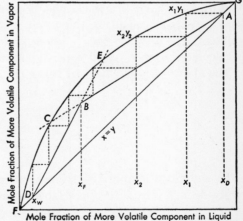

$$y_m = \frac{O_{m+1}}{V_m} x_{m+1} - \frac{W}{V_m} x_w \qquad (4)$$

This straight line of slope $O_m/V_m$ is also drawn on the $x = y$ diagonal, and passes through the $x = y$ diagonal at $x = x_w$.

This graphical method of McCabe and Thiele is illustrated in Figure 9. Throughout this book, unless otherwise specified, $x$ will indicate the mole fraction

**Figure 9.** Graphical Method of McCabe-Thiele

of the more volatile component in the liquid, while $y$ will indicate the mole fraction of the more volatile in the vapor.

The line $FDAG$ is the 45-degree $x = y$ diagonal. $ABC$ of slope $O_n/V_n$, called the *enriching line*, corresponds to equation (2a). Line $DBE$ of slope $O_m/V_m$, called the *exhausting line*, corresponds to equation (4). Thus, Sorel's method may now be solved graphically.

Knowing the composition of the product, we therefore know $x_D$, the mole fraction of the more volatile component in the distillate. Since no fractionation takes place from the vapor from the top plate to the condensed product, it follows that $x_D = y$. Therefore $x_1$ is found by going vertically at the abscissa $x = x_D$ to the diagonal $x = y$, thus obtaining point $A$. In Figure 1, composition of liquid and vapor at any point in the column is found by drawing horizontal and vertical steps between the liquid and vapor curves. The same procedure is followed here, except that the steps are drawn between the equilibrium curve $FCEG$ and the enriching and exhausting lines. Thus, if $x_1$ is the composition of the liquid on one plate, $x_2$ is that on the plate below, $x_3$ on the next, and so on.

The diagram of Figure 9 is drawn for continuous distillation, that is, with a definite reflux ratio, $O_{n+1}/V_n$. In other words, part of the material reaching the top of the column is taken off as product, while the remainder is returned to the column as reflux. Now, if we consider a batch fractionation column under total reflux, we find that the number of moles returning to the column is the same as the number of moles reaching the head of the column. Therefore

$$O_{n+1} = V_n, \text{ and } \frac{O_{n+1}}{V_n} = 1 \tag{5}$$

With a slope $O_{n+1}/V_n$ equal to 1, the enriching and exhausting lines, $ABC$ and $DBE$, coincide with the 45-degree diagonal, $FDAG$, and the McCabe-Thiele diagram becomes that of Figure 10.

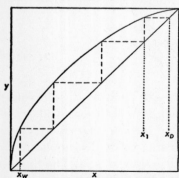

***Algebraic Solution.*** Several mathematical methods for analyzing and predicting column performance have been developed. These equations have been developed for the purpose of simplifying the graphical methods used, so that in certain special cases an elementary substitution in a formula will immediately give the results formerly obtained by the steps drawn on the McCabe-Thiele diagram.

**Figure 10.** McCabe-Thiele Diagram for Total Reflux

***Fenske and Underwood Equation.*** It has been seen that when a column is operating on total reflux, the slope of the line determined by $O_{n+1}/V_n$ and

$O_m/V_m$ becomes equal to 1, and thus corresponds to the diagonal $x = y$. Fenske[3] and Underwood[4] independently have combined this fact with the consideration of the relative volatility for ideal solutions, and have developed an equation for determining conditions existing in a column under total reflux.

If $\alpha$ is the relative volatility,

$$\frac{y_A}{y_B} = \alpha \frac{x_A}{x_B} \tag{6}$$

for any plate, and

$$\frac{y_A}{y_B} = \alpha^n \frac{x_A}{x_B} \tag{7}$$

where
$n$ = number of theoretical plates in the column
$x_A$ = mole fraction $A$ in liquid
$y_A$ = mole fraction $A$ in vapor
$x_B$ = mole fraction $B$ in liquid
$y_B$ = mole fraction $B$ in vapor

Underwood has developed the expression in the form

$$n = \frac{\log \frac{x_0(1 - x_n)}{x_n(1 - x_0)}}{\log \alpha} \tag{8}$$

where $x_0$ = mole fraction more volatile component in liquid
$x_n$ = mole fraction more volatile component in vapor

One plate should be subtracted from the $n$ determined from the above equations in order to adjust for the single plate obtained in going from the still pot to the column. Both the above equations then reduce to the easily usable form

$$n + 1 = \frac{\log \left(\frac{x_A}{x_B}\right)\left(\frac{y_B}{y_A}\right)}{\log \alpha} \tag{8a}$$

**Smoker Equation.** The Fenske and Underwood equation was developed assuming total reflux. Smoker[5] has now developed an equation making possible the prediction of the plates necessary to effect a given separation between any desired concentrations and at any fixed reflux ratio. It is applicable to a discontinuous still or to either section of a continuous still. The Smoker equation is derived as follows:

Using Raoult's law in the form

$$y = \frac{\alpha x}{1 + (\alpha - 1) x} \tag{9}$$

construct the vapor-liquid equilibrium line of Figure 11. Any desired operating line is constructed from the straight-line formula

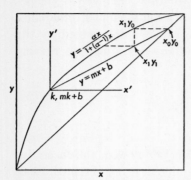

$$y = mx + b \tag{10}$$

The quadratic equation

$$m(\alpha-1)x^2 + [m+b(\alpha-1)-\alpha]x + b = 0 \tag{11}$$

is obtained by eliminating $y$ between equations (9) and (10). Only one of the roots of equation (11) will be between 0 and 1. Representing this root by $k$, and substituting in equation (10)

$$x = k \tag{12}$$

**Figure 11.** Development of the Smoker Equation

$$y = mk + b \tag{13}$$

Equations (12) and (13) represent the coordinates of the point of intersection of the vapor-liquid equilibrium curve and the operating line. If the origin of coordinates is shifted from $x = y = 0$ to this intersection point, then

$$x' = x - k \tag{14}$$

$$y' = y - (mk + b) \tag{15}$$

The operating line is then represented by

$$y' = mx' \tag{16}$$

and the vapor equilibrium curve is

$$y' + mk + b = \frac{\alpha\,(x' + k)}{1 + (\alpha - 1)\,(x' + k)} \tag{17}$$

When $x' = 0$, $y' = 0$ and equation (17) becomes

$$mk + b = \frac{\alpha k}{1 + (\alpha - 1)\,k} \tag{18}$$

By eliminating $b$ between equations (17) and (18) and rearranging,

$$y' = \frac{\sigma x'}{[1 + (\alpha - 1)k]^2 + (\alpha - 1)\,[1 + (\alpha - 1)k]x'} \tag{19}$$

If we set

$$C = 1 + (\alpha - 1)k, \tag{20}$$

then equation (19) becomes

$$y' = \frac{\alpha x'}{C^2 + C(\alpha - 1)x'} \qquad (21)$$

Equation (21) is Raoult's law expressed in coordinates determined by the intersection of the original Raoult equation and any operating line. Solving for $x'$,

$$x' = \frac{C^2 y'}{\alpha - C(\alpha - 1)y'} \qquad (22)$$

In Figure 11, let $x_0'$, $y_0'$ represent any pair on the operating line, $y' = mx'$. If the stepwise procedure of McCabe and Thiele is followed, the successive points on the operating line and on the vapor-liquid curve are obtained. Since coordinates of points on the operating line are related by equation (16), and those on the vapor-liquid equilibrium curve by equation (22),

$$y_0' = mx_0' \qquad (23)$$

$$x_1' = \frac{C^2 y_0'}{\alpha - C(\alpha - 1)y_0'} \qquad (24)$$

Eliminating $y_0'$ between equations (23) and (24) expresses $x_1'$ in terms of $x_0'$

$$x_1' = \frac{mC^2 x_0'}{\alpha - mC(\alpha - 1)x_0'} \qquad (25)$$

Similarly, $y_1' = mx_1'$ and $\qquad\qquad\qquad\qquad\qquad\qquad (26)$

$$x_2' = \frac{C^2 y_1'}{\alpha - C(\alpha - 1)y_1'} = \frac{mC^2 x_1'}{\alpha - mC(\alpha - 1)x_1'} \qquad (27)$$

Eliminating $x_1$ from equations (25) and (27) expresses $x_2'$ in terms of $x_0$

$$x_2' = \frac{m^2 C^4 x_0'}{\alpha^2 - mC(\alpha - 1)(\alpha - mC^2)\, x_0'} \qquad (28)$$

Proceeding in the same stepwise fashion, it can be shown that

$$x_3' = \frac{m^3 C^6 x_0'}{\alpha^3 - mC(\alpha - 1)(\alpha^2 + \alpha mC^2 + m^2 C^4)x_0'} \qquad (29)$$

Inspection of equations (25), (28), and (29) results in the generalization for $n$ steps

$$x_n' = \frac{m^n C^{2n} x_0'}{\alpha^n - mC(\alpha - 1)\left(\dfrac{\alpha^n - m^n C^{2n}}{\alpha - mC^2}\right) x_0'} \qquad (30)$$

Solving for $n$ gives the final Smoker equation,

$$n = \frac{\log \dfrac{x'_0\left(1 - \dfrac{mC(\alpha - 1)}{\alpha - mC^2}\, x'_n\right)}{x'_n\left(1 - \dfrac{mC(\alpha - 1)}{\alpha - mC^2}\, x'_0\right)}}{\log \dfrac{\alpha}{mC^2}} \tag{31}$$

The above equation involves only two assumptions: Raoult's law, and constant molal overflow. An illustrative problem is solved by the Smoker equation on page 34.

For the case of total reflux, $R = \infty$, $m = 1$, $b = 0$, $k = 0$, $C = 1$, and the Smoker equation becomes

$$n = \frac{\log \dfrac{x_0(1 - x_n)}{x_n(1 - x_0)}}{\log \alpha} \tag{32}$$

which is recognized as a form of the Fenske equation.

***Transfer Units.***   Chilton and Colburn[6] have proposed another mathematical method for analyzing difficulty of separation in a packed column. In the methods so far considered, a separation required a number of *theoretical plates*. The concept of theoretical plates implies that for any given plate, the composition of vapor passing through the plate is equal to the difference between the composition of the entering vapor and the corresponding equilibrium vapor. The transfer unit concept is more fundamental, being so defined that the composition of vapor passing through a plate is equal to the mean value of the difference between the entering vapor and the corresponding equilibrium vapor.

The following terminology used by Chilton and Colburn will be used in the development of the transfer unit equations:

$A$ = interface area, sq ft
$G$ = mass velocity of gas or vapor, lb per hr per sq ft
$H$ = height of packed section, ft
$H.E.T.P.$ = height equivalent theoretical plate
$H.T.U.$ = height transfer unit
$K$ = absorption coefficient (gas film), lb moles per (hour) (sq ft) (atm)
$Ka$ = absorption coefficient (gas film), lb moles per (hour) (cu ft packed column) (atm)
$L$ = liquid rate, lb moles per hr
$M_m$ = average molecular wt of vapor stream
$S$ = cross-sectional area (over which $G$ is measured), sq ft
$V$ = vapor rate, lb moles per hr

$a$ = surface area of packing per unit of packed volume, sq ft per cu ft
$p$ = partial pressure of diffusing components, atm
$p^*$ = equilibrium partial pressure of diffusing component out of liquid, atm
$\triangle p = p - p^*$
$w$ = rate of transfer of diffusing component, lb moles per hr
$x$ = mole fraction of diffusing component in liquid
$y$ = mole fraction of diffusing component in gas, $= p/\pi$
$y^*$ = equilibrium mole fraction of diffusing component out of liquid $= p^*/\pi$
$\triangle y = y - y^*$
$\pi$ = total press., atm
$\alpha$ = relative volatility $= \dfrac{y^*(1 - x)}{(1 - y^*)x}$

The transfer unit calculations are developed as follows:

As the vapor moves up the column, it becomes progressively richer in the lower boiling component, or in other words, the partial pressure of the low boiling material increases. As was assumed for previous mathematical treatments, the number of moles of material passing successive points remains constant. Therefore the differential rate of increase in the moles of low boiling material in the vapor is

$$dw = \frac{dpGS}{\pi M_m} \tag{33}$$

It has also been shown previously that the vapor above a given section or plate was in equilibrium with the liquid on the section or plate. The rate of increase $dw$ must therefore also be equal to the rate of transfer by diffusion of the lower boiling component from the plate, and also of the higher boiling component to the plate, or

$$dw = K\triangle pdA = Ka\triangle pSdH \tag{34}$$

Combining and rearranging equations (33) and (34)

$$\frac{dp}{\triangle p} = \left( \frac{Ka\pi M_m}{G} \right) dH \tag{35}$$

which, in the integrated form, gives

$$\int_{P_1}^{P_2} \frac{dp}{\triangle p} = \frac{Ka\pi M_m H}{G} \tag{36}$$

Solving the above equation for $H$ would give the height of packed section necessary to perform a given separation.

The above equation requires a knowledge of the total number of moles passing through the column. The necessity of knowing this term may be eliminated by considering the problem from a slightly different angle. The degree of enrichment of the vapor above the liquid, or the increase in partial pressure of the vapor, can be used as a measure of the difficulty of separation. Thus, if the enrichment is large or if the partial pressure increases considerably, the separation would be considered easy. The number of transfer units could then be defined as

$$T.U. = \int_{p_1}^{p_2} \frac{dp}{\triangle p} = \int_{y_1}^{y_2} \frac{dy}{\triangle y} \tag{37}$$

A solution of equation (37) in the general case was developed by Thormann.[7] Knowing the relationship between the vapor composition $y$ and the liquid composition $x$ leaving any cross section above or below the feed line from equations 2b and 4a, which in Chilton and Colburn's terminology become

$$y = \frac{L}{V} x + \left(1 - \frac{L}{V}\right) x_p \tag{38}$$

above the feed, and below the feed

$$y = \frac{L}{V} x - \left(\frac{L}{V} - 1\right) x_w \tag{39}$$

and making the usual simplifying assumptions (page 12), it is then necessary only to choose values of $x$ between $x_w$ and $x_p$, calculate values of $y$ corresponding to each from equations (38) and (39) and then at the same values of $x$ obtain $y^*$ from the equilibrium curve. If a plot is then made of $1/\triangle y$ vs. $y$, the transfer units necessary for the separation may be obtained by a graphical integration between the limits of $y_1$ and $y_2$, the composition of vapor entering and leaving the column respectively. The values of $\triangle y$ can also be obtained from a McCabe-Thiele diagram. A typical problem solved by this method in Chapter IV, page 32, will make the procedure clear.

If the column is operated at total reflux, then $L/V = 1$, and from equations (38) and (39) $y = x$. Then the relationship between $y^*$ and $x$ can be expressed as

$$y^* = \frac{\alpha x}{1 + (\alpha - 1)x} \tag{40}$$

Equation (37) can now be integrated to give

$$T.U. = \frac{2.3}{\alpha - 1} \log \frac{y_2(1 - y_1)}{y_1(1 - y_2)} + 2.3 \log \frac{(1 - y_1)}{(1 - y_2)} \tag{41}$$

This equation holds only for total reflux and where $\alpha$ is constant, the same limitations that hold for the Fenske equation. Use of equations (8) and (41), therefore, gives a direct relationship between transfer units and theoretical plates under the limitations given above.

In cases of near-ideal mixtures with low relative volatilities, the transfer units and theoretical plates may be equal as shown in Table 1, where equations (8) and (41) are used for the calculations.

**TABLE 1**

| $y_1$ | $y_2$ | $\alpha$ | $T.U.$ | $n$ |
|-------|-------|----------|--------|-----|
| 0.01 | 0.99 | 1.08 | 119.5 | 119.5 |
| 0.50 | 0.99 | 1.08 | 61.0 | 59.8 |
| 0.01 | 0.99 | 2.5 | 10.7 | 10.0 |
| 0.50 | 0.99 | 2.5 | 6.9 | 5.0 |

However, for nonideal mixtures and for mixtures of higher relative volatility, the difference may be considerable.

Collins and Lantz[8] have proposed the use of the term *plate equivalents* to express the efficiency of the column while operating under a finite reflux ratio. Plate equivalents are the number of plates which would be required at total reflux to give the same separation as is obtained at the given finite reflux. The plate equivalents may be calculated by using the Fenske equation, compositions of the vapor and liquid being taken during the distillation with finite reflux ratio.

## REFERENCES

1. SOREL, "La rectification de l'alcool", Paris, 1893
2. McCABE, W. L., and THIELE, E. W., *Ind. Eng. Chem.*, **17,** 605 (1925)
3. FENSKE, M. R., *ibid.*, **24,** 482 (1932)
4. UNDERWOOD, A. J. V., *Trans. Inst. Chem. Engrs.*, **10,** 112 (1932)
5. SMOKER, E. H., *Trans. Am. Inst. Chem. Engrs.*, **34,** 165 (1938)
6. CHILTON, T. H., and COLBURN, A. P., *Ind. Eng. Chem.*, **27,** 255 (1935)
7. THORMANN, K., *Chem. App.*, **14,** 61 (1927)
8. COLLINS, F. C., and LANTZ, V., *Proc. Am. Petroleum Inst.*, **26,** [III], 72 (1946)

# Column Characteristics

IN ORDER to be in a position to decide on the type of column to use to carry out a given fractionation, we must know what properties make one column more suitable than another. The following characteristics of a column are usually considered in evaluating its efficiency:

1. Number of theoretical plates
2. Holdup
3. Throughput
4. Pressure drop

*Theoretical Plates.* When the vapors above a liquid at its boiling point are in equilibrium with the liquid, the enrichment obtained by removing the vapor from the system and condensing it is equivalent to the enrichment that would be obtained by a distillation through a column of one theoretical plate. Referring to Figure 9, each horizontal step from the diagonal line to the vapor-liquid curve represents a theoretical plate, each successive step giving greater enrichment. It is fundamental, therefore, that the higher the number of theoretical plates, the greater will be the separating power of the column. An important derived function which is frequently used to express the efficiency of a column is height equivalent to a theoretical plate, *H.E.T.P.*[1], obtained by dividing the height of the column by the number of theoretical plates calculated as in the following chapter. A low *H.E.T.P.* is, of course, most desirable.

*Holdup.* The operating holdup of a column is defined as the amount of charged material in the column system above the surface of the material in the pot when the column is operating under the desired conditions. The holdup is an extremely important characteristic of a column, especially when small amounts of materials are being fractionated, because it is sometimes a measure of the sharpness of separation obtainable. The distinction between *sharpness* of separation and *degree* of separation should be noted. For example, if we have two columns, *A* and *B*, both capable of giving pure samples of the individual components of a charged mixture, the degree of separation is the same. However, if in column *A* we obtain 90 per cent of the charged mixture

22

as pure components in the distillate, leaving 10 per cent as impure intermediate fractions, and in column *B* we obtain only 70 per cent of the material pure, leaving 30 per cent impure, then column *A* gives the *sharper* separation.

Figure 12 pictures a batch distillation column operating at maximum efficiency separating a mixture of two components, with ⊙⊙⊙ being the lower boiling and ⊗⊗⊗ the higher boiling constituent of the mixture. In (a) pure material is being taken off at the top, while the higher boiling component is just starting into the column. As more of the lower boiling material is taken off, more of the other component must rise into the

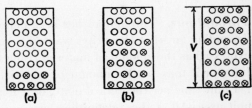

**Figure 12.** Effect of Column Holdup

column in order to have continuous operation. The closer this latter material comes to the top of the column, the less capable is the column of separating it completely from the lower boiling material. In (b) pure material is still being taken off at the head, but there is more of the mixture present in the column. Finally, in (c) all the pure material has been removed, and the impure mixture must be distilled until the pure higher boiling component rises to fill the column completely. The greater the volume indicated by *V*, the greater will be the intermediate cut between the pure components.

Colburn and Stearns[2] have discussed the effect of holdup under varying conditions. They propose that, since column holdup increases the spread between distillate and still composition, the effect would be toward a sharper separation. The importance varies with the ratio of the volume of holdup to the volume of original charged material. Also, when the rate of change of plate composition with per cent takeoff is large, as, for example, when sharp separations are already being made, the effect of holdup will be to increase the sharpness of separation. Rose[3] has shown that column holdup will give a poorer separation because of the concentration of the more volatile material in the column and its depletion in the still. The importance of this effect will depend on the ratio of the holdup to the amount of any single component present in the original charge.

***Static Holdup.*** The static holdup is the amount of adsorbed material held by a given column system after it has been allowed to drain for a specified period of time after a fractionation has been completed. As would be expected, the static holdup depends upon the area of surface and the type of surface with which the distilling material comes into contact within the column proper.

The static holdup will depend not only on the packing used but also on the character of the material being distilled. A given packing will hold up a greater quantity of a viscous material than of a highly fluid one. For example, it was found[4] that two spiral screen columns which had respective static hold-ups of 28 cc and 5 cc of benzene held up 40 cc and 7.5 cc of β-pinene, respectively.

**Throughput.**  Throughput has been defined in a number of different ways, depending on what the writer wanted to emphasize. For example, it may be expressed as the amount of material rising to the head of the column per unit time, or it may be the amount of material rising to the head of the column per unit time per theoretical plate, or it may be the amount per unit time per unit area. All of these definitions are useful under certain conditions. However, in this book, unless otherwise specified, throughput will be defined as the total volume of material rising to the head of the column per unit time. This definition is also applied to the term *boilup rate.*

The advantages of a high throughput are readily seen. For two columns of the same number of theoretical plates and the same holdup, the column with the higher throughput would be better. The time required for distillation is shortened and, therefore, as a corollary, larger volumes of material can be charged to a given column for fractionation in a reasonable time.

**Flooding and Loading Velocities.**  The maximum throughput of a column is determined by the point at which the column floods. As the rate of throughput increases, more vapor rises in the column and more liquid flows back down the column, until at some rate the vapor bubbles through the liquid violently enough to carry with it a large amount of liquid, and slugs can be seen in the column. This point is called the *flood point.* For any given vapor rate there is a definite liquid rate above which flooding occurs. Similarly, for any given liquid rate the maximum vapor velocity is fixed. The flood point is marked by a very definite and sudden increase in pressure drop.

In many cases loading velocity and flooding velocity have been used interchangeably. However, this is not strictly correct. White[5] has defined the loading point as the point at which the logarithmic curve of pressure drop vs. gas velocity first deviates from a slope of approximately 2. This is illustrated in Figure 13.

At point $L$ the pressure drop increases suddenly with a slight increase in vapor velocity. This is the loading point. At the point $F$, the flood point, the pressure drop increases even more rapidly with vapor velocity. The greater the loading point and flood point, the more practical will be the column, other factors being equal.

*Pressure Drop.*   The pressure drop is defined as the difference in pressure between the still pot and the column head. The pressure in the still pot is always greater than it is at the column head. Some force is required to drive the vaporized material up through the column, that is, to overcome the frictional resistance offered by the pack-ing, and by the liquid reflux flowing down through the packing. This force is equal to the pressure drop. It may vary from a small fraction of a millimeter of mercury for small columns to 100 milli-meters or more for the larger type. A column with a low pressure drop is desired, especially for vacuum frac-tionations. If a column has a pressure drop (*p.d.*) of 5 millimeters, the actual pressure in the pot will be 5 millimeters above that recorded at the head. There-fore, if a fractionation run in this column

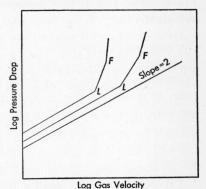

Figure 13.  Loading and Flooding Velocities

shows a pressure of 2 millimeters measured at the head, the actual pressure in the pot is 7 millimeters. This is quite serious if the column charge is unstable at boiling points above that obtained at 2 millimeters, since the material in the pot might be boiling 30 C above the material at the head. Other things being equal, then, a column with a low pressure drop is to be preferred.

Naturally, the ideal packed column would have a large number of plates with a large throughput and minimum pressure drop and holdup. However, we usually have to compromise to some extent to obtain optimum efficiency. For example, in columns with removable packing, lower *H.E.T.P.* is usually obtained with finer packing. But, since the packing is finer, more surface is exposed and so the holdup is greater. Also, with finer packing the pressure drop increases and the throughput decreases. If we wish to increase the throughput, we can do so at the expense of the *H.E.T.P.* by increasing the packing size. In this case, then, we also decrease the pressure drop. However, in the cases just given the column with the finer packing would also give more theoretical plates and a lower *H.E.T.P.* Therefore, if the columns were com-pared on the basis of holdup or pressure drop per theoretical plate, the columns might be equal.

A word of warning should be given about interpreting literature results of efficiency tests run on columns. For example, suppose two columns of the same theoretical plate value are being compared as to holdup and pressure drop. At first glance it might seem that the column having the lower holdup and pressure drop would be the better column. As we shall see later, in certain types of columns the *H.E.T.P.* increases if the diameter of the column is appreciably increased. Suppose, for example, that column *A* has the dimensions 100 cm in length by 5 mm in diameter, while column *B* is 150 cm by 10 mm. Assume, also, that both of these columns give the same number of theoretical plates. Because of the increased length and diameter of column *B* over column *A*, column *B* would have a greater holdup and pressure drop. Therefore, if the results of these tests were reported as cubic centimeters of holdup per theoretical plate, column *A* would undoubtedly be considered the better column. However, one other factor should also be considered, and that is throughput. If the diameter of column *B* is enough larger than column *A* to affect the *H.E.T.P.*, the throughput will also be increased appreciably. Suppose we run the two columns for the same period of time. We will then have more distillate from column *B* than from column *A*, and the importance of the greater holdup of column *B* will be minimized. Therefore, we can say that if we have only a small amount of material we can use column *A*, and if we have a large amount of material use column *B* and still take the same amount of time.

Similarly, if only the *H.E.T.P.* of a column is reported, a great divergence of comparative figures can be obtained by varying the diameter and length of the column. If two packings are being compared in columns of the same length but different diameters, the column with the larger diameter will usually have the larger *H.E.T.P.* Again, however, the throughput will usually be larger in the column of larger diameter.

Pressure drop and holdup are also affected, as we shall see, by increase in vapor velocity and the consequent increase in throughput. If the pressure drops for two packings are reported, the throughputs should also be known. Figures favoring one or the other of the packings in the matter of pressure drop and holdup may very easily be obtained by running the favored column at a lower rate of speed. Again, though, we see that the second column will have put through a larger quantity of distillate in a given time.

Several attempts have been made to find a term to express an efficiency factor which will give a comparative idea of the effectiveness of different columns. Willingham, Sedlak, Westhaver, and Rossini[6] suggest that an efficiency factor be defined as the throughput in milliliters of liquid per hour divided by the holdup in milliliters per theoretical plate. This may also be expressed as the number of theoretical plates through which the material being fractionated passes per unit of time. Podbielniak[7] proposed for this factor the ratio of the reflux rate in cubic centimeters per hour to the holdup in cubic centimeters per plate. This factor is the inverse of one of several proposed earlier by Bragg[8] and used by Collins and Lantz[9].

While such concepts are useful, it is probably true that no single term can express all the factors necessary for evaluating a column.

## REFERENCES

1. PETERS, W. A., *Ind. Eng. Chem.*, 15, 402 (1923)
2. COLBURN, A. P., and STEARNS, R. F., *Trans. Am. Inst. Chem. Engrs.*, 37, 295 (1941)
3. ROSE, A., WELSHANS, L. M., and LONG, H. H., *Ind. Eng. Chem.*, 32, 673 (1940)
4. STALLCUP, W. D., FUGUITT, R. E., and HAWKINS, J. E., *Ind. Eng. Chem.*, Anal. Ed., 14, 503 (1942)
5. WHITE, A. McL., *Trans. Am. Inst. Chem. Engrs* , 31, 390 (1935)
6. WILLINGHAM, C. B., SEDLAK, V. A., WESTHAVER, J. W., and ROSSINI, F. D., *Ind. Eng. Chem.*, 39, 706 (1947)
7. PODBIELNIAK, W. M., *Ind. Eng. Chem.*, Anal. Ed., 13, 639 (1941)
8. BRAGG, L. B., *Trans. Am. Inst. Chem. Engrs.*, 37, 19 (1941)
9. COLLINS, F. C., and LANTZ, V., *Ind. Eng. Chem.*, Anal. Ed., 18, 673 (1946)

# IV

## Theoretical Plates and Reflux Ratio Required for a Given Separation

PROBABLY the first and most important piece of information that should be known before a column is chosen for a given fractionation is the approximate number of plates required to effect a desired separation. If the liquid-vapor curve (page 2) for the materials under consideration is known, the problem of estimating the plates required for a given separation is relatively simple. Suppose, for example, we wish to fractionate a mixture of benzene and toluene to obtain pure benzene and pure toluene. The amount of intermediate fraction will not be considered here. Using the vapor-liquid data available, the corresponding curve as well as the $x = y$ diagonal are drawn as in Figure 14.

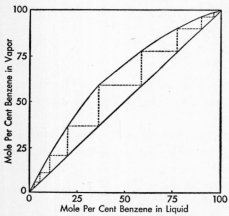

**Figure 14.** Plates Required for Separating Benzene and Toluene in 99 Per Cent Purity

On the McCabe-Thiele diagram it was seen how it was possible to obtain any desired enrichment by progressing in a stepwise fashion. Further, it was seen that every step represented a theoretical plate. Therefore, if we decide on an initial and final concentration in our distillation, we can obtain the required number of steps by drawing the steps between the chosen concentrations. However, if we take 100 per cent as the final purity of one of the components, the stepwise process becomes impossible since infinitely small steps must be drawn in the region where the vapor-liquid curve approaches the $x = y$ diagonal. If, instead of drawing steps between 0 per cent and 100 per cent, we use 1 per cent and 99 per cent as our desired purities and then use a suitable safety factor to estimate the plate requirements to obtain 100 per cent distillate, we can obtain a working basis for deciding on the proper efficiency of the column to be used. If the vapor-liquid curve approaches the $x = y$ diagonal in the manner shown in Figure 15 (a), the plates calculated between 1 per cent and 99 per cent should be multiplied by 1.5 to 2. If, on the other hand, the curve is the shape of (b), then the factor to be used is 3. This is a very rough approximation but it does give an adequate number of plates for the separation under consideration. For example, for the separation shown in Figure 14, 10 plates are necessary as shown on the figure. However, this is under total reflux, and so, using the safety factor of 1.5 to 2, we obtain 15 to 20 plates as being a safe value to use for the actual separation.

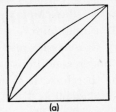 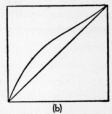

(a)                              (b)

**Figure 15.** Irregular Equilibrium Curves

If the mixture being distilled can be treated as an ideal solution, and the relative volatility $\alpha$ is known, the problem becomes even more simple since it is necessary only to substitute in one of the several formulas available. Fenske's formula for calculating the minimum number of plates required for the separation of materials at total reflux is

$$n = \frac{\log\left(\frac{x_A}{x_B}\right)\left(\frac{y_B}{y_A}\right)}{\log \alpha} \qquad (1)$$

Where a total condenser is used, one plate should be subtracted for the still. If a partial condenser is used, two plates should be subtracted, one for the still and one for the condenser.

As an example of the use of the Fenske[1] formula, suppose it is desired to separate a mixture of $n$-heptane and methylcyclohexane into a distillate containing 99 mole per cent $n$-heptane, while the residue will contain 99 mole per cent methylcyclohexane. Then

$$n + 1 = \frac{\log\left(\frac{99}{1} \times \frac{99}{1}\right)}{\log 1.074}$$

$$n + 1 = 129, \text{ or}$$
$$n = 128$$

The above formula is for a column operating under total reflux, that is, with no distillate being removed.

***Reflux Ratio.*** In the discussion of the theory of distillation the importance of scrubbing action (page 5) was emphasized. The maximum scrubbing action of a given column will be obtained when the vapors rising in the column are washed by the total amount of condensate at the head, or in other words, when no distillate is being taken off. Since this condition of total reflux gives the most efficient fractionation, it is axiomatic that minimum theoretical plates are required at total reflux. As a corollary, therefore, in a column of infinite theoretical plates, a minimum of reflux is required. Since in all fractionations it is necessary to remove some of the product as distillate, it is not possible to operate under conditions corresponding to total reflux. For any given fractionation, therefore, it is necessary to know the optimum amount of material to be taken off as distillate as compared with the amount returned to the column as reflux. The ratio of the amount of material returned as reflux to the amount of distillate is called the *reflux ratio*. Any fractionation, therefore, must be performed at conditions between those of a minimum number of plates at total reflux, and a minimum reflux with an infinite number of plates.

If a method could be used for determining the minimum reflux ratio required to perform a given separation, then the limiting conditions of minimum plates at total reflux and minimum reflux ratio with infinite plates would be defined. Such a formula[1] is given below:

$$R_{\min} = \frac{1}{\alpha - 1}\left(\frac{x_{cA}}{x_{fA}} - \alpha\,\frac{x_{cB}}{x_{fB}}\right) \tag{2}$$

where
$R$ = the reflux ratio
$x_{cA}$ and $x_{cB}$ = the mole fractions of $A$ and $B$ in the distillate
$x_{fA}$ and $x_{fB}$ = the mole fractions of $A$ and $B$ in the feed

Smoker[2] has also given two formulas for use in estimating the minimum number of plates required at infinite reflux, and of minimum reflux with infinite plates:

$$n_{\min} = \frac{\log \dfrac{x_o(1 - x_f)}{x_f(1 - x_o)}}{\log \alpha} \tag{3}$$

$$\frac{R_{\min}}{1 - R_{\min}} = \frac{x_o - \dfrac{\alpha x_f}{1 + (\alpha - 1)x_f}}{x_o - x_f} \tag{4}$$

where $x_f$ and $x_o$ refer to feed and overhead compositions, or to any two liquid compositions in the column as long as $x_o$ is greater than $x_f$. Equation (3) is also a form of the Fenske equation.

It has been observed previously that in continuous distillation the conditions throughout the column remain constant, while in batch fractionation there is continuous change. Rose[3] has therefore suggested a method of evaluating the requirements of a column based not upon the difference between still and product compositions, but upon the shape of the distillation curve desired (see page 42). He introduces the concept of a *standard separation*, and defines it as a separation in which the first 40 per cent of material distilled from a 50-50 mole per cent solution has an average purity of greater than 95 per cent. To estimate the conditions necessary to obtain this separation, Rose has developed the following formulas, using only the term $\alpha$ and a constant.

$$n_{max} = \frac{3.6}{\log \alpha} \tag{5}$$

$$n_{opt} = \frac{2.85}{\log \alpha} \tag{6}$$

$$n_{min} = \frac{2.3}{\log \alpha} \tag{7}$$

where $n$ = number of plates.

By the same method of calculation the same author has obtained formulas for determining the corresponding reflux ratios.

$$R_{min} = \frac{2}{3} n_{max} \tag{8}$$

$$R_{opt} = n_{opt} \tag{9}$$

$$R_{max} = \frac{3}{2} n_{min} \tag{10}$$

where $R$ = reflux ratio.

For example, if the optimum number of plates has been calculated to be 15, then a reflux ratio of 15 to 1 should be used. If the maximum number of plates is 15, then the minimum allowable reflux ratio is 10 to 1. It should be remembered that these formulas estimate conditions required for the standard separation, and not necessarily to give pure components.

Where a large number of plates is available, Dodge and Huffman[4] recommend the use of the following formula:

$$n_{min} = \frac{2.303}{\alpha - 1} \left[ \log \frac{x_D}{x_f} + \alpha \log \frac{1 - x_f}{1 - x_D} \right] \tag{11}$$

where $x_D$ and $x_f$ are the mole fractions of the more volatile component in the distillate and in the feed, respectively.

For a rough approximation of the number of plates required to give products each of 99 per cent purity at total reflux, Colburn and Schoenborn[5] propose the following formula:

$$n = \frac{4 \times 2.3}{\alpha - 1} \tag{12}$$

All the above methods of estimating plates depend on a knowledge of either $\alpha$ or the vapor-liquid equilibrium curve. In the majority of laboratory fractionations, such data are not available. A very rough estimation of the plates required for the standard separation based only on the difference in boiling points has been proposed:[3]

$$n_{opt} = \frac{T_B + T_A}{3(T_B - T_A)} \tag{13}$$

where $T_B$ and $T_A$ are the boiling points of the higher and lower boiling components, respectively, in degrees Kelvin. It should be remembered that this is only a rough approximation, but it usually tells, for example, whether 10 or 30 plates are required.

*McCabe-Thiele Solution.* The total method of McCabe and Thiele[6] for solving fractionation problems is usually applied to continuous commercial fractionations. It is also worthy of consideration here because it has become a classic in the science of fractional distillation.

In continuous fractionation the charge, called the feed, is admitted to the column at some point above the still. The reason for this is as follows. Suppose that in a batch fractionation we are separating a mixture of 50-50 mole per cent benzene and toluene. At some time during the fractionation, pure benzene will be refluxing at the head while pure toluene will exist in the still. As we progress up the column from the still to the head, the composition of the material existing in the column will vary from pure toluene to benzene. At some point in the column the composition will be 50 mole per cent benzene and 50 mole per cent toluene, the composition of the starting charge. If, now, at this point additional feed of the same composition is added at the boiling point of the mixture, conditions in the column will become stabilized and pure benzene may be taken off continuously at the top while toluene is taken off at the bottom. The rate of feed is adjusted so that addition of feed is equal to the combined rates of takeoff from the top and bottom. The advantages of such a system are obvious where a large amount of material must be fractionated and where the initial and final concentrations of materials are known.

A typical problem solved by the McCabe-Thiele method is as follows: It is desired to separate a 50-50 mole per cent solution of benzene and toluene so that the distillate contains 95 mole per cent benzene, and the material from the bottom of the column will contain 95 mole per cent toluene. How many theoretical plates are required, and at what point in the column will the feed be introduced?

The equilibrium diagram $AFED$ and the $x = y$ 45-degree diagonal $ABCD$ are drawn as on Figure 16.

A reasonable reflux ratio is assumed. In this case a ratio of 5 to 1 will be used. The slope of the enriching line $BE$ will be $O_n/O_n+D$ or $O_n/V_n$ and the slope of the exhausting line $CF$ will be $O_m/V_m$, as derived on page 14. To apply these formulas, assume a basis of 100 moles of feed mixture. Since we want 5 mole per cent of benzene in the still and 95 mole per cent of benzene in the distillate, an over-all material balance of the column gives:

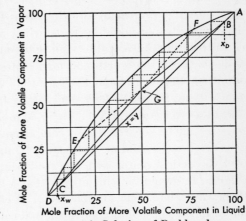

Figure 16. Solution of Problem by McCabe-Thiele Method

$$(0.05)\,(100) = 0.95\,D + 0.05\,W$$
$$= 0.95\,D + 0.05\,(100 - D)$$

which gives

$$D = 50 \text{ moles}$$
$$W = 50 \text{ moles}$$

We have assumed the reflux ratio, $O/D$ equal to 5. Therefore

$$O_n = 5D, \text{ or } 250$$
$$V_n = O_n + D, \text{ or } 300.$$

Below the feed plate, $V_n = V_m = 300$, $W = 50$, and $O_m = 350$.

Therefore, the slope of the enriching line $BE$ is

$$\frac{O_n}{V_n} = \frac{250}{300} = 0.833$$

and the exhausting line $CF$ is

$$\frac{O_m}{V_m} = \frac{350}{300} = 1.17$$

These two lines are now drawn on the diagram. The enriching line is drawn so that it intersects the 45-degree diagonal at $B$, where $x = 95$ per cent, while the exhausting line intersects at $C$, or where $x = 5$ per cent. These lines are now completely defined. It will be seen that these two lines intersect at $G$, or where $x = 50$ per cent, the composition of the feed. Now, the plates are determined by drawing steps from the enriching and exhausting lines to the vapor-liquid curve, starting at $B$ and progressing downward to $C$. In this example, it will be seen that counting downward from $B$, the point $G$ lies between the fourth and fifth plates. It is here, then, that the feed is admitted. Between $G$ and $C$ there are $4+$ plates. Therefore, there must be 4 or 5 plates below the feed. The total solution of the problem, then, reveals that at a reflux ratio of 5 to 1, a 50-50 mole per cent mixture of benzene and toluene can be separated into components containing at the head 95 mole per cent benzene and at the bottom 95 mole per cent toluene, by a column of 9 theoretical plates with the feed being introduced at the center of the column. It should be remembered that a bubble plate is not equivalent to a theoretical plate. The suitable factor of efficiency should therefore be introduced in the construction of the actual column.

It should be obvious from an examination of the diagram that as the reflux ratio is increased, the theoretical plates required for the separation decrease, since the slopes of the exhausting and enriching lines approach the $x = y$ diagonal. The minimum plates required are calculated when the reflux ratio is equal to $\infty$, that is, where no distillate is being taken off. An economical balance must be computed, therefore, which takes into account the relationship between the size of the column and the heat and time required for a given separation.

Smoker's equation[7] (page 18)

$$
n = \frac{\log \dfrac{x_o' \left(1 - \dfrac{mC(\alpha - 1)}{\alpha - mC^2} x_n'\right)}{x_n' \left(1 - \dfrac{mC(\alpha - 1)}{\alpha - mC^2} x_o'\right)}}{\log \dfrac{\alpha}{mC^2}}
\tag{14}
$$

does algebraically what the McCabe-Thiele diagram does graphically. Let us assume the same problem as was solved above by the McCabe-Thiele method. An average $\alpha$ of 2.60 is assumed. Then, in the section above the feed plate,

$$
m = \frac{R}{R + 1} = \frac{5}{6} = 0.833
$$

$$
b = \frac{x_p}{R + 1} = \frac{0.95}{6} = 0.158
$$

To obtain $k$, the following equation is solved:

$$m(\alpha - 1)k^2 + [m + b(\alpha - 1) - \alpha]k + b = 0$$

$$0.833\,(2.60 - 1)k^2 + [0.833 + 0.158\,(2.60 - 1) - 2.60]k + 0.158 = 0$$

$$1.3328k^2 - 1.514k + 0.158 = 0$$

$$k = 0.1178$$

$$\text{and } C = 1 + (\alpha - 1)k = 1.1885$$

$$\text{Further } x'_n = x_f - k$$

$$= 0.50 - 0.1178 = 0.3822$$

$$\text{and } x'_o = x_p - k$$

$$= 0.95 - 0.1178 = 0.8332$$

When these values are substituted in the Smoker equation, the plates required above the feed are obtained:

$$n = \frac{\log \dfrac{0.8332\left(1 - \dfrac{(0.883)(1.1885)(2.6 - 1)(0.3822)}{2.6 - 0.833(1.885)^2}\right)}{0.3822\left(1 - \dfrac{(0.833)(1.1885)(2.6 - 1)(0.8332)}{2.6 - 0.833(1.1855)^2}\right)}}{\log \dfrac{2.6}{0.833(1.1885)^2}}$$

or $n = 4$ (approx.)

When similar calculations are made below the feed, a little over 4 plates are found to be necessary. Therefore, a total of 9 plates is necessary, which is the same solution as was obtained from the McCabe-Thiele method.

The number of transfer units required for the same problem is obtained by the method described on page 20. In this case values of $x$ were chosen and the corresponding values of $y$ and $y^*$ were read from the enriching or exhausting line and the equilibrium curve respectively of Figure 16. As mentioned previously, the value of $y$ can also be calculated from equations (38) and (39), page 20.

The data of Table 2 were used in solving the problem:

**TABLE 2**

| $x$ | $y$ | $y^*$ | $\triangle y$ | $\dfrac{1}{\triangle y}$ |
|---|---|---|---|---|
| 0.0625 | 0.0688 | 0.1188 | 0.05 | 20.0 |
| 0.125 | 0.1400 | 0.2325 | 0.0925 | 10.8 |
| 0.25 | 0.2875 | 0.4312 | 0.1437 | 6.9 |
| 0.3125 | 0.3613 | 0.5125 | 0.1512 | 6.6 |
| 0.375 | 0.4325 | 0.5800 | 0.1475 | 6.8 |
| 0.4375 | 0.5075 | 0.6438 | 0.1363 | 7.3 |
| 0.500 | 0.5813 | 0.7000 | 0.1187 | 8.4 |
| 0.5625 | 0.6313 | 0.7567 | 0.1254 | 8.0 |
| 0.625 | 0.6813 | 0.8050 | 0.1237 | 8.1 |
| 0.6875 | 0.7325 | 0.8500 | 0.1175 | 8.5 |
| 0.750 | 0.7880 | 0.8900 | 0.1020 | 9.8 |
| 0.8125 | 0.8375 | 0.9225 | 0.0850 | 11.7 |
| 0.875 | 0.8875 | 0.9525 | 0.0650 | 15.4 |
| 0.9375 | 0.9375 | 0.9788 | 0.0413 | 24.2 |

The graph $y$ vs. $1/\triangle y$ is drawn in Figure 17.

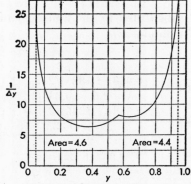

**Figure 17.** Determination of Transfer Units

Measurement of the area below the curves gives 4.6 transfer units below the feed plate, and 4.4 units above. For this problem, then, the number of transfer units calculated corresponds to the number of theoretical plates.

### REFERENCES

1. FENSKE, M. R., *Ind. Eng. Chem.*, **24**, 482 (1932)
2. SMOKER, E. H., *ibid.*, **34**, 509 (1942)
3. ROSE, A., *ibid.*, **33**, 594 (1941)
4. DODGE, B. F., and HUFFMAN, J. R., *ibid.*, **29**, 1434 (1937)
5. COLBURN, A. P., and SCHOENBORN, E. M., *Trans. Am. Inst. Chem. Engrs.*, **41**, 645 (1945)
6. McCABE, W. L., and THIELE, E. W., *Ind. Eng. Chem.*, **17**, 605 (1925)
7. SMOKER, E. H., *Trans. Am. Inst. Chem. Engrs.*, **34**, 165 (1938)

# Separation to Be Expected

IT IS FREQUENTLY the reaction of the research worker, when he sees the immense possibility of improvement in efficiency obtained by the transition from the older Vigreux or Hempel columns to the more efficient packed columns, to attribute to the efficient column ability of separation far beyond its capacity. The difficulties involved in the separation of materials with what are usually considered large boiling point differences are not generally recognized by the worker without a basic knowledge of the theory of fractional distillation. For example, it requires 8 or 9 plates in a column operating at a reflux ratio of 3 to 1 to separate a 50-50 mole per cent mixture of benzene and toluene, with a boiling point difference of 32 degrees, into distillate consisting of 95 mole per cent benzene and residue consisting of 95 mole per cent toluene. To raise these percentages to 99 per cent, about 13 to 15 plates are required at the same ratio.

These plate requirements may, of course, be lowered somewhat by an increase in the reflux ratio. When it is considered how often it is necessary to separate materials boiling much closer than 32 degrees with no better fractionating equipment than a one-plate still with no reflux control whatever, the advantages—even the necessity—of an efficient column become apparent at once.

In Table 3 are given data for some fractionations. The first seven examples are fractionations of actual reaction mixtures, and so contained some foreshots and tails not listed. The columns in these cases were operated so as to give the maximum number of plates during the fractionation. The remaining examples are test mixtures. In some of these later cases more efficient separation could have been obtained by varying the operating conditions. However, they do give a very good indication of the separation to be expected.

In an 85-plate column[1] the following materials were separated:

| | |
|---|---|
| 4.9 grams t-butylethylene | b 41 C |
| 5 grams intermediate, | |
| 21 grams neohexane | b 50 C |
| 13.9 grams intermediate, | |
| 5.31 grams 1,1,2-trimethylcyclopropane | b 56 C |
| 4.78 grams intermediate, | |
| 8 grams 1-chloro-2,2-dimethylbutane, | b 115 C |

## TABLE 3

| Lower Boiling Component | Inter-mediate Cut | Higher Boiling Component | Boiling Point Difference | Plates in Column | Ref-erence |
|---|---|---|---|---|---|
| n-Propanol 60 g | 4.1 g | t-Amyl carbinol 7.2 g | 38° | 9 | 1 |
| t-Butylethylene 1.4 g | 0.8 g | Neohexane 1 g | 9° | 20 | 1 |
| Pinacolyl chloride 247 g | 157.0 g | 1-Chloro-2,2-dimethylbutane 198 g | 6° at 252 mm | 87 | 1 |
| n-Propanol 16.5 g | 1.9 g | n-Propyl-neohexyl ether 7.2 g | 49° | 9 | 1 |
| t-Amyl carbinol 7.6 g | 1.5 g | n-Propyl-neohexyl ether 11 g | 11° | 9 | 1 |
| Pivalic acid 70.7 g | 16.9 g | Chloropivalic acid 237 g | 47° at 51 mm | 12 | 1 |
| 1-Hexene 23.7 g | 6.3 g | n-Octane 29.9 g | 60° | 13 | 2 |
| Benzene 25 wt % | 55 wt % | Toluene 20 wt % | 32° | 11 | 3 |
| Benzene | 100 wt %* | Ethylene dichloride | 3.5° | 21 | 3 |
| Carbon tetrachloride 25.3 g | 18.2 g | Toluene 53.5 g | 33° | 10 | 4 |

*No pure component was obtained. Initial fraction contained about 73 per cent benzene.

Figure 18 is the distillation curve obtained from the fractionation of the methyl esters of a mixture of fatty acids obtained from hydrogenated fish

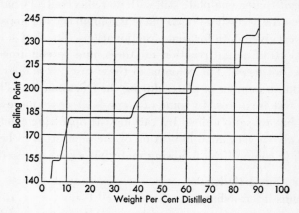

**Figure 18.** Distillation Curve from Fractionation of Fatty Acids

oil. The fractionation was run using intermittent takeoff (page 100) from a 15-plate helix-packed column at a pressure of 10 mm of mercury.

We have seen that the ease of separation of a binary system is indicated by $\alpha$, the relative volatility of the compounds. The larger the $\alpha$, the greater will be the difference in the vapor pressures of the components, and consequently the easier it will be to separate them. To give some idea of the relative volatility to be expected, a number of $\alpha$ values are given in Table 4. The values of $\alpha$ are calculated from the data of Willingham, Taylor, Pignocco, and Rossini[5] (see page 144). The $\alpha_A$ and $\alpha_B$ are calculated at temperatures corresponding to the boiling points of the lower and higher boiling components of the mixture, A and B respectively.

**TABLE 4**

| | | Boiling Point C | | | | |
|---|---|---|---|---|---|---|
| | System | A | B | Difference | $\alpha_A$ | $\alpha_B$ |
| A | 2,5-Dimethylhexane | 109.103 | 109.429 | 0.326 | 1.009 | 1.009 |
| B | 2,4-Dimethylhexane | | | | | |
| A | n-Heptane | 98.426 | 99.238 | 0.812 | 1.024 | 1.022 |
| B | 2,2,4-Trimethylpentane | | | | | |
| A | 2,3,4-Trimethylpentane | 113.467 | 114.760 | 1.293 | 1.036 | 1.036 |
| B | 2,3,3-Trimethylpentane | | | | | |
| A | 2,2,4-Trimethylpentane | 99.238 | 100.934 | 1.696 | 1.049 | 1.049 |
| B | Methylcyclohexane | | | | | |
| A | n-Heptane | 98.426 | 100.934 | 2.508 | 1.074 | 1.076 |
| B | Methylcyclohexane | | | | | |
| A | 2,2,4-Trimethylpentane | 99.238 | 125.665 | 26.427 | 2.219 | 1.995 |
| B | n-Octane | | | | | |
| A | n-Heptane | 98.426 | 125.665 | 27.239 | 2.278 | 2.088 |
| B | n-Octane | | | | | |
| A | Toluene | 110.623 | 138.347 | 27.724 | 2.236 | 2.068 |
| B | p-Xylene | | | | | |
| A | Toluene | 110.623 | 139.102 | 28.479 | 2.296 | 2.107 |
| B | m-Xylene | | | | | |
| A | n-Hexane | 68.740 | 98.426 | 29.686 | 2.618 | 2.330 |
| B | n-Heptane | | | | | |
| A | Benzene | 80.103 | 110.623 | 30.520 | 2.604 | 2.333 |
| B | Toluene | | | | | |

Several other systems have been reported, giving $\alpha$ at only one temperature as indicated in Table 5.

In Figure 19, (a) and (b), the value of $\alpha$ is plotted against temperature difference. Figure 19 (a) shows the lower $\alpha$ and boiling point differences. As would be expected, the curve is close to a straight line. In Figure 19 (b), however, the values vary considerably from a straight-line formula. These differences are caused partly by the wide temperature range over which each $\alpha$ is measured, and partly by variation from Raoult's law.

**TABLE 5**

| System | α | Boiling Point Difference, C | Reference |
|---|---|---|---|
| 2,4-Dimethylpentane<br>2,2,3-Trimethylbutane | 1.006 | 0.2 | 6 |
| 2,2-Dimethylpentane<br>2,4-Dimethylpentane | 1 045 | 1.5 | 6 |
| 2,2-Dimethylpentane<br>2,2,3-Trimethylbutane | 1.051 | 1 7 | 6 |
| Benzene<br>Ethylene dichloride | 1.11 | 3.5 | 7 |
| Toluene<br>Ethylene dichloride | 2.23 | 26.3 | 8 |

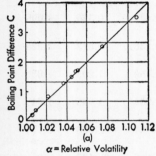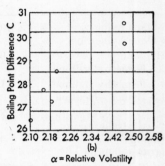

**Figure 19.** Boiling Point Differences—Alpha Curves

As the boiling point difference and α increase, the number of plates required to separate the mixture decreases rapidly. Table 6 is calculated from the Fenske equation (page 15), using selected values of α, and values of 99 mole per cent more volatile in the distillate and 1 mole per cent more volatile in the still.

**TABLE 6**

| α | Plates Required | α | Plates Required |
|---|---|---|---|
| 1.00 | ∞ | 1.30 | 35 |
| 1.05 | 188 | 1.40 | 27 |
| 1.10 | 96 | 1.60 | 19 |
| 1.15 | 66 | 2.00 | 13 |
| 1.20 | 50 | 2.50 | 10 |
| 1.25 | 41 | 3.00 | 8 |

It should be remembered that these values are calculated for total reflux and also for ideal systems. For practical fractionation, these minimum plate values should be multiplied by a factor of about 2 (see page 28).

Formulas for roughly estimating the $\alpha$ of hydrocarbons have been given by Griswold[9]. For materials boiling within 5 degrees of each other,

$$\alpha_c = 1 + \frac{T_B - T_A}{10.56 + 0.0633T} \tag{1}$$

where $T$ is the boiling point in degrees Kelvin at atmospheric pressure. For wider boiling materials,

$$\alpha_w = 1 + \alpha_c(4.4 + 2.3 \log T)\left(\frac{T_B - T_A}{T}\right) \tag{2}$$

The formula developed by Edgeworth-Johnstone[10] for nonpolar liquids at atmospheric pressure is:

$$\log \alpha = \frac{T - T_A}{T} \log T_A + \frac{T_B - T}{T} \log T_B + \frac{T_B - T_A}{T} \log R \tag{3}$$

where
$$R = \text{gas constant (82.048)}$$
$$T_A \text{ and } T_B = \text{absolute atmospheric boiling points}$$
$$\alpha = \text{relative volatility at } T$$

This equation applies when $\alpha$ for the system can be assumed equal to $P_A/P_B$.

Melpolder and Headington[11] have also developed a method for calculating the relative volatility of nonpolar binary mixtures from the boiling points of the components. These values are sufficiently accurate to be used in distillation systems involving many theoretical plates and small boiling point differences. On the basis of the following,

$$\log \frac{P_1}{P_2} = \log \alpha = K\left(\frac{t_2 - t_1}{T}\right) \tag{4}$$

where $P_1$ and $P_2$, and $t_1$ and $t_2$ are, respectively, the pressures and temperatures of the components of the system, the temperature being measured in degrees centigrade, $T$ is the absolute boiling point of the mixture, and $K$ is a constant which is a function of temperature and pressure, Melpolder and Headington have used precise vapor pressure and temperature measurements to evaluate $K$. The following formula is the result:

$$\log \alpha = \frac{t_2 - t_1}{T}\left(7.30 - 1.15 \log P + \frac{T}{179 \log P}\right) \tag{5}$$

which, for atmospheric pressure, becomes

$$\log \alpha = \frac{t_2 - t_1}{T}(3.99 + 0.001939T) \tag{6}$$

This formula is useful if the components under consideration do not deviate from Raoult's law, and if the temperature difference is not large.

As examples of the agreement between values in Table 4 and those obtained from equation (6), Table 7 has been constructed.

**TABLE 7**

| System | Temperature, C | α from Table 4 | α from Equation (6) |
|---|---|---|---|
| n-Heptane- | 98.426 | 1.074 | 1.074 |
| Methylcyclohexane | 100.934 | 1.076 | 1.075 |
| 2,3,4-Trimethylpentane- | 113.467 | 1.036 | 1.037 |
| 2,3,3-Trimethylpentane | 114.760 | 1.036 | 1.037 |
| 2,2,4-Trimethylpentane- | 99.238 | 2.219 | 2.158 |
| n-Octane | 125.665 | 1 995 | 2.065 |
| Benzene- | 80.103 | 2.604 | 2.531 |
| Toluene | 110.623 | 2.333 | 2.376 |

The data collected from a fractionation are usually recorded and analyzed in the form of a *distillation curve*. If the compositions of the various pure products are known and recognizable in the fractions of the distillate, the curve may have the form shown in Figure 20, where the percentage of one component in each fraction is plotted against either the weight (or volume) distilled or the percentage of the total charge distilled.

The flat, horizontal portions at 0 and 100 per cent of the more volatile component are, of course, the pure components, while the sloping portion of the curve is the intermediate fraction. If the composition of the fractions is unknown, a plot of the physical properties of the fractions against amount distilled can be made, as shown on page 104.

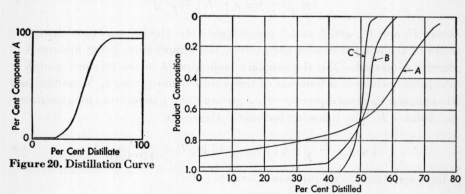

**Figure 20.** Distillation Curve

**Figure 21.** Change in Distillation Curve with Change in Alpha

In Figure 21 three distillation curves are shown. Rose[12] has shown that for an ideal two-component system with an α of 1.25 (boiling point difference of about 8 degrees at 100 C), 10 plates are required for curve $A$, 20 for $B$, and 30 for $C$, provided proper reflux is used in each case and holdup is negligible. This separation is dependent not only on $\alpha$, but also on the number $n$ of plates in the column. As a result of this fact an efficiency factor $E$ equal to $\alpha^n$ may be set up.

Figure 22 shows the actual curves obtained[4] from the fractionation of a mixture of 60 weight per cent toluene and 40 weight per cent carbon tetrachloride through a 10-plate column packed with glass helices.

Curve $A$ was obtained at a reflux ratio of 3 to 1, curve $B$ at a reflux ratio of 10 to 1, while curve $C$ was obtained using the technique of intermittent takeoff (page 100) at a rate equivalent to a reflux ratio of 10 to 1.

Smoker and Rose[3] have devised a method for predicting the shape of a distillation curve before the fractionation is run. The data required are the vapor-

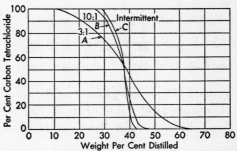

Figure 22. Change in Distillation Curve with Change in Reflux Ratio

liquid equilibrium diagram, the theoretical plates in the system, the reflux ratio, and the composition of the charge. In this case, as in the case above, the holdup of the column is assumed to be negligible. Experience has shown that this assumption is frequently justified, since a holdup of less than 10 per cent of the total volume of any component in the starting charge will have little effect on the shape of the distillation curve. In Chapter IV an example was given for determining the number of plates necessary to give a desired distillate and residue composition when the feed composition and the reflux ratio are set. By the same method, then, it is also possible to calculate the charge composition necessary to give desired distillate and residue if the number of plates and reflux ratio are specified. To use the method of Smoker and Rose, the charge composition for a number of distillate compositions is determined with a fixed reflux ratio and plate value. When these feed compositions are plotted against the corresponding distillate compositions in an example calculated at a reflux ratio of 2.44 and for 11 theoretical plates, curve $B$, Figure 23, is obtained.

This gives, in effect, a second vapor-liquid equilibrium curve, except that the coordinates have been changed to account for the conditions of a reflux ratio of 2.44 and a system of 11 theoretical plates. This curve may now be treated in a manner exactly analogous to the way in which curve $A$ would

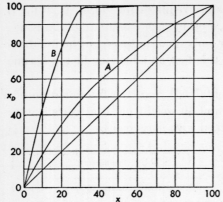

**Figure 23.** Prediction of Distillation Curve

be treated. The Rayleigh[13] equation,

$$\ln W = \int_{x_c}^{x} \frac{dx}{x_D - x} \qquad (7)$$

relates the fraction of the original charge remaining in the pot $W$ to the pot composition $x$ and the distillate composition $x_D$. For different assumed charge compositions $x_c$, the distillate compositions $x_D$ are read from curve $B$ and values of the function $1/(x_D - x)$ are determined. These are plotted as shown in Figure 24.

The numerical value of $\ln W$ can then be found for any value of $x$ by taking the area under the curve from the assumed $x$ to $x_c$. When the values

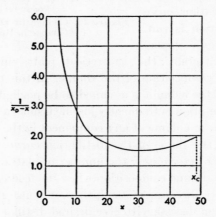

**Figure 24.** Prediction of Distillation Curve

of $W$ are determined, the corresponding values of the fraction distilled $D$ immediately become known since $D = 1 - W$. Therefore, the value of $x_D$, the mole per cent more volatile component in the distillate, is found for corresponding values of $D$, and the final distillation curve is drawn.

## REFERENCES

1. CARNEY, T. P., *Ph. D. Thesis, The Pennsylvania State College* (1941)
2. WHITMORE, F. C., and ZOOK, H., *J. Am. Chem. Soc.*, **64**, 1783 (1942)
3. SMOKER, E. H., and ROSE, A., *Trans. Am. Inst. Chem. Engrs.*, **36**, 285 (1940)
4. CARNEY, T. P., *Unpublished work*
5. WILLINGHAM, C. B., TAYLOR, W. J., PIGNOCCO, J. M., and ROSSINI, F. D., *J. Research Nat. Bur. of Standards*, **35**, 219 (1945)
6. FAWCETT, F. S., *Ind. Eng. Chem.*, **38**, 338 (1946)
7. SMITH, E. R., and MATHESON, H., *J. Research Nat. Bur. of Standards*, **20**, 641 (1938)
8. COLBURN, A. P., and STEARNS, R. F., *Trans. Am. Inst. Chem. Engrs.*, **37**, 291 (1941)
9. GRISWOLD, J., *Ind. Eng. Chem.*, **35**, 247 (1943)
10. EDGEWORTH-JOHNSTONE, R., *ibid.*, **35**, 826 (1943)
11. MELPOLDER, F. W., and HEADINGTON, C. E., *ibid.*, **39**, 766 (1947)
12. ROSE, A., *ibid.*, **33**, 594 (1941)
13. RAYLEIGH, LORD, *Phil. Mag.*, 534 (1904)

# CHAPTER

# VI

## Selection of Proper Column

THE SELECTION of the proper fractionating column for carrying out a given fractionation is dependent on a number of factors. The quantity of material to be distilled, the relative vapor pressure or boiling point difference of the components to be separated, the sharpness of separation desired, the actual boiling points of the components, and the pressure at which the fractionation is to be run are the principal data to be known or estimated before deciding on a column.

Mixtures of materials are fractionated for two purposes: to analyze an unknown mixture, or to purify a certain compound or compounds. In each case the most important consideration is to have a column capable of separating the mixture into fractions, at least some of which will be pure samples of each of the important components in the starting mixture. In Chapter IV the methods of estimating the number of theoretical plates required for a given fractionation were discussed. Naturally, a special column cannot be built for every laboratory fractionation. Therefore, the distillation will have to be fitted to an available column. It is only necessary that the column used have at least the number of plates estimated as being required, but any increase in this number will not be wasted. Since a larger number of theoretical plates in a column requires a smaller reflux ratio to perform a given separation, the excess efficiency of the column used may to some extent be balanced by decreasing the reflux ratio, thus increasing the takeoff rate and decreasing the time required for completion of the distillation. As a rough general rule, though, the reflux ratio should be approximately equal to the number of theoretical plates determined for the column while operating under total reflux.

In the ordinary laboratory the choice of a column usually will not be very wide. If 15-, 50-, and 100-plate columns are available in sizes which will handle from about 10 to 500 cc of charged material, the laboratory is equipped to fractionate practically all the mixtures obtained in ordinary chemical research.

In addition to the three types of columns suggested above, a micro column (Chapter XXI) and a column of about 20 plates capable of distilling a charge of several liters are also recommended as standard equipment. This latter column is particularly useful in fractionating starting materials which are obtained from industrial laboratories in *practical* grades. A practical grade may mean a material of a purity anywhere between 50 and 90 per cent, and even in the more refined commercial products there are sometimes enough impurities present to eliminate their use in a reaction without further purification. A great deal of time is saved if a large amount of material of this kind can be fractionated in one batch. In special problems such as those encountered in petroleum research, larger and more efficient columns having over 100 theoretical plates are necessary.

Assume, now, that we have several columns available, all having enough plates to give the required degree of separation. The next limiting factor is the amount of charge available for fractionation. The operating holdup of the column determines what starting charge may be handled satisfactorily. Obviously, a charge of 50 grams could not be fractionated practically through a column having a 25-gram holdup. As we have seen, sharpness of separation is a function of the holdup. As an arbitrary standard, then, the operating holdup of a column should not be more than approximately 10 per cent of the amount of any single component in the charge if this component is desired pure. Naturally, if the holdup is less it is advantageous in the matter of sharpness of separation.

As a result of the fact that sharpness of separation is approximately a linear function of the ratio of the charge to holdup,[1] it is quite possible to have a decrease in the sharpness of separation even though the number of theoretical plates of a column is increased. Such would be the case where increases in plate efficiency are also accompanied by increase in holdup. Both the number of theoretical plates and the holdup should be taken into consideration where sharpness of separation is a desirable factor. For columns of the same number of theoretical plates, a sharper separation is obtained in the same length of time if the holdup relative to the charge is decreased.

The *H.E.T.P.* of a given type of column should be considered before actually deciding on that type as the column for use, especially if the number of plates required is quite high. If the column may be extended through two or three floors of a building, then the *H.E.T.P.* from the standpoint of total column height alone is not important. However, if the column has to be fitted into an ordinary sized room, a column giving a lower *H.E.T.P.* would be used, even though some desirable properties available in a different type of column would have to be sacrificed.

Different types of packings and columns will be considered in detail in subsequent chapters in this book. On the surface, though, there are two factors to be considered: first, ease of construction and/or cheapness of the commercially constructed unit, and, second, generality of usefulness.

The all-glass columns described are readily constructed by anyone knowing the rudiments of glass blowing. The helix type of packing is available from several commercial sources if the builder of the column does not wish to make it himself. Some of the metal packings are quite difficult to construct and when finally made are difficult to encase in the column tube so that no channeling will occur. Commercially made columns are usually relatively expensive.

By generality of usefulness is meant use at all temperatures, pressures, and with all types of chemical compounds. Glass is the only material that is completely resistant to corrosion. In addition, it has no tendency to catalyze decomposition of the material being fractionated as do some metal packings. If a column is to be in general use in a laboratory, it is desirable that it be capable of handling any type of compound.

While a cursory reading of the literature available would seem to indicate that for a given size packing, particularly of the helix type, metal packings give higher efficiency than glass, this is probably actually not the case. Glasgow and Schicktanz[2] have studied packing composed of 2-mm to 4-mm balls made from glass, lead, and copper. They concluded that, for the same size packing, the heat conductivity and the nature of the material of the packing have no effect on the efficiency of separation, liquid holdup, or throughput of the still. It is probable that this same thing would also be true for the helix packing, provided packings of the same size were being compared. For example, packings described as "1/16-inch" made from glass and from steel may differ considerably in the diameter of the material making up the helices. It is believed that if glass helices could be made of the same thickness and to the same standards of uniformity as can those of steel, the efficiency would not vary for the same size packing. Fine glass, which would give more volume per cent free space, is usually too fragile.

Because of the nature of the construction of some of the packings described later they cannot be made from glass, and so some relatively corrosion resistant material such as stainless steel must be used. These metal packings do have the advantage of being able to withstand harder usage than glass, both during distillation and during the removal and replacement of packing.

## REFERENCES

1. ROSE, A., WELSHANS, L. M., and LONG, H. H., *Ind. Eng. Chem.*, **32**, 673 (1944)
2. GLASGOW, A. R., JR., and SCHICKTANZ, S. T., *J. Research Nat. Bur. Standards*, **19**, 593 (1937)

# VII

## *Bubble Plate Columns*

BUBBLE PLATE COLUMNS are not usually considered in the category of laboratory fractionating columns. Their one advantage is in high throughput. However, this advantage is frequently nullified by the large holdup which decreases the sharpness of separation. In the normal laboratory fractionation it is usually desired to have a sharper separation, even if speed of operation has to be sacrificed.

The ordinary bubble plate column has the general form shown in Figure 6. The vapor passes up through the vapor riser $A$ and is deflected downward to the plate by the bubble cap $B$, escaping at the base of the cap. On each plate is a layer of liquid whose depth is determined by the height $h$ of the overflow pipe $C$ above the surface of the plate. The lower end of this overflow pipe is sealed by the liquid on the plate below, thus preventing vapor from passing up through this passage. The vapor escaping through the base of the bubble cap thus passes under the surface of the liquid on the plate. There is some heat exchange between the vapor and the liquid, involving condensation and reevaporation of the more volatile components. This washing of the vapor by the liquid on the plate takes place all the way up the column, each plate evolving vapor richer in the more volatile component than did the plate below it.

As can be seen, a large quantity of material is held up as liquid on the plates themselves, thus reducing the value of this type of column for small-scale laboratory fractionations.

It should be remembered that an actual bubble plate in a column is not equal to a theoretical plate. A column having 30 bubble plates may actually give a separation equivalent to only 10 theoretical plates. This becomes evident when we remember that a theoretical plate is one having the vapor in *equilibrium* with the liquid. Several factors contribute to the lack of equilibrium on a bubble plate. The vapor bubbles rising through the liquid may be too large. Velocity of the vapors can be too rapid, causing entrainment of liquid. The overflow of liquid from the plate above may not mix thoroughly with that on the plate below, or the vapor may pass out through only one side of the bubble cap.

The efficiency of a bubble plate column[1] is expressed as the actual number of plates in the column divided by the number of theoretical plates required to give the same enrichment as that given by the column under consideration. In actual practice plate efficiencies usually run from 40 per cent to 70 per cent, although if the column is not correctly designed and operated the efficiency may drop as low as 15 per cent.

***Bruun Column.*** Bruun[2] has developed a special type of bubble cap tower

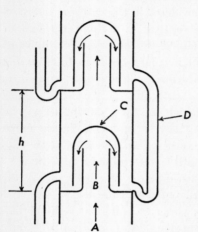

Figure 25. Bruun Column

which gives excellent results, with few of the undesirable features of the standard bubble plate column. The general structure of the column is shown in Figure 25.

The vapors enter the column through *A* and rise through the vapor riser *B*, then down between the outside wall of the riser and the loose cap *C*. In the bottom of the cap are cut fine slits, thus forcing the vapor to pass below the surface of the liquid on the plate in a fine spray. Overflow from one plate to the one below is by means of the side arm *D*.

Data for several column sizes are available. Columns I, II, and III have the dimension *h* (Figure 25) equal to 20 mm, 40 mm, and 80 mm, respectively.

TABLE 8

| *Column* 25 mm ID | *Column height cm* | *Throughput ml/min* | *Plates* —1 | *H.E.T.P.* cm |
|---|---|---|---|---|
| Column I 5 sections | 10 | 5.1 9.8 21.5 | 5.4 4.8 3.7 | 1.9 2.1 2.7 |
| Column II 5 sections | 20 | 4.5 10.3 24.6 | 4.4 4.2 3.7 | 4.5 4.8 5.4 |
| Column III 5 sections | 40 | 4.8 20.7 | 5.7 4.9 | 7.1 8.2 |

The data of Table 8 were collected using benzene-carbon tetrachloride. Similar tests with *n*-heptane-methylcyclohexane gave results not appreciably different.

The maximum vapor velocities (see page 145) allowable in these columns are given in Table 9, the test liquid being benzene.

TABLE 9

| Column | Throughput ml/min | Vapor velocity | |
|---|---|---|---|
| | | cm/sec | ft/sec |
| Column I | 30 | 31.3 | 1 |
| Column II | 64 | 65.5 | 2.2 |
| Column III | 41 | 42.4 | 1.4 |

In a column of 100 sections[3] spaced as in column I, the plate values of Table 10 were obtained:

TABLE 10

| Throughput ml/min | Plates |
|---|---|
| 8 | 84.2 |
| 10 | 72.6 |
| 5 | 70.6 |

When 1500 ml of a mixture of 10 mole per cent n-heptane (bp 98.4 C) and 90 mole per cent toluene (bp 110 C) was fractionated through the above column at a takeoff rate of 1 ml per min and a reflux ratio of 6:1, approximately 125 ml of practically pure heptane, 150 cc of intermediate mixture, and the remainder practically pure toluene were obtained. The operating holdup of this column is approximately 70 ml. The maximum vapor velocity is 31.3 cm per sec (1 ft per sec) or about 30 ml of benzene per minute.

To give some idea of the separation effected by columns of this type, binary mixtures of 50 mole per cent benzene-50 mole per cent ethylene dichloride (mixture A) boiling 3.5 degrees apart, and 10 mole per cent n-heptane-90 mole per cent toluene (mixture B) were fractionated through columns of types I, II, and III, containing 100, 52, and 26 sections respectively, with the results stated in Table 11.

TABLE 11

| Mixture | Throughput ml/min | Takeoff ml/min | Reflux ratio | Mole per cent lower boiling constituent in distillate | | |
|---|---|---|---|---|---|---|
| | | | | I | II | III |
| A | 2 | 0.1 | 20:1 | 99.9 | 93 | 80 |
| B | 7 | 0.1 | 7:1 to 10:1 | 99.9 | 99 | 93 |

While the holdup of the Bruun column is well above that obtained from, for example, a Fenske column with the same plates and throughput, it is still much less than the standard bubble plate column. The holdups for types I and II are about 0.7 ml and 0.14 ml per section respectively.

One thing should be noted concerning this type of column. The spacing of the sections is dependent on the vapor velocity. For higher vapor velocities, it is necessary to have a column of type II, while at lower velocities type I is preferred. Thus it is necessary to have two different columns, one to operate at low vapor velocities at atmospheric pressure, the other to use under reduced pressure where the vapor velocities are much greater.

*Othmer Column.*    The next successful attempt to improve on the design of the bubble plate column so as to eliminate the undesirable features was made by Othmer.[4] In Figure 26, the arrows drawn in the upper plate assembly indicate the path of rising vapor, while those in the lower indicate the path of the descending liquid. The liquid on the plate $A$ is thoroughly washed by the vapor passing through the ten or twelve 4-mm holes, $B$. The lower trap is vented at $C$ to prevent siphoning, and the overflow from the plate is discharged from the trap through the tube $D$. There are three of these outlet tubes around the circumference of the trap instead of two as shown in the drawing. The outlet tubes come within 1 mm of the side of the column so that the liquid flows down the inner wall to the next lower plate. These columns have been made in units of 4, 6, and 8 plates with glass flanges on the ends for assembling. Inlet or take-off tubes, not shown in the drawing, may be placed anywhere along the length of the sections.

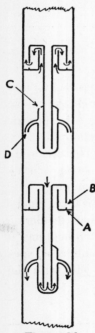

When heat is no longer applied to the still pot on this column, a partial vacuum is caused by the condensation of vapors. This causes the liquid on the plate to be drawn under the cap, and gases bubble up through this liquid and thence pass down the inner riser tube. If it is desired to avoid this draining from the plates, it may be done in three ways: (1) by making the diameter of the cap larger in relation to that of the column and thus decreasing the amount of liquid held up by the plate and increasing the capacity under the cap, (2) by decreasing the height of the lower trap so that it is less than that on the plate and vapors may be drawn down the overflow tube, or (3) by placing an auxiliary trap on the still pot which will allow air to come in at the column base on a shutdown. This last is the most practical. These columns have been made in sizes from 1 inch to 2.5 inches in diameter, being used un-

**Figure 26.**
Othmer Column

der both superatmospheric and subatmospheric pressures. The smaller sizes have been made from heavy glass tubing to withstand pressures up to 75 pounds per square inch.[5]

Some of the operating characteristics of this column are as follows[5]: In a 2-inch diameter column having 12 actual plates, the theoretical plate value varied from 7 to 12. With the system acetic acid-water, superficial vapor velocities varied from 0.66 feet per second and 2.0 feet per second to give an overhead (principally water) of 15 to 45 cc per minute. The operating holdup is about 20-25 cc per plate, while the pressure drop is about 1.5 inches of distilling liquid per plate.

***Palkin Column.*** Palkin[6] has developed the gauze-plate column shown in Figure 27 to eliminate the danger of blowing of vapors up through the trap tubes, and to insure the complete mixing of reflux from the plate above with

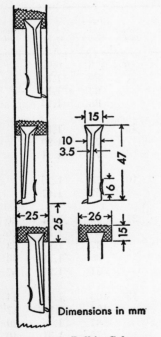

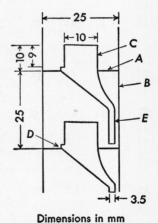

**Figure 27.** Palkin Column          **Figure 28.** Oldershaw Column

the scrubbing medium on any plate. The plates are made from 40-mesh nickel wire screen. The operation of this type column is evident from the figure. As can be seen from Figure 27 the screen is made slightly larger in diameter than the column tube so as to form a squeeze fit in the tube.

The Palkin column has been used quite successfully for the distillation of α- and β-pinene mixtures.

*Oldershaw Column.* A second laboratory column using glass plates has been developed by Oldershaw.[7] It consists of a series of perforated plates *A* sealed into a tube *B*. Each plate is equipped with a baffle *C* to direct the flow of liquid, a weir *D* to maintain liquid level on the plate, and a drain pipe *E*, as in Figure 28. The dimensions assigned in Figure 28 are for column I, Table 12.

An *H.E.T.P.* of less than an inch is obtained at a slower rate of throughput, while plate efficiencies (page 49) as high as 103 per cent were also observed under these conditions.

The operating characteristics of five columns of the Oldershaw type are given in Table 12.

### TABLE 12

| Column | Inside column diameter mm | Diameter plate perforations mm | Number of perforations per plate | Distance between plates mm | Through-put ml/min | Theoretical plates | Actual plates | Plate efficiency | H.E.T.P. inches | Holdup ml | Reference |
|--------|---------------------------|-------------------------------|----------------------------------|----------------------------|--------------------|--------------------|---------------|------------------|------------------|-----------|-----------|
| I   | 25 | 0.85 | 42 | 25 | 6     | 10   | 10 | 100 | 0.98 |    | 7 |
|     |    |      |    |    | 13    | 8.9  |    | 89  | 1.10 |    |   |
|     |    |      |    |    | 18    | 8.8  |    | 88  | 1.12 |    |   |
|     |    |      |    |    | 24    | 8.6  |    | 86  | 1.14 |    |   |
| II  | 25 | 1.1  | 44 | 25 | 15    | 8.4  | 10 | 84  | 1.17 |    | 7 |
|     |    |      |    |    | 26    | 7.7  |    | 77  | 1.28 |    |   |
|     |    |      |    |    | 28    | 7.5  |    | 75  | 1.31 |    |   |
| III | 25 | 1.35 | 44 | 25 | 12.5  | 7.8  | 10 | 78  | 1.26 |    | 7 |
|     |    |      |    |    | 23.5  | 6.7  |    | 67  | 1.47 |    |   |
| IV  | 25 | 0.85 | 42 | 25 | 9     | 35.1 | 37 | 95  | 1.04 | 20 | 7 |
|     |    |      |    |    | 14    | 32.9 |    | 89  | 1.10 | 26 |   |
|     |    |      |    |    | 22    | 32.2 |    | 87  | 1.13 | 53 |   |
|     |    |      |    |    | 28    | 31.8 |    | 86  | 1.14 | 58 |   |
|     |    |      |    |    | 40*   | 30.0 |    | 81  | 1.21 | 67 |   |
| V   | 32 | 0.85 | 81 | 30 | 17    | 15.5 | 15 | 103 | 1.14 | 14 | 7 |
|     |    |      |    |    | 18.3  | 15.3 |    | 102 | 1.16 | 17 |   |
|     |    |      |    |    | 36.8  | 13.0 |    | 87  | 1.36 | 39 |   |
|     |    |      |    |    | 52    | 11.7 |    | 78  | 1.51 | 40 |   |
|     |    |      |    |    | 70.5  | 10.3 |    | 69  | 1.71 | 44 |   |
|     |    |      |    |    | 75.0* | 10.0 |    | 67  | 1.76 | 45 |   |
| VI  | 27 | 0.9  | 80 | 25 | 21.7  | 17.2 | 30 | 57  | 1.71 | 47 | 8 |
|     |    |      |    |    | 46.7  | 19.4 |    | 65  | 1.52 | 53 |   |
|     |    |      |    |    | 63.3  | 16.7 |    | 56  | 1.77 | 59 |   |

*Indicates maximum rate.

Collins and Lantz[8] have studied column VI, Table 12, under various operating conditions, with the results shown in Table 13.

**TABLE 13**

| Throughput cc/min | Reflux ratio (to 1) | Theoretical plates | Plate efficiency per cent | Operating holdup ml |
|---|---|---|---|---|
| 21.7 | 27 | 17.1 | 57 | 47 |
| 38.3 | 27 | 17.4 | 58 | 50.5 |
| 46.7 | 27 | 18.0 | 60 | 53 |
| 55.0 | 27 | 17.0 | 57 | 55.5 |
| 63.3 | 27 | 16.6 | 55 | 59 |
| 46.7 | 64 | 18.2 | 61 | 53 |
| 46.7 | 42 | 18.0 | 60 | 53 |
| 46.7 | 13 | 14.9 | 50 | 53 |

The pressure drop in the Oldershaw column is greatly influenced by the type of material being distilled. Because of the capillary action of the bubble plate holes, material of higher surface tension will give a greater pressure drop, as is shown[8] in Table 14. The data were collected using column VI, Table 12.

**TABLE 14**

| n-HEPTANE | | METHYLCYCLOHEXANE | | BENZENE | | FORMIC ACID | |
|---|---|---|---|---|---|---|---|
| Through-put ml/hr | Pressure drop per actual plate mm Hg | Through-put ml/hr | Pressure drop per actual plate mm Hg | Through-put ml/hr | Pressure drop per actual plate mm Hg | Through-put ml/hr | Pressure drop per actual plate mm Hg |
| 1500 | 0.5 | 1500 | 0.62 | 1500 | 0.82 | 200 | 0.88 |
| 2500 | 0.55 | 2500 | 0.65 | 2500 | 0.87 | 600 | 1.02 |
| 3500 | 0.60 | 3500 | 0.71 | 3500 | 1.00 | 800 | 1.09 |
| 4500 | 0.70 | 4500 | 0.85 | 4280* | 1.17 | 1000 | 1.18 |
| 5230* | 0.80 | 5230* | 0.97 | | | 1125* | 1.13 |

*Flood point

The heat loss of vacuum jacketed columns of the type of column VI, Table 12, has been studied using refluxing n-heptane. At a throughput of about 5000 ml per hour, the rate of condensation due to heat loss (determined as on page 148) was about 200 ml per hour. This rate of condensation is very nearly independent of the feed rate for a material of given boiling point and heat of vaporization, although the loss may vary from column to column. In a vacuum jacketed column 1 inch by 48 inches, Goldsbarry and Askevold[9] found a sidewall condensation of 305 ml per hour.

Studies were also carried out[8] to determine pressure drop using a mixture of *n*-heptane-methylcyclohexane at various pressures. In Table 15 the distillation pressure is in millimeters of mercury, and the pressure drop is in millimeters of mercury per actual plate.

**TABLE 15**

| Throughput ml/hr | Pressure drop at 760 mm | Pressure drop at 500 mm | Pressure drop at 250 mm |
|---|---|---|---|
| 1500 | | | 0.668 |
| 2000 | 0.598 | 0.624 | 0.724 |
| 2500 | 0.612 | 0.649 | 0.852 |
| 3000 | 0.632 | 0.718 | Floods |
| 3500 | 0.675 | 0.802 | |
| 4000 | 0.719 | Floods | |

Goldsbarry and Askevold[9] studied a 1-inch by 48-inch Oldershaw column at various finite reflux ratios. The results shown in Table 16 were obtained, using *n*-heptane-methylcyclohexane.

**TABLE 16**

| Reflux ratio | Liquid reflux return rate cc/hr | Plate equivalents |
|---|---|---|
| ∞ | 2600 | 28.4 |
| ∞ | 3800 | 27.2 |
| 120:1 | 2600 | 25.2 |
| 120:1 | 3800 | 24.2 |
| 80:1 | 2600 | 24.0 |
| 80:1 | 3800 | 23.2 |
| 40:1 | 2600 | 21.6 |
| 40:1 | 3800 | 20.6 |
| 10:1 | 2600 | 10.2 |
| 10:1 | 3800 | 9.8 |
| 4:1 | 2600 | 5.2 |
| 4:1 | 3800 | 4.8 |

A comparison between the construction of the Oldershaw column and that of Bruun shows that the liquid drains completely from the former, while on the latter the layer of liquid remains constant even after the column has been shut down. This characteristic might be either an advantage or a disadvantage, depending on the type of fractionation to be run. In a fractionation involving a large amount of material or taking a great deal of time, it might be necessary to shut down the operation in the middle of a run. In this case the column of Bruun would be preferable, since the fractionated material on the plates would not draw back into the still and so some time would be saved in attaining equilibrium when the operation was started again. However, in a batch fractionation completed without shutdown, the column of Oldershaw would be superior, since the static holdup would be much smaller and a good material balance would be obtained.

## REFERENCES

1. MURPHREE, E.V., *Ind. Eng. Chem.*, **17, 747** (1925)
2. BRUUN, J.H., *Ind. Eng. Chem.*, Anal. Ed., **8, 214** (1936)
3. BRUUN, J.H., and FAULCONE, W.B.M., *ibid.*, **9, 192** (1937)
4. OTHMER, D.F., *Ind. Eng. Chem.*, **22, 322** (1930)
5. OTHMER, D.F., *Private communication*
6. PALKIN, S., *Ind. Eng. Chem.*, Anal. Ed., **3, 377** (1931)
7. OLDERSHAW, C.F., *ibid.*, **13, 265** (1941)
8. COLLINS, F.C., and LANTZ, V., *ibid.*, **18, 673** (1946)
9. GOLDSBARRY, A W., and ASKEVOLD, R.J., *Proc. Am. Petroleum Inst.*, **26,** [III], 18 (1946)

# VIII

## *Unpacked Columns*

IN THE LIGHT of the present knowledge of fractionation and of the development of high-efficiency fractionating columns, the usefulness of the old unpacked columns has become rather limited. However, in many laboratories such columns are the only fractionating equipment available. A description of the various unpacked columns is included in this book so that the reader may select the best of these and compare its characteristics with those of the more efficient packed columns.

There is still a definite use for the simple unpacked column as, for example, in the stripping of a low boiling solvent from a reaction mixture. Even though there is considerable difference in the boiling points of the solvent and the desired dissolved product—as much as 100 C—some loss is caused by entrainment when the solvent is evaporated from an open vessel. A column of several plates serves to eliminate this entrainment and gives good separation of the solvent from the solute.

An unpacked column usually allows much faster throughput, is more easily constructed, and is simpler to operate. Consequently, it is to be preferred to a packed column, where a very wide difference of boiling points exists between the components to be separated.

A large number of columns, some very simple and some unduly complex, were used in early works and are still being used by those unfamiliar with present-day fractionating technique. Some of these are shown in Figure 29. Of these, the Wurtz, the Pear, and the LeBel-Henninger are little better than spray traps. In the last type, the condensed liquid flows down the sides and through the side tubes, forming a liquid seal in the U portion of the arm. This seal is constantly changing because of the continuous flow of liquid down the column. The Glinsky, operating on somewhat the same principle, is only a little better.

It has been shown that in these columns where controlled reflux is introduced, the efficiency of the column is actually decreased. This indicates that the small enrichment which these columns do give is caused by the partial condensation on the side of the tube. By controlled reflux is meant the return to the system as liquid of a portion of the vapors reaching the top of the column.

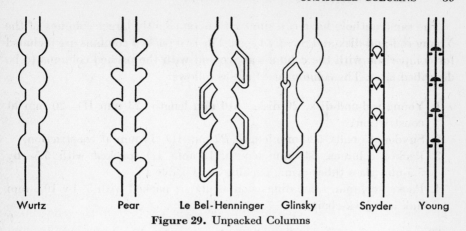

Wurtz    Pear    Le Bel-Henninger    Glinsky    Snyder    Young

**Figure 29.** Unpacked Columns

In the investigation of some of these less efficient columns, Hill and Ferris[1] have used the method of Peters[2] for comparing efficiencies. The enrichment factor $E$, defined as

$$E = \frac{C_D (1 - C_L)}{C_L (1 - C_D)} \tag{1}$$

is determined for the test mixture, benzene-carbon tetrachloride, where

$C_D$ = molar concentration of $CCl_4$ in vapor (or distillate)
$C_L$ = molar concentration of $CCl_4$ in liquid in still.

The average $E$ for this mixture was found to be 1.18. The enrichment from the still pot to the head was then determined, and a constant $K$ for each column was calculated from

$$\frac{C_D}{C_L} = 1.18^K \text{ or } K = \frac{\log C_D - \log C_L}{\log 1.18} \tag{2}$$

This gives a method of estimating the efficiency of one column with respect to another. However, it is by no means as good as the accepted method of determining theoretical plates. The data collected by Hill and Ferris are given in Table 17.

**TABLE 17**

| Reflux ratio | Open tube | Wurtz | Pear | LeBel-Henninger | Glinsky | 5.5 by 5.5 mm Glass tubes | Vigreux |
|---|---|---|---|---|---|---|---|
| | | | | EFFICIENCIES, CALCULATED AS $K$ | | | |
| 0* | 0.9 | 1.1 | 1.1 | 1.0 | 1.3 | 1.3 | 1.2 |
| 2 | | 0.8 | 0.9 | 0.9 | 1.3 | 1.4 | 1.4 |
| 5 | | 0.5 | 0.8 | 1.1 | | 1.4 | 1.5 |
| 9 | | | 0.8 | 0.9 | | 1.9 | 1.4 |

* Indicates no insulation, total takeoff.

The same authors have run similar tests on slightly larger columns of the Young rod-and-disk and Snyder types. The two packed columns are included for comparison with the columns above and with the packed columns to be described later. The columns used are as follows:

1. Young rod-and-disk, 20 disks, 610 mm length, 23 mm ID (20 mm at constriction)
2. Snyder, 15 balls, 520 mm length, 22 mm ID (14 mm at constriction)
3. Packed columns, 545 mm length, 18 mm ID, packed with 5.5- by 5.5-mm glass tubes (same packing as in Table 17)
4. Packed column, same dimension as above, packed with 5- by 10.5-mm link iron jack-chain.

The Young column consists of a tube constricted at intervals along its length, and a series of disks through which runs a rod, the whole rod and disk unit being free from the sides of the column. Each disk on the length of the rod coincides with a constriction in the column tube. The descending liquid and rising vapors are interrupted at these points, giving some increase in scrubbing action.

The Snyder column also consists of a tube constricted at intervals. However, instead of the rod and disk discussed above, this column utilizes small hollow balls to interrupt the flow of liquid and vapor. Each constriction carries a ball which is free to rise from the seat of the constriction as vapor rises or liquid descends. It is prevented from moving more than a short distance up the column by indentations at its maximum allowable height. The diameter of the balls should be such that the annular area between the ball and the unconstricted part of the tube is approximately the same as the area of the tube at the point of constriction.

The data on these columns are given in Table 18.

## TABLE 18

| | | EFFICIENCIES, CALCULATED AS $K$ | | | |
|---|---|---|---|---|---|
| Reflux ratio | Takeoff rate cc/min | Young rod and disk | Snyder | Glass tube | Jack-chain |
| 9 | 2 | | | 3.5 | |
| 9 | 2.1 | | | | 4.3 |
| 9 | 1 | | 4.6 | | |
| 9 | 1.8 | | 3.7 | | |
| 2 | 1 | 1.7 | | | |
| 2 | 1.4 | 1.5 | | | |

For the packed columns, the rate of throughput given is both the point of highest efficiency and the flood point. For the Young and Snyder columns, the faster rate is the flood point while the other rate is the throughput giving highest efficiency. The Snyder column is somewhat better than the tube-packed column. However, while this column is fairly good (being in some measure a cross between an open tube and a bubble tray column), it is tedious to construct, fragile, and considerably exceeded in efficiency by other simple packed columns.

Simons and Wagner[3] have also run a series of tests on the enrichment accomplished by these unpacked columns when a mixture of alcohol and water is fractionated. Their results in general corroborate the comparisons given above.

*Vigreux Column.* From the standpoint of ease of operation, ease of construction, relative efficiency, and throughput, the Vigreux is probably the most practical of the columns described in this chapter. The Vigreux column is very simple to construct. A spot on the wall of the tube is heated to red heat and then pressed inward and slightly downward with a carbon pencil one or two millimeters in diameter, or with some other small tool. The depth of the indentations should be more than one-half the diameter of the tube. The prongs should be in such a position that they interrupt the flow of vapor up through the column. An indentation is made on one side of the tube, then another directly opposite. The tube is then rotated through 45 degrees and two more indentations are made opposite each other and slightly higher or lower than the first two on the tube. This procedure is followed until the tube is indented from a point slightly above the joint to just below the take-off line. Characteristics of several Vigreux columns are given in Table 19.

**TABLE 19**

| Column length cm | Plates | H.E.T.P. cm | Holdup cc | References |
|---|---|---|---|---|
| 30 | 2.5 | 11.75 | | 4 |
| 107.5 | 6.6 | 16.25 | | 4 |
| 30 | 5 | 6 | 1.65 | 5 |
| 68.6* | 6 | 13.7 | | 6 |

*1.09 ID

Cooper and Fasce[7] (see Figure 115) and later Weston[8] (see Figure 116) have described small Vigreux columns, 7 mm ID and 34 cm long. When a 36 volume per cent mixture of methanol in water was distilled through the column of Cooper and Fasce, the results shown in Table 20 were obtained:

**TABLE 20**

| Charge | % Methanol (approx) | % Intermediate (approx) | Water |
|---|---|---|---|
| 2 cc | 20 | 12 | Remainder |
| 5 cc | 31 | 1 | Remainder |
| 10 cc | 35 | Less than 1 | Remainder |

This column, when operated at 20 to 40 drops per minute, has a holdup of about 0.4 – 0.5 cc. About 30 minutes are required for a 10 cc charge if the boiling point difference of the components is about 15 C.

When 10 cc of a 50-50 volume per cent mixture of 2-chloro- and 1-chlorobutane was distilled through the Weston column, 4 cc of the former boiling at 69 C and 3.5 cc of the latter boiling at 78 C were recovered. With a 10 cc charge of a 50-50 volume per cent solution of aniline and nitrobenzene, 3.5 cc of aniline boiling at 71 C and 2.5 cc of nitrobenzene boiling at 83 C were recovered at a pressure of 10 mm.

Table 21 gives a comparison of three Vigreux columns examined under similar conditions.[9] The plate values were determined under total reflux, a reflux head similar to that shown in Figure 49 being used. A reflux period of one half hour was allowed for equilibrium to be established before samples were taken for analysis. The column jackets were not heated but were simply insulated by air jackets. The jackets for columns I and III consisted of a 24-mm OD tube, while column II required a 36-mm tube.

**TABLE 21**

| Column | Length cm | Diameter cm | Throughput cc/min | Plates | H.E.T.P. cm | Holdup cc |
|---|---|---|---|---|---|---|
| I | 46 | 1.2 OD | 0.9 | 8.5 | 5.4 | |
| | | | 1.6 | 6.5 | 7.1 | 3.0 |
| | | | 4.9 | 6.0 | 7.7 | 3.7 |
| | | | 9.0 | 6.0 | 7.7 | 4.1 |
| | | | 2.7* | 2.5 | 18.4 | |
| II | 46 | 2.4 OD | 2.0 | 4.5 | 10.2 | 5.8 |
| | | | 4.0 | 3.8 | 12.1 | |
| | | | 8.5 | 4.0 | 11.5 | 7.2 |
| III | 65 | 1.2 OD | 0.9 | 9.5 | 6.8 | 4.2 |
| | | | 4.9 | 7.2 | 9.0 | 4.8 |
| | | | 9.0 | 6.8 | 9.6 | 5.2 |

* Indicates no reflux control, total takeoff.

The value of reflux control is shown in the data for column I. When operated at a throughput that would have given approximately 6 theoretical plates under total reflux at equilibrium, this column gave only 2.5 plates when there was no reflux control, and consequently no possibility of reaching optimum equilibrium.

The jacket of a Vigreux column should not be heated to the reflux temperature as is done with other columns (see page 95). Instead, the jacket temperature should be held about 25 degrees below the reflux temperature. Because there is no packing surface, the walls of the column tube must be used as an area of contact. Therefore the sides of the tube must be kept at such a temperature that an appreciable quantity of material will condense on them, thus giving opportunity for ascending vapor to contact downflowing liquid.

## REFERENCES

1. HILL, J.B., and FERRIS, S.W., *Ind. Eng. Chem.*, **19**, 379 (1927)
2. PETERS, W.A., *ibid.*, **16**, 1126 (1924)
3. SIMONS, J.H., and WAGNER, E.C., *J. Chem. Ed.*, **9**, 122 (1932)
4. BAILEY, A.J., *Ind. Eng. Chem.*, Anal. Ed., **13**, 487 (1941)
5. BAKER, R.H., BARKENBUS, C., and ROSWELL, C.A., *ibid.*, **12**, 468 (1940)
6. FENSKE, M.R., *Ind. Eng. Chem.*, **26**, 1169 (1934)
7. COOPER, C.M., and FASCE, E.V., *ibid.*, **20**, 420 (1928)
8. WESTON, P.E., *Ind. Eng. Chem.*, Anal. Ed., **5**, 179 (1933)
9. CARNEY, T.P., *Unpublished work*

# IX

*Packed Columns*

FROM THE POINT OF VIEW of laboratory fractionation, the packed column is by far the most important type. Almost anything that could be fitted into a tube has been tested as packing at one time or another, but a very small percentage of those tested are good enough to warrant any use whatever in the light of present high-efficiency demands.

In this chapter will be considered the five best types of packing to be used in laboratory or in semiplant columns. These are the Fenske, the Podbielniak, the Stedman, the McMahon, and the Lecky-Ewell packings.

*Fenske Packing.* This type of packing[1] consists of single turn glass or metal helices. Although Fenske was not the first to report on glass helices,[2] his name has become associated with all types of this packing because of the great amount of excellent work he has done with these columns. The helices are dropped individually into the column (page 114) and result in a closely spaced packing, causing continuous change in direction of the flow of liquid and vapor and resulting in maximum contact with a good throughput. The helices may be made in any size and from almost any material. As would be expected, the *H.E.T.P.* decreases with decrease in size.

This type of packing is probably the best possible for general laboratory use. One great advantage of this packing over others is that it can be made from glass as well as stainless steel and so can be used to handle almost any type chemical without danger of corrosion or catalytic action. While the glass helices are not quite as efficient as metal helices, still the advantage of generality of usefulness is often reason enough to choose this packing over others, especially in laboratories where the number of columns must be limited and a particular column is not available for each different type of compound. The glass helix packing has been used with materials boiling as high as 300 C at the pressure used, and it has been used equally effectively at low temperatures. It has been used under pressures of several atmospheres, and at pressures as low as is practical with any fractionation.

The dimensions of some columns using Fenske packing, together with their operating characteristics, are shown in Table 22. In the table, *M* is the packing material, *d* is the diameter of the helices in inches, *L* is the length of the packed section in centimeters, $D$ is the diameter of the column in millimeters, $n$ is theoretical plates, $p.d.$ is pressure drop in millimeters of mercury, $H$ is operating holdup in cubic centimeters, $T$ is throughput in cubic centimeters per hour, and $R$ is the reference.

### TABLE 22

| M | d | L | D | n | p.d. | H | T | R |
|---|---|---|---|---|------|---|---|---|
| Glass | ⅛ | 315 | 8 | 67 | | 4 | 6 | 3 |
| | | 315 | 8 | 52.5 | | 10 | 12 | |
| | | 315 | 8 | 40 | | 10 | 18 | |
| | | 315 | 8 | 34 | | 14 | 24 | |
| | | 150 | 8 | 30 | | | | |
| | | 38 | 10 | 8 | | | | |
| | | 41 | 10 | 10-12 | | 9 | 550 | |
| | | 43 | 10 | 11 | | 7.7 | 157 | 4 |
| | | 43 | 10 | 11 | | 8.5 | 471 | |
| | | 80 | 12 | 18 | | | 678 | |
| | | 135 | 14 | 23 | | | | |
| | | 150 | 14 | 30 | | | | 3 |
| | | 40 | 14 | 10.5 | | | | |
| | | 300 | 18 | 30-35 | | | | 5 |
| | | 157 | 20 | 41.5 | | 55 | 1800 | 6 |
| | ¼ | 205 | 35 | 22 | | 280 | 8500 | 6 |
| Stainless steel | 3⁄32 | 70 | 8 | 27 | | 5.8 | 201 | 4 |
| | | 81 | 12 | 37 | | 20 | 452 | |
| | | 366 | 15 | 135 | 21.3 | | 740 | 7 |
| | | 366 | 20 | 130 | 21.3 | | 1240 | |
| | | 366 | 25 | 125 | 21.3 | | 1560 | |
| | | 265 | 25.4 | 140 | 1.8 | 168 | 500 | 4 |
| | | 265 | 25.4 | 126 | 6.3 | 202 | 1000 | |
| | | 265 | 25.4 | 88 | 50.2 | 300 | 3000 | |
| | | 227 | 50.8 | 58 | 0.52 | 783 | 2026 | |
| | | 227 | 50.8 | 54 | 2.6 | 880 | 4052 | |
| | | 227 | 50.8 | 44 | 31.7 | 1364 | 12156 | |
| | | 259 | 50.8 | 68 | 4 | | 2000 | 1 |
| | | 259 | 50.8 | 44 | 23 | | 7400 | |
| | 1⁄16 | 72 | 8 | 55 | | 88 | 151 | 4 |
| | | 105 | 25.4 | 65 | 1.3 | 78 | 500 | |
| | | 105 | 25.4 | 62 | 4.3 | 96 | 1000 | |
| | | 105 | 25.4 | 43 | 28 | 142 | 3000 | |
| | 5⁄32 | 86.5 | 20 | 13 | | 18.5 | 2200 | 6 |
| | | 1160 | 33 | 101 | 45 | | 3400 | |
| | | | 33 | | 119 | | 5500 | |
| | | 259 | 51 | 19 | | | 3500 | 1 |
| | | 259 | 51 | 24.5 | 22 | | 14000 | |

TABLE 22 (*Continued*)

| M | d | L | D | n | p.d. | H | T | R |
|---|---|---|---|---|---|---|---|---|
| Aluminum | 3/16 | 259 | 51 | 23.5 | 26 | | 20200 | 1 |
| | 1/4 | 259 | 51 | 17 | 3 | | 19500 | 1 |
| | | 259 | 51 | 17.5 | 10 | | 21300 | |
| Nickel | 1/8 | 30.5 | 6 | 8 | | | 300 | 9 |
| | | 30.5 | 6 | 11 | | | 60 | |
| | | 1250 | 33 | 94 | 39 | | 2500 | |
| | | 1250 | 33 | 122 | 80 | | 4200 | |
| | | 259 | 51 | 45 | ca 31 | | 10000 | |
| | 5/32 | 259 | 51 | 22.5 | 10 | | 11500 | 1 |
| | | 259 | 51 | 35 | 25 | | 18200 | |

When the number of turns per helix was increased, the results shown in Table 23 were obtained, indicating that the single turn helices are preferred.

TABLE 23

| M | L | D | n | p.d. | T | R |
|---|---|---|---|---|---|---|
| 2 & 3 turn wire | 140 | 2.03 | 17 | | 1.3 | 10 |
| 6 turn #24 Lucerno | 396 | 5.26 | 10.5 | 0.12 | 8.3 | 10 |
| | | | 9.5 | 0.12 | 11.6 | |
| | | | 10.0 | 0.20 | 15.6 | |
| | | | 10.0 | 0.28 | 20.3 | |
| | | | 9.5 | 0.10 | 7.8 | |
| | | | 9.5 | 0.20 | 15.7 | |

Table 24 gives the data obtained when a 1-inch by 48-inch Fenske column packed with 1/8-inch glass helices is operated under finite reflux ratios.

TABLE 24

| Reflux ratio | Liquid reflux return rate, cc/hr | Plate equivalents |
|---|---|---|
| ∞ | 1500 | 31 |
| ∞ | 2150 | 29.8 |
| 80:1 | 1500 | 26.2 |
| 80:1 | 2150 | 23.8 |
| 40:1 | 1500 | 23.4 |
| 40:1 | 2150 | 21.2 |
| 10:1 | 1500 | 14.6 |
| 10:1 | 2150 | 13.8 |
| 4:1 | 1500 | 8.2 |
| 4:1 | 2150 | 7.6 |

*Podbielniak Spiral Packing.* The original Podbielniak packing[12] consisted of a continuous wire spiral wound six or seven turns per inch and fitted snugly into a tube, the diameter of which was determined by the volume of throughput and sharpness of separation desired. Whereas other packings obtain contact between liquid and vapor at the wetted surface of the packing, the Podbielniak spiral owes its efficiency to the fact that the liquid flowing down the column distributes itself into very thin capillary films formed between the spiral turns themselves, and between the spiral and the column wall. The spiral has been made from both glass and metal and seems to give about the same efficiency with either. However, the difficulty involved in making a glass spiral of the proper pitch to fit snugly into the column makes this material rather impractical.

The special advantage claimed for this type of packing is its low holdup, which property might be predicted from the nature of the packing. Whereas other packings expose a great amount of surface which is capable of holding liquid, spiral packing has no such large surface. The spiral itself acts as a natural guide to drain liquid from the column, and very little of the actual column space is occupied by the packing. The pressure drop, too, should be low for this packing since the frictional resistance to the vapor rising through the column is low.

At velocities much above those listed below, the *H.E.T.P.* increases rapidly. Increasing column diameters also increase *H.E.T.P.* This, too, is easily understandable. The larger the column diameter, the greater will be the free space in the middle of the column up through the center of the spiral. This gives added chance for vapor to rise through the column without ever coming into contact with refluxing liquid. Therefore either the column diameter or the throughput must be reduced to obtain the maximum number of plates.

**TABLE 25**

| Length cm | Diameter mm | Plates | Holdup | Throughput | Pressure drop | Reference |
|---|---|---|---|---|---|---|
| 137 | | 10 | 3.0 | | | 8 |
| 150 | 4.5 | 14 | 2.38 | 0.79 | 0.28 | 4 |
| | 4.5 | 15 | 2.85 | 1.58 | 0.75 | |
| | 4.5 | 16 | 4.64 | 2.63 | 1.60 | |
| 30.5 | 6.0 | 6.5 | | 1 | | 9 |
| | 6.0 | 4 | | 5 | | |
| | 3.0 | 8 | | 0.6 | | |
| | 3.0 | 8 | | 2.2 | | |
| 128 | 3.7 | 7 | 1.2 | 150 | | 6 |

This packing was designed originally for low temperature work, but it has been used in the range from −190 to 300 C.

Table 25 gives some of the characteristics of the original Podbielniak spiral packing.

*Podbielniak Heli-Grid Packing.* A highly improved wire packing has been developed[13] along the same lines as the original Podbielniak type. This material, called *Heli-Grid* because of its resemblance to an ordinary grid, is used in two different forms. The first consists of coils of sectorlike sections

**TABLE 26**

| Height cm | Diameter mm | Plates | Throughput cc/hr | Holdup cc | Reference |
|---|---|---|---|---|---|
| 91.4 | 5.7 | 75 | 75 | 1.5 | 13 |
|  |  | 63 | 87 |  |  |
|  |  | 45 | 112 |  |  |
|  |  | 40 | 150 | Flood |  |
| 91.4 | 8.0 | 100 | 125 | 4 | 13 |
|  |  | 80 | 160 |  |  |
|  |  | 64 | 210 |  |  |
|  |  | 50 | 250 | Flood |  |
| 35.0 | 11.0 | 39 | 200 | 5.9 | 13 |
|  |  | 32 | 245 | 6.1 |  |
|  |  | 25 | 315 |  |  |
|  |  | 23 | 375 |  |  |
| 91.4 | 11.0 | 100 | 200 | 7.3 | 13 |
|  |  | 80 | 245 |  |  |
|  |  | 65 | 315 |  |  |
|  |  | 56 | 375 | Flood |  |
| 274.0 | 11.0 | 150 | 300 |  | 7 |
| 91.4 | 25.0 | 92 | 500 | 32.8 | 14 |
|  |  | 73 | 1000 | 38.9 |  |
|  |  | 58 | 1500 | 44.2 |  |
|  |  | 48 | 2000 | 51.3 |  |
| 91.4 | 13.0 | 100 | 300 | 11.4 | 13 |
|  |  | 80 | 375 |  |  |
|  |  | 62 | 500 |  |  |
|  |  | 55 | 550 |  |  |
| 183.0 | 13.0 | 100 | 300 |  | 7 |
| 366.0 | 16.0 | 200 | 720 |  | 7 |

wound around each other and around a very small core wire to yield a number of uniform nonflooding vapor passageways lined with capillary liquid reflux films extending between vertically adjacent wire loops. The second form consists of wire stage *staircases* wound around a central solid core and around each other in concentric telescoping layers if necessary to obtain larger diameters and capacities. The diameter of these coils is usually about 0.01 inch, with the spacing between the wires approximately equal to the wire diameter.

Data on this improved packing are given in Table 26.

The time required for the 91.4 cm by 25.0 mm column to reach equilibrium has been determined by Brandt, Perkins, and Halverson[14] to be approximately eight hours. The time did not vary appreciably as the throughput was raised from 500 cc to 2000 cc per hour, nor did preflooding affect the time. Preflooding, as has been mentioned, does increase the operating efficiency of the Podbielniak packing.

The operating pressure drops of the columns of reference 7 in Table 26 at the throughput given are 12.1, 8.5, and 19.2 mm of mercury, respectively.

Because the packing operates on the basis of capillary formation and attraction, channeling is almost completely eliminated. Thus, for the same height of packing, the *H.E.T.P.* should not change with change in diameter. Similarly, the number of plates should be proportional to the height of the column.

***Stedman Packing.*** Stedman packing[15] is made of wire cloth which has been embossed and trimmed into flat, truncated, conical disks. A semicircular hole is cut out of one side of the cone and extends about two-thirds of the distance from the edge of the cone to the flat in the center. These cones are then welded together, alternately base to base and edge to edge, to form the pattern shown in Figure 30. The disks fit tightly into the column so that the only vapor passageway is through the cut-out semi-circular hole on the side of the cone. The vapor, after passing through each cell, must pass between the containing tube and the gauze around both sides of the axis before passing to the next cell.

The liquid flows down the sides of the cone in a thin film, comes together at the base of the cone, and again spreads in a film over each disk. This spreading of the liquid in a thin film serves to make

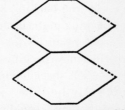

**Figure 30.** Stedman Packing

each portion of the liquid on a cell completely homogeneous in composition. The vapor, rising through the passageways in each cell, comes into contact with the liquid on both the inside and outside of the cell, thus giving excellent contact and facilitating the maximum heat exchange and approach to equilibrium conditions.

The data shown in Table 27 have been collected on Stedman[16] packings of different sizes:

**TABLE 27**

| Packing | Height cm | Diameter cm | Plates | Throughput cc/hr | Holdup cc |
|---|---|---|---|---|---|
| | 30.5 | 2.54 | 24 | 378 | — |
| | 30.5 | 2.54 | 20 | 942 | — |
| | 30.5 | 2.54 | 17 | 1,416 | — |
| #105 | 61 | 0.95 | 20 | 91 | — |
| | 61 | 0.95 | 53.6 | 129 | 7.57 |
| | 61 | 0.95 | 56.4 | 140 | 7.19 |
| | 61 | 0.95 | 56.4 | 151 | 7.95 |
| | 61 | 0.95 | 44.8 | 189 | 8.71 |
| | 61 | 0.95 | 37.7 | 231* | 12.11 |
| #104 | 61 | 1.91 | 43.2 | 98 | 8.71 |
| | 61 | 1.91 | 50.3 | 151 | 10.60 |
| | 61 | 1.91 | 30.6 | 598 | 24.61 |
| | 61 | 1.91 | 27.8 | 636* | — |
| #112 | 61 | 2.50 | 38.7 | 129 | 8.33 |
| | 61 | 2.50 | 48.4 | 151 | 9.09 |
| | 61 | 2.50 | 24.2 | 1,060 | 36.00 |
| | 61 | 2.50 | 24.2 | 1,083* | 36.00 |
| #114 | 61 | 2.50 | 23.0 | 1,400 | 23.5 |

*Indicates initial flood point.

A second type of Stedman packing has also been developed[16] for use in larger diameter columns. Although these columns are not strictly for laboratory use, the packing is worthy of mention here because it is probably the best packing material for larger scale semiplant columns, and seems to have more potentialities for development along that line than any of the other high-efficiency packings described. This packing is made in single circular sheets, each sheet having an upturned lip around the circumference and fitting tightly into the column tube. The sheet is punched, blanked, and embossed, having formed on it a regular pattern of raised triangular pyramids. The pyramids are located on ⅜-inch equilateral triangular centers. The sheets are also perforated with ³⁄₁₆-inch diameter holes located on ⅜-inch triangular centers between the pyramids. To arrange the sheets in a column, the upper sheet is rotated so that the valleys at the junction of the bases of the pyramids come immediately above the apexes of the pyramids of the lower sheet. The sheets are welded together at this point of contact and the holes of the lower sheet are, by such an arrangement, located directly below the apex of the pyramid of the upper sheet. These holes act as vapor passageways, causing the vapor to flow directly into the pyramid above.

The data of Table 28 represent some of the operating characteristics of this semiplant column packing.

**TABLE 28**

| Packing | Height inches | Diameter inches | Plates | Throughput gal/hr | Holdup gal |
|---------|--------|----------|--------|-----------|--------|
| #128 | 36 | 2.08 | 13.1 | 0.4 | 0.08 |
|  | 36 | 2.08 | 39.0 | 0.6 | 0.08 |
|  | 36 | 2.08 | 22.3 | 0.5 | 0.26 |
|  | 36 | 2.08 | 22.0 | 2.75* | 0.21 |
| #107 | 36 | 3.08 | 25 2 | 0.5 | 0.05 |
|  | 36 | 3.08 | 33.2 | 0.65 | 0.05 |
|  | 36 | 3.08 | 20.2 | 6.0 | 0.34 |
|  | 36 | 3.08 | 19.4 | 6.8 * | 0.40 |
| #115 | 36 | 6.08 | 30.1 | 2.0 | 0.45 |
|  | 36 | 6.08 | 30.8 | 2.8 |  |
|  | 36 | 6.08 | 17.3 | 23.5 |  |
|  | 36 | 6.08 | — | 24.0 * |  |
| #116 | 24 | 12.0 | 16.1 | 12.0 | 0.55 |
|  | 24 | 12.0 | 16.7 | 15.0 | 0.40 |
|  | 24 | 12.0 | 9.5 | 90.0 | 0.92 |
|  | 24 | 12.0 | — | 93.0 * | — |

*Indicates initial flood point.

Packing #116 is a 12-inch hexagon instead of the circular plates of #107, #115, and #128.

Borns, Coffey and Garrard[17] have published data on the #107 packing (3.08 inches) in a 12-foot column. This data, shown in Figure 31, indicates the change in plate value with throughput, and also the change in plate value with routine use over a period of time. It can be seen that at higher throughputs the *H.E.T.P.* of the older packing is almost twice that obtained when new packing is used. At a boil-up rate of 18.5 liters per hour, the three-year-old column reached equilibrium in about 10 hours, while at a rate of 9 liters per hour, 13 hours were required. It was observed that more time was required to reach equilibrium with the old packing than with new packing. The pressure drop, too, increased with increase in time. At a throughput of

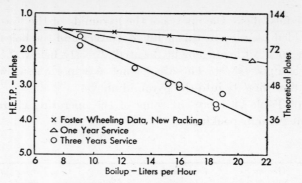

Figure 31. Effect of Service Time on H.E.T.P. of
Stedman Packing No. 107

20 liters per hour, the pressure drop increased from 18 mm to 30.5 mm over
a three-year period.

*McMahon Packing.*  A packing which has operating characteristics similar
to the Stedman packing has been designed by McMahon.[18]  This packing
consists of squares of ¼-inch by ¼-inch 100- by 100-mesh 0.0045-inch wire
size brass cloth, stamped into shapes resembling Berl saddles. As would be
expected, packings made from ⅜-inch squares and from ⁵⁄₁₆-inch squares had
a larger throughput, but they also had a larger *H.E.T.P.* McMahon believes
that mesh size is of secondary importance provided it is fine enough to allow
formation of a continuous film of refluxing liquid across the wires. This
packing was designed originally to give a lightweight, low heat capacity
column in which height and diameter were to be kept at a minimum for the
rectification of liquid air. A column 2⅞ inches inside diameter and 18 inches
long gave approximately 12 theoretical plates while fractionating liquid air.

Further investigations of the characteristics of this packing have been
made on columns 6 inches in diameter[19] using packing of the ¼-inch size
made from both brass and monel wire cloth. The density of these packings
is approximately 26.0 pounds per cubic foot.

Data of columns constructed from sections of 6-inch standard monel pipe
are given in Table 29. These data were obtained using benzene-ethylenedi-
chloride.

Although the Stedman packing shows a lower *H.E.T.P.* than the Mc-
Mahon packing, the latter has several desirable features. The column may
be packed very easily, requires no machined sides, and may be dumped just
as easily for cleaning. The throughput and holdup are of the same order of
magnitude for the two, but the McMahon type has an appreciably lower

## TABLE 29

| Packing material | Length inches | Boilup rate gal/hr | Pressure drop in. H₂O/ft | Theoretical plates | H.E.T.P. inches |
|---|---|---|---|---|---|
| Brass | 57 | 12.2 | 0.26 | 27.4 | 2.1 |
|  |  | 16.8 | 0.65 | 23.0 | 2.5 |
|  |  | 21.5 | 1.31 | 19.2 | 3.0 |
| Brass | 105* | 11.9 | 0.25 | 45.5 | 2.3 |
|  |  | 16.5 | 0.63 | 41.9 | 2.5 |
|  |  | 21.7** | 1.15 | 30.1 | 3.5 |
| Monel | 57.5 | 12.8 | 0.25 | 17.3 | 3.3 |
|  |  | 17.5 | 0.50 | 16.6 | 3.5 |
|  |  | 22.3 | 0.97 | 14.6 | 3.9 |

*One redistributor used.
**Holdup at this rate was 0.21 gal per ft.

pressure drop, making it more desirable for reduced pressure work. The mechanical disadvantages of the McMahon packing are that it is not rigid when in the column and may be subject to change. Also, loose wires resulting from fraying edges may collect at various places in the column or piping and cause difficulties.

*Lecky and Ewell Packing.* A number of investigators (Widmer, Midgely, etc.) have used the long path method of increasing or trying to increase the effective height of a column. Lecky and Ewell[20] have used this same formula but with better results. The Lecky-Ewell packing is a continuous flat spiral of metal gauze enclosed between two concentric glass tubes in such a manner that there is no leakage between the walls of the tubes and the edge of the packing. The liquid or vapor thus must traverse a long path as in the Widmer (see page 76). However, there is a very essential difference between the two columns. In the Lecky-Ewell column there is a liquid-vapor contact on both sides of the screen as the vapor and liquid move up and down the column. The liquid spreads out in very thin films on the gauze, thus insuring intimate contact with the vapor. This type of packing has a relatively small holdup and pressure drop, and allows a large throughput. However, it must be made of metal and is rather difficult to construct, great care being necessary to obtain a tight fit of the packing inside the concentric tubes. The data of Table 30 illustrate the characteristics of the Lecky-Ewell packing. All packing is pitched at 76 turns per foot.

Reed[23] notes that if two or more turns of this packing slip together, the boilup rate will be lowered appreciably.

It will be noted that the holdup for column III below is somewhat out of line. In this column an inner rod of 1.8 cm OD was used with a 3.7-cm diam-

**TABLE 30**

| No. | Packing diameter cm | Height cm | Plates | Throughput cc/hr | Operating holdup cc | References |
|---|---|---|---|---|---|---|
| I | 1.91 | 43.2 | 25 | 100 | 6.25 | 20 |
| | | 43.2 | 25 | 200 | 7.5 | |
| | | 43.2 | 25 | 300 | 9.5 | |
| | | 43.2 | 24.3 | 500 | 12.2 | |
| | | 43.2 | 21 3 | 700 | 21.3 | |
| | | 86.4 | 50 | | 20.0 | |
| II | 1.27 | 43.2 | 25 | 100 | 4.50 | |
| | | 43.2 | 25 | 300 | 6.25 | |
| | | 43.2 | 23.4 | 400 | 11.7 | |
| III | 3.7 | 116.8 | 70 | | 66.5 | 21 |
| IV | 1.0 | 116.8 | 64 | | 9.0 | 21 |
| V | 1.27 | 165.0 | 75 | 320 | | 22 |
| VI | 1.27 | 95.3 | 42 | 150 | 6.5 | 23 |
| | | | 40 | 200 | 7.0 | |
| | | | 40 | 250 | 7.5 | |
| | | | 39 | 300 | 7.5 | |
| | | | 35 | 340 | 7.75 | |

eter packing, while with column IV a 0.25-cm OD rod was used with a 1.0-cm packing, thus making the effective volume of the former considerably larger, and accounting for the increased holdup. The static holdup for column III is 28 cc, while for column IV it is only 5 cc.

These columns operate very well under reduced pressure. At a pressure of 20 mm of mercury a very sharp separation of α- and β-pinene boiling 7 degrees apart was effected[21] through columns III and IV. During these distillations column III had a pressure drop of 2 mm at a reflux rate of 2.5 ml per min, while in column IV the drop was 2.5 mm at a rate of 0.8 ml per min. A pressure drop of the order of 1 mm per foot is obtained at optimum conditions for the above packing.

The packing itself is made by punching washers from 60- by 60- or 80- by 80-mesh metal gauze (the size does not seem to make much difference). Each washer is cut along an axis and then spot welded to form a long continuous spiral. A glass tube or a nickel rod is run through the inside hole, and this unit is then fitted tightly inside a second tube. It is important that a tight fit be obtained. This may be accomplished by stamping the washers so that when the spiral is formed the edges will be turned up at an angle of 45 degrees with the side. The packing unit may then be forced into the tube and a snug fit will be obtained.

# REFERENCES

1. FENSKE, M. R., LAWROWSKI, S., and TONGBERG, C. O., *Ind. Eng. Chem.*, **30, 297** (1938)
2. WHITMORE, F. C., and LUX, A. R., *J. Am. Chem. Soc.*, **55,** 2795 (1933)
3. BAILEY, A. M., *Ind. Eng. Chem.*, Anal. Ed., **13,** 487 (1941)
4. WHITMORE, F. C., et al., *J. Am. Chem. Soc.*, **62,** 795 (1940)
5. KISTIAKOWSKY, G. B., RUHOFF, J. R., SMITH, H. A., and VAUGHAN, W. E., *ibid.*, **57,** 876 (1935)
6. FAY, J. W. J., *Annual Rep. on the Progress of Chemistry*, **XL,** 216 (1943)
7. WILLINGHAM, C. B., and ROSSINI, F. D., *J. Research Nat. Bur. Standards*, **37,** 15 (1946)
8. BAKER, R. H., BARKENBUS, C., and ROSWELL, C. A., *Ind. Eng. Chem.*, Anal. Ed., **12,** 468 (1940)
9. ROSE, A., *Ind. Eng. Chem.*, **28,** 1210 (1936)
10. FENSKE, M. R., TONGBERG, C. O., and QUIGGLE, D., *ibid.*, **26,** 1169 (1934)
11. GOLDSBARRY, A. W., and ASKEVOLD, R. J., *Proc. Am. Petroleum Inst.*, **26,** [III], 18 (1946)
12. PODBIELNIAK, W. M., *Ind. Eng. Chem.*, Anal. Ed., **3,** 177 (1931)
13. PODBIELNIAK, W. M., *ibid.*, **13,** 639 (1941)
14. BRANDT, P. L., PERKINS, R. B., JR., and HALVERSON, L. K., *Proc. Am. Petroleum Inst.*, **26,** [III], 57 (1946)
15. STEDMAN, D. F., *Trans. Am. Inst. Chem. Engrs.*, **33,** 153 (1937)
16. BRAGG, L. B., *ibid.*, **37,** 19 (1941)
17. BORNS, W. J., COFFEY, B. L., and GARRARD, L. G., *Proc. Am. Petroleum Inst.*, **26,** [III], 32 (1946)
18. MCMAHON, H. O., *Ind. Eng. Chem.*, **39,** 712 (1947)
19. FORSYTHE, W. L., JR., STACK, T. G., WOLF, J. E., and CONN, A. L., *ibid.*, **39,** 714 (1947)
20. LECKY, H. S., and EWELL, R. H., *Ind. Eng. Chem.*, Anal. Ed., **12,** 544 (1940)
21. STALLCUP, W. D., FUGUITT, R. E., and HAWKINS, J. E., *ibid.*, **14,** 503 (1942)
22. EWELL, R. H., and WELCH, L. M., *Ind. Eng. Chem.*, **37,** 1224 (1945)
23 REED, C. R., *Proc. Am. Petroleum Inst.*, **26,** [III], 14 (1946)

# CHAPTER

# X

# *Miscellaneous Packings*

AMONG THE EARLY COLUMNS developed in an attempt to raise the efficiency of separation above that obtained by simple distillation were those of Hempel, Widmer, Dufton, and Midgely. In none of these columns was any attempt made to control reflux. Consequently, the only washing action obtained was from the condensation of vapors on the sides of the tube or on the packing as the material progressed up the column.

The Hempel column consisted of a tube packed with glass rods or beads. It may be disregarded since it is little more than a spray trap.

The Widmer[1] packing consists of a glass spiral wound into the annular

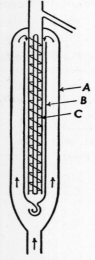

**Figure 32.** Widmer Column

spaces between two glass tubes. The hot vapors from the distilling pot rise through the outer jacket A, then pass down through another jacket B, and are finally led up through the column proper. The total effect is that the column is heated by vapors from the pot. This is theoretically unsound since these heating vapors are hotter than the vapors rising in the column. We shall see later (page 95) that superheating of the vapors in the column can decrease the plate value very markedly.

Data for two Widmer columns are given in Table 31.

## TABLE 31

| Column | Height cm | Plates | Throughput cc/min | Holdup cc | Reference |
|--------|-----------|--------|-------------------|-----------|-----------|
| 1 | 36 | 4.4 | | 2.2 | 2 |
| 2 | 32 | 5 | 1.4 | 2.0 | 3 |
| | | 4.5 | 6.0 | 2.9 | |

Column 2 had the following dimensions (Figure 32): A = 36 mm OD., B = 18 mm OD., and C = 8 mm OD. The spiral had a pitch of 2 turns per inch.

Before Widmer, Dufton[4] had used the same type of spiral packing except that it was made of copper. No difference in efficiency was noted. Midgely[5] coated the spirals of Widmer and Dufton with Carborundum and obtained considerably increased efficiency.

Hall and Bachman[6] have used a 7.5-cm Midgely column consisting of a 50-turn flat copper spiral in a height of 47.5 cm, coated with 40- to 60-mesh silicon carbide, and obtained an *H.E.T.P.* of 2.7 cm. The column flooded at a throughput of 1.8 liters per hour.

The modified Widmer consists of a column of the Widmer spiral packing, but differing in the method of heating the column jacket. The vapors rise directly from the pot into the column, while the jacket is externally heated. When the column jacket temperature is properly controlled, a slight improvement over the original Widmer is obtained. However, none of the Widmer type columns is very efficient and the results obtained with this type column do not appear to justify the labor required for their construction or the time consumed in their operation. A well operated Vigreux will give the same results with less time and trouble.

In further efforts to improve efficiencies of fractionation, almost every material that would fit inside a tube and allow vapor passage has been tested for packing. Many of these, of course, were of no worth. Single-link jack-chain showed some value. Its principal advantage lay in the fact that columns were quite easily packed with it, and so it could be used with larger columns. Carborundum has been used in a number of different forms, both as a coating for other packing and as crushed chips. Ordinary carding teeth of all sizes, and double-cross-wire forms have been used with some improvement over older columns. Probably the only reason that they would be used now would be because of their availability. Examples of the characteristics obtained by the use of these packings are given in Table 32.

**TABLE 32**

| Packing | Column length cm | Column diameter cm | Plates | Throughput l/hr | Pressure drop inches | Reference |
|---|---|---|---|---|---|---|
| #16 single jack-chain | 101.6 | 5.26 | 7.5 | 2.9 | 0.12 | 7 |
| | | | 7.5 | 6.3 | 0.24 | |
| | | | 7.0 | 8.7 | 0.31 | |
| | | | 5.5 | 10.7 | 0.47 | |
| | | | 5.5 | 14.2 | 0.39 | |
| | 182.9 | 5.26 | 12.5 | 2.0 | 0.12 | 7 |
| | | | 13.5 | 5.7 | 0.20 | |
| | | | 14.0 | 8.1 | 0.31 | |
| | | | 13.5 | 9.9 | 0.55 | |
| | | | 10.0 | 11.5 | 0.55 | |
| Carding teeth bent ¼″ | 294.6 | 1.70 | 25.0 | 1.6 | | 7 |
| | | | 27.0 | 1.3 | | |

**TABLE 32** (*Continued*)

| Packing | Column length cm | Column diameter cm | Plates | | Throughout l/hr | Pressure drop inches | Refer-ence |
|---|---|---|---|---|---|---|---|
| Carding teeth ⁷⁄₃₂″ | 259 | 5.1 | 24 | | 6.1 | 6.0(mm) | 8 |
| | | | 29 | | 14.8 | 30.0 | |
| | | | 52 | * | 4.6 | 6.0 | |
| | | | 40 | * | 14.4 | 46.0 | |
| Carding teeth bent ⁷⁄₃₂″ | 73.7 | 1.70 | 13.0 | | 1.3 | | 7 |
| | | | 13.5 | | 1.5 | | |
| | | | 14.5 | | 1.4 | | |
| Carding teeth straight ⁷⁄₃₂″ | 287 | 1.70 | 30.5 | | 1.4 | 1.77 | 7 |
| | | | 26.5 | | 1.3 | 1.18 | |
| | 167.6 | 2.03 | 26.5 | | 1.5 | | 7 |
| | | | 25.5 | | 1.9 | | |
| | 106.7 | 5.26 | 2.5 | | 3.8 | 0.51 | 7 |
| | | | 3.0 | | 9.6 | 0.16 | |
| | | | 6.5 | | 8.8 | 0.47 | |
| | 182.9 | 5.26 | 20.0 | | 4.7 | 0.31 | 7 |
| | | | 20.0 | | 7.7 | 0.59 | |
| | | | 20.5 | | 9.0 | 1.34 | |
| Carding teeth bent ⁵⁄₁₆″ | 30.5 | 0.6 | 3.3 | | 0.216 | | 7 |
| | | | 6.0 | | 0.036 | | |
| Double-cross-wire forms | 139.7 | 2.03 | 20.5 | | 1.4 | | 7 |
| | 76.2 | 5.26 | 10.0 | | 2.8 | 0.08 | 7 |
| | | | 7.0 | | 4.5 | 0.20 | |
| | | | 8.5 | | 5.6 | 0.39 | |
| | | | 7.5 | | 6.4 | 0.63 | |
| | 142.2 | 5.26 | 18.5 | | 2.0 | 0.32 | 7 |
| | | | 16.0 | | 3.0 | 0.47 | |
| | | | 15.0 | | 4.9 | 0.95 | |
| 6-mesh Carborundum | 259 | 5.1 | 20 | | 1.3 | 5.0 (mm) | 8 |
| | | | 40.5 | | 4.2 (flood) | 79.0 | |
| | | | 60 | * | 0.9 | 4.0 | |
| | | | 62 | * | 3.9 | 79.0 | |
| | | | 51 | * | 2.2 | 9.0 | |
| | | | 57 | * | 3.7 | 51.0 | |

*Indicates prewetting of packing.

The standard Berl saddles and Raschig rings have been used for some time. However, their chief use now is in semiplant or even plant size columns. The carbon rings are particularly in demand since they are completely resistant to corrosion. Some types of clay or stoneware are attacked by chemicals, particularly by hot caustic solutions. Characteristics of these packings are shown in Table 33.

**TABLE 33**

| Packing | Column length cm | Column diameter cm | Plates | Through-put l/hr | Pressure drop mm | Holdup cc | Reference |
|---|---|---|---|---|---|---|---|
| 4 x 4 mm Berl saddles | 121.9 | 1.1 | 24 | | | 12.0 | 9 |
| | 68.58 | 1.9 | 21 | | | 14.7 | 9 |
| 1.27 cm clay Berl saddles | 259 | 5.1 | 15.5 | 5.0 | 2 | | 8 |
| | | | 15.5 | 17.7 | — | | |
| | | | 13.5 | 0.6 | — | | |
| | | | 18 | 16.1 | — | | |
| 1.27 cm aluminum Berl saddles | 259 | 5.1 | 14.5 | 4.0 | — | | 8 |
| | | | 25 | 19.3 | 26 | | |
| 4 x 4 mm stoneware Raschig rings | 116.8 | 1.1 | 22 | | | 11.0 | 9 |
| ⅜″ x ⅜″ stoneware Raschig rings | 259 | 5.1 | 16 | 0.7 | < 1 | | 8 |
| | | | 14.5 | 4.5 | 5 | | |
| | | | 15.5 | 7.4 | 9 | | |
| | | | 22 | 11.2 | 22 | | |
| ½″ x ½″ stoneware Raschig rings | 259 | 5.1 | 12 | 6 | 2 | | 8 |
| | | | 20.5 | 18.2 | 27 | | |
| | | | 13.5* | 8.6 | 4 | | |
| | | | 17 * | 17 | 17 | | |
| ¼″ x ¼″ carbon Raschig rings | 259 | 5.1 | 17 | 4.5 | 20 | | 8 |
| | | | 20.5 | 1.7 | 4 | | |
| | | | 21 | 5.3 | 29 | | |
| ½″ x ½″ carbon Raschig rings | 259 | 5.1 | 9.5 | 4 | 1 | | 8 |
| | | | 17 | 16 | 20 | | |
| | | | 12.5* | 2.9 | 1 | | |
| | | | 16 * | 14 | 16 | | |
| | 305 | 5.1 | 15 | | | | 10 |
| ¼″ x ¼″ glass Raschig rings | 259 | 5.1 | 18 | 4.1 | — | | 8 |
| | | | 19.5 | 9.6 | 15 | | |

*Indicates column preflooded before operation.

## REFERENCES

1. WIDMER, G., *Helv. Chim. Acta.*, **7,** 59 (1924)
2. BAKER, R. H., BARKENBUS, C., and ROSWELL, C. A., *Ind. Eng. Chem.*, Anal. Ed., **12,** 468 (1940)
3. CARNEY, T. P., *Unpublished work.*
4. DUFTON, A. F., *Phil. Mag.*, **41,** 633 (1921)
5. MIDGELY, T., *Ind. Eng. Chem.*, Anal. Ed., **1,** 86 (1929)
6. HALL, H. J., and BACHMAN, G. B., *ibid.*, **10,** 548 (1938)
7. FENSKE, M. R., TONGBERG, C. O., and QUIGGLE, D., *Ind. Eng. Chem.*, **26,** 1169 (1934)
8. FENSKE, M. R., LAWROWSKI, S., and TONGBERG, C. O., *ibid.*, **30,** 297 (1938)
9. STALLCUP, W. D., FUGUITT, R. E., and HAWKINS, J. E., *Ind. Eng. Chem.*, Anal. Ed., **14,** 503 (1942)
10. WHITMORE, F. C., and SURMATIS, J. D., *J. Am. Chem. Soc.*, **63,** 2200 (1941)

# Rotary Distillation Columns

INSTEAD OF THE STATIONARY PACKINGS discussed up to this point, various rotary distillation columns have spinning center parts which serve to disperse the vapor and liquid through each other in the column, thus assuring intimate contact. These columns are of three types, the spinning band columns of Lesesne and Lochte,[1] the rotating cones of Pegram, Urey, and Huffman[2] and of Mair and Willingham,[3] and the rotating drum column of Willingham, Sedlak, Westhaver, and Rossini.[4]

Westhaver[5] in his development of the theory of rectification through an open tube has shown that an increase in effectiveness may be accomplished in any one or all of three ways: by decreasing the diameter of the rectifying section, by decreasing the throughput, or by increasing the diffusion coefficient in the gas phase. In a static apparatus for a given temperature and composition, the diffusion coefficient of the gas phase is substantially constant. The purpose of the rotating type column, then, is to change from laminar flow such as is met with in open tubes, to turbulent flow, where the diffusion coefficient is markedly increased.

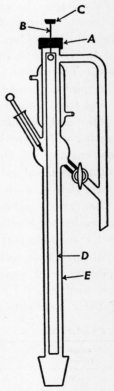

The spinning band type is shown in Figure 33. A number of the column heads described in Chapter XV may be used with this column, but the head shown is probably the best suited since it affords a minimum of holdup. This column depends for its efficiency on the contact obtained between liquid and vapor in an annular space between a rapidly spinning wire ribbon and the sides of a glass tube. The spinning band acts to throw the liquid condensate out from the center so that it is contacted by the rising vapor which is also agitated by the band. The packing gland $A$ is included so that the column can be operated under vacuum. However, this gland can be eliminated by the use of an electromagnetic type motor operating the spinning

**Figure 33.** Spinning Band Column

band, which is completely sealed inside the column. A wire *B*, attached to the motor *C*, extends through the packing gland and is attached to the band *D*. This band may be of any stiff, corrosion-resistant metal ribbon. A thickness of about 1 mm is recommended. The band extends down through the column proper *E*. Speed of rotation is regulated by the speed of the motor. The tube *E* is the only bearing required for *D*. The data of Table 34 were collected by Lesesne and Lochte,[1] using a column 37.5 cm long, 6 mm ID, with a spinning band of flat nichrome wire 4 mm in diameter.

**TABLE 34**

| Reflux rate drops/sec | Rotation rpm | Plates | H.E.T.P. inches |
|---|---|---|---|
| 1 | 1,000 | 15 | 1.0 |
| 2 | 1,000 | 9.4 | 1.5 |
| 1 | 0 | 4 | 3.8 |

When a mixture of 1 cc methanol and 1 cc water was fractionated through this column, the sample was completely separated into pure methanol and pure water except for a single intermediate cut of 0.06 cc. As would be expected, the holdup of such a column is very small. The effective free space of the column is the distance between the rotating band and the column walls. The column walls offer the only effective holdup area for liquids since the spinning band throws practically all the liquid with which it comes into contact out toward the walls. Therefore, the smaller the tube of the column proper and the smaller the clearance between the band and the wall, the smaller will be the holdup. However, this decrease in size and clearance will also cut down on the total throughput. Since the holdup is so small, the rotating band column offers great possibilities along the lines of semimicro work, that is, work involving a minimum charge of about 2 cc.

Baker[6] has increased the potentialities of the spinning band column by increasing the length considerably. Instead of having a single length of ribbon as the spinning portion, he uses short 30-cm lengths of ribbon connected by links made from soft monel metal wire having a diameter of 0.20 cm. When a spinning band composed of 30-cm strips of 6-mm by 1-mm monel ribbon was used in a 6.7 mm ID column tube 545 cm long, the results shown in Table 35 were obtained.

**TABLE 35**

| Throughput cc/min | Rotation rpm | Plates | H.E.T.P. cm | Holdup cc (operating) |
|---|---|---|---|---|
| 2.7 | 950 | 70 | 7.8 | 7.9 |
| 5 | 950 | 48 | 11.4 | |
| 2.7 | 1,900 | 70 | 7.8 | |

In both the columns described above, it was observed that increase in speed of rotation of the spinning band had no effect on the plate value of the column.

Huffman and Urey[7] used a type of the metal rotating cone column shown in Figure 34 for the classical work of separating heavy water from ordinary water. The upturned cone A rotates within the stationary cone B. In a column 35 feet high they installed 621 pairs of cones. On the basis of calculations of the efficiency per plate obtained from smaller cones, this large column should have given over 500 theoretical plates when operating smoothly. Actually, they calculated an operational value of over 400 theoretical plates. In this large column, also, the speed of rotation did not appreciably affect the column efficiency.

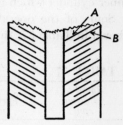

**Figure 34.** Rotating Cone Column

Mair and Willingham[3] have used this same type column. With a column 56 cm long by 5.08 cm ID, containing 77 rotating cones A and 78 stationary cones B, all at angles of 30 degrees to the horizontal plane, the results shown in Table 36 were obtained. The holdup was 1.3 to 1.6 ml per theoretical plate.

**TABLE 36**

| Throughput ml/min | Rotation rpm | Plates | H.E.T.P. cm | Pressure drop mm of Hg |
|---|---|---|---|---|
| 0.8 | 1,500 | 50 | 1.12 | 1.00 |
| 2 | 1,500 | 47.5 | 1.18 | 1.07 |
| 4.7 | 1,500 | 58.7 | 1.30 | 1.30 |
| 7 | 1,500 | 53.7 | 1.04 | 1.53 |
| 9.4 | 1,500 | 49.5 | 1.13 | 1.69 |
| 2.8 | 500 | 51.2 | 1.09 | 1.07 |
| 4.8 | 500 | 60.0 | 0.93 | 1.15 |
| 5.2 | 500 | 59.7 | 0.94 | 1.23 |
| 6.7 | 500 | 54.7 | 1.02 | 1.46 |
| 8.5 | 500 | 49.6 | 1.13 | 1.61 |
| 1.0 | 250 | 52.7 | 1.06 | 0.61 |
| 3.4 | 250 | 59.3 | 0.94 | 0.84 |
| 3.7 | 250 | 48.1 | 1.16 | 0.81 |
| 5.6 | 250 | 45.4 | 1.23 | 0.92 |

It will be observed in the above data that the speed of rotation has no significant effect on the column efficiency. There is also no significant difference in *H.E.T.P.* with throughput from 1 to 10 ml per min. The maximum throughput is about 10 ml per min.

The best of the rotary distillation columns from the point of view of practical laboratory distillation is that of Willingham, Sedlak, Westhaver, and Rossini.[4] This column, besides having very low holdup, *H.E.T.P.*, and pressure drop, also permits of a high throughput. The rotating portion consists of a closed cylinder, instead of the band previously described. The rectifying section consists of an annular space 1.09 mm in width, formed by the inside surface of a stationary outer cylinder and the outside surface of a rotating closed inner cylinder which is 7.44 cm in outside diameter and 58.4 cm in length.

Some of the operating characteristics of this rotating tube column are shown in Table 37, the values being based on a rectifying section of 1 meter.

**TABLE 37**

| Speed of rotation rpm | Throughput ml/hr | Pressure drop mm of Hg | Number of plates | Holdup ml |
|---|---|---|---|---|
| 0 | 1000 | 0.23 | | 12.6 |
| | 1500 | — | 7 | 14.5 |
| | 2000 | 0.40 | | 15.9 |
| | 3000 | 0.66 | | 18.2 |
| | 4000 | 0.83 | 5 | 20.1 |
| 1000 | 1000 | 0.30 | | |
| | 1500 | — | 15 | * |
| | 2000 | 0.51 | 14 | |
| | 3000 | 0.88 | 12 | |
| | 4000 | 1.20 | 11 | |
| 2000 | 1000 | 0.37 | | * |
| | 1500 | — | 21 | |
| | 2000 | 0.74 | 20 | |
| | 3000 | 1.13 | 19 | |
| | 4000 | 1.50 | 18 | |
| | 4500 | 1.77 | — | |
| 3000 | 1000 | 0.44 | | |
| | 1500 | — | 69 | |
| | 2000 | 0.90 | 55 | |
| | 3000 | 1.39 | 40 | |
| | 4000 | 2.00 | 35 | |
| | 4500 | 2.40 | | |
| 4000 | 1000 | 0.50 | | * |
| | 1500 | — | 105** | |
| | 2000 | 1.11 | 83 | |
| | 3000 | 1.89 | 61 | |
| | 4000 | 2.97 | 50 | |
| | 4500 | 3.86 | | |

*The holdup value is calculated for the amount of material on the wall of the outside tube. It is independent of speed of rotation.
**Extrapolated value.

These results are shown graphically in Figure 35.

From the above data it is seen that increase in throughput has the same effect on this column as on others discussed previously, namely, an increase in pressure drop and holdup, and a decrease in the number of theoretical plates.

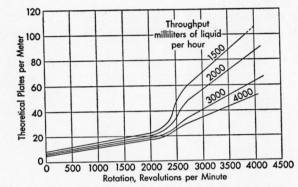

**Figure 35.** Characteristics of Rotary Concentric-Tube Column

The curves in Figure 35 show very strikingly the change from laminar flow to turbulent flow in the range of speed of rotation of 2300 rpm, as is predicted by the theory of Westhaver.[5] The very low pressure drop of this column should also be noted since this is an important factor when reduced pressure fractionations are being run.

The chief disadvantages of these columns lie in the fact that they are mechanical in nature and so are subject to all the imperfections associated with mechanical parts, and that the spinning band is made of metal. At atmospheric pressure where no packing gland is necessary at the head, suitable adjustment can usually be made without too much difficulty. However, when operating under reduced pressure care must be taken to maintain a tight seal at the gland. An ordinary graphite rope gland has been used to maintain a pressure of 1 mm for a period of 7 hours. Occasional tightening down of the thread is necessary since the rapidly rotating shaft wears away the packing, causing slight leakage after a period of time.

## REFERENCES

1. LESESNE, S. D., and LOCHTE, H. L., *Ind. Eng. Chem.*, Anal. Ed., **10**, 450 (1938)
2. PEGRAM, G. B., UREY, H. C., and HUFFMAN, J., *Phys. Rev.*, **49**, 883 (1936)
3. MAIR, B. J., and WILLINGHAM, C. B., *J. Research Nat. Bur. of Standards*, **22**, 519 (1939)
4. WILLINGHAM, C. B., SEDLAK, V. A., WESTHAVER, J. W., and ROSSINI, F. D., *Ind. Eng. Chem.*, **39**, 706 (1947)
5. WESTHAVER, J. W., *Ind. Eng. Chem.*, **34**, 126 (1942)
6. BAKER, R. H., BARKENBUS, C., and ROSWELL, C. A., *Ind. Eng. Chem.*, Anal. Ed. **12**, 468 (1940)
7. HUFFMAN, J. R., and UREY, H. C., *Ind. Eng. Chem.*, **29**, 531 (1937)

# Effect of Variables on Column Characteristics

THE MAJOR FACTORS affecting the operating characteristics of a column may be divided roughly into two classes: first, those which are a part of the column construction, such as height, diameter, and packing; and second, those which are a part of the operation, such as reflux ratio, throughput, etc.

There is no sharp line of demarcation between the effects of factors in one group and those in another. For example, both height of the column and throughput affect the pressure drop. The effect of each variable with respect to all other factors will be considered for different types of columns. When a change in any one factor is compared, it is understood that all other factors remain constant, that is, that conditions throughout the system are the same for both cases.

*Effect of Column Height.* Increase in column height for the same packing always increases the number of theoretical plates obtainable from the system. However, this increase in plate value is not always directly proportional to the increase in length. The reason for this lack of proportional increase in plate value is that in longer columns there is more chance for "channeling" to take place, that is, the liquid may run down through the packing in channels while the vapor passes up through in other channels. Thus efficient washing does not take place, reducing the number of plates. This condition exists in a column in which the packing has become unevenly distributed or, if the column is excessively long, channeling may occur because of a tendency of the liquid to flow chiefly along the column walls.

The Fenske metal helices show substantially no change in *H.E.T.P.* with column height over the range of the data available. For the glass helices, however, there is a decided increase in *H.E.T.P.* with increase in length for shorter columns, that is, up to about 150 cm in length. For longer columns there is no increase (see Figure 37). It is probable that the glass helices are too fragile to permit proper tamping to eliminate voids while packing, and that these data are deceptive, while the data on metal packing are more reliable and reproducible.

The columns of Stedman and of Lecky and Ewell show very slight increase of *H.E.T.P.* with increase in length for the short columns studied (Figures 39 and 40). The Podbielniak packing shows no change of *H.E.T.P.* with

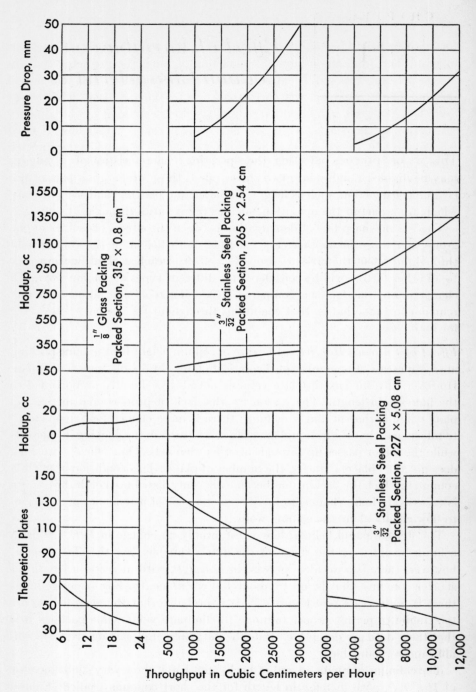

**Figure 36.** Operating Characteristics of Fenske Packing

increase in height for short columns. From the way these latter packings operate, and from the nature of channeling, it might be predicted that increase in plates would be approximately proportional to the increase in height. These packings owe their efficiency to the fact that liquid flows over a more or less capillary surface, and the flow is directed by the capillary attraction of this surface. Only one path is possible for liquid flow. It must spread out over the openings on the surface of the packing, and so be directed downward in a steady flow. No matter how high the column is built, the same type of conditions of flow at the top as at the bottom will prevail.

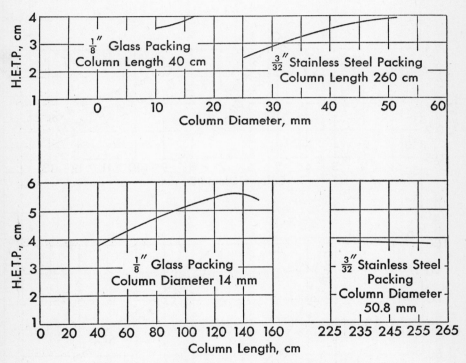

**Figure 37.** Operating Characteristics of Fenske Packing

It is obvious that increasing the height of any column will also increase the holdup for a given diameter and throughput. This follows simply from the fact that there is more volume in the column which must be filled with vapor and liquid.

Increase in the height of all types of columns increases the pressure drop. This, too, is easily understood since it will require more force to push the material to the greater height and through the added packing.

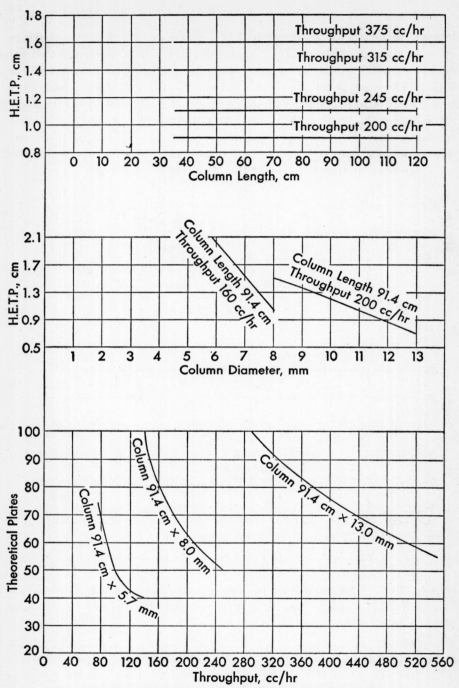

**Figure 38.** Operating Characteristics of Podbielniak Heli-Grid Packing

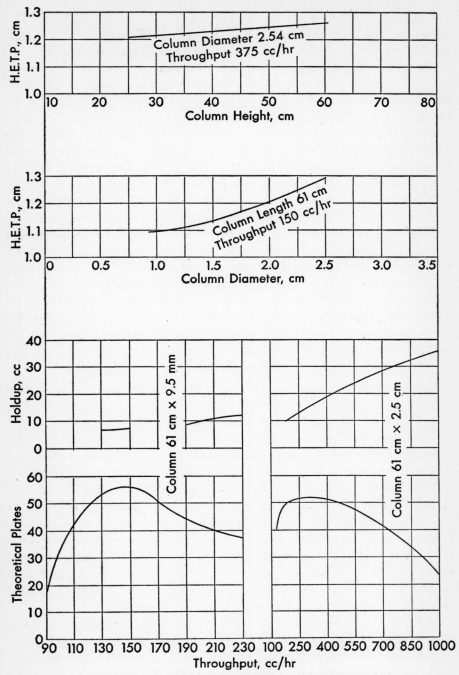

**Figure 39.** Operating Characteristics of Stedman Packing

*Effect of Column Diameter.* The channeling effect again becomes apparent with increase in diameter. Increase in diameter increases the *H.E.T.P.* of the Fenske and Stedman columns for the same throughput (Figures 37 and 39). No change is observed for the Lecky-Ewell column. The Podbielniak Heli-Grid (and Midgely) packing shows the peculiar property of decrease in *H.E.T.P.* with increase in diameter. This may be explained by a consideration not only of the diameter-*H.E.T.P.* relationship, but also of the relationship of throughput to plates (Figure 38). It will be seen that the number of plates decreases (*H.E.T.P.* increases) *very* sharply with increase in throughput, or in other words, with increase in vapor velocity. The curves of Figure 38 are drawn showing the change of *H.E.T.P.* with diameter at constant volume of throughput. However, as the diameter of the column increases, the vapor velocity decreases even though the volume of throughput remains the same. This amounts to the same thing as decreasing the volume of throughput in another column, and as a result the *H.E.T.P.* is decreased.

Increase in diameter also increases the amount of holdup in the same way that increase in height does—by increasing the volume of the system.

As mentioned above, increase in diameter decreases the vapor velocity for the same volume of throughput. As a corollary, the increase in diameter will permit a larger volume of throughput at a given vapor velocity.

*Effect of Vapor Velocity or Throughput.* When conditions in a given column are being compared, the vapor velocity increases in proportion to the throughput. In this discussion, then, the two terms are synonymous.

Two general statements can be made concerning the effect of increased throughput: the pressure drop always increases, and the holdup always increases in any type of column with increase in throughput. These effects are rather obvious. With increase in throughput with a column of constant volume, the amount of distilling material per unit column volume must of necessity increase. The pressure drop increases because of the increased force necessary to drive the larger amount of material up through the column.

Another effect of change in throughput is observed in the change of plate values or *H.E.T.P.* Decrease in plate value is probably caused by inefficient contact either because of channeling or because the vapor velocity is so great that heat exchange at a maximum efficiency is not possible.

The plate value for the Lecky-Ewell column falls off much more slowly with increase in throughput than do other columns. In fact, the *H.E.T.P.* is fairly constant over a wide range, and falls off only at rather high velocities.

In the Stedman column, a peak efficiency is observed, the plate value increasing and then decreasing with increasing throughput. It is believed that

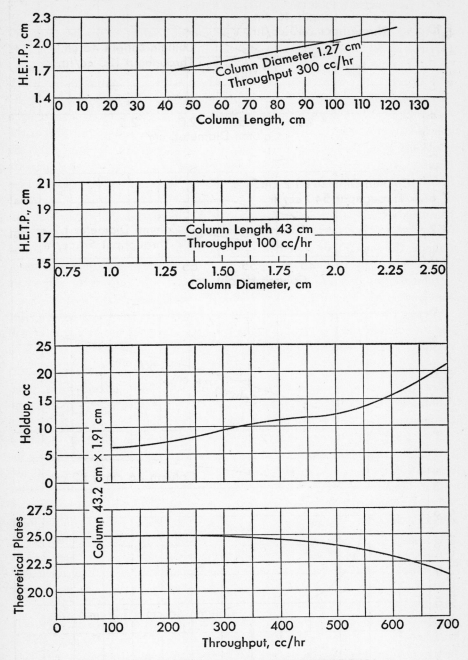

**Figure 40.** Operating Characteristics of Lecky-Ewell Packing

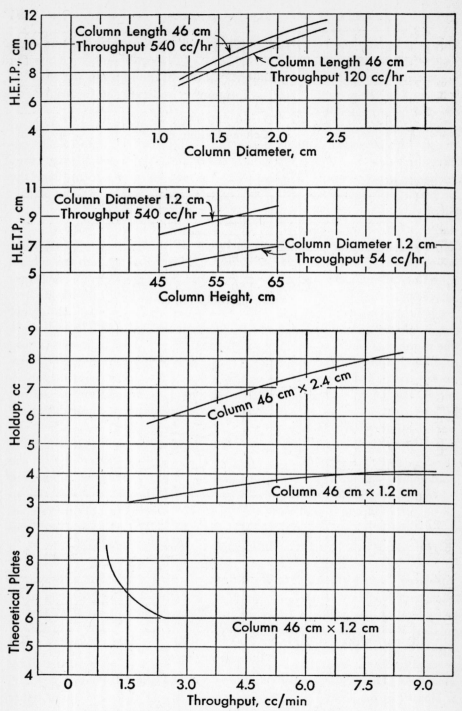

**Figure 41.** Operating Characteristics of Vigreux Columns

this peak is near the velocity at which the refluxing material keeps the surface of the packing completely wetted. This peak has been observed, also, in some studies of the Fenske metal packing. It will be remembered that the efficiency of these metal packings increases considerably if the packing is flooded before fractionation is begun.

The plate values of the Podbielniak Heli-Grid packing decrease tremendously with increase in vapor velocity. This effect must be caused almost entirely by vapors moving up through the column so rapidly that adequate heat exchange is not possible. The nature of the packing seems to preclude the probability of channeling, although spray or entrainment may be involved.

*Effect of Heating Jacket.* The effect of heat applied to the column jacket becomes more apparent as the temperature of fractionation increases. For example, materials boiling at 60-70 C can be fractionated through any column with only an unheated air jacket for insulation without any appreciable loss of efficiency. As the temperature increases, the heat loss becomes greater. Such heat removed from the system decreases the number of individual vaporizations possible up through the column system. As a result, a decrease in the number of plates is observed. However, even with poor temperature control, some appreciable enriching of the vapors occurs if the column is supercooled. If the column is superheated, the detrimental effect is greatly magnified. This becomes clear from a consideration of the process of fractionation which, as we know, consists of a series of vaporizations and condensations, vaporization of lower boiling materials taking place as the result of heat obtained from the condensation of the higher boiling components. Now, if the temperature of the jacket is appreciably above that of the material in the column, a certain amount of the distilling components will never be allowed to condense once they are vaporized from the pot, but instead will pass up through the column to the head with practically no enrichment. For example, for a material boiling at 180 C, the column plate value will be decreased from 90 plates to about 20 if the column is superheated by 20 degrees.

*Effect of Reflux Ratio.* The importance of the proper reflux ratio on the sharpness of separation is shown strikingly in Figure 22. The materials under consideration there have a boiling point difference of 32 degrees. With this mixture it is possible to get some pure components with a reflux ratio of only 3 to 1. As the boiling point difference decreases, the reflux ratio must be increased to obtain separation as shown in the distillation curves calculated by Rose (see Figure 21).

Rose[1] has made an excellent theoretical study of the influence of reflux ratio on the sharpness of separation in batch distillation and has reached the following conclusions:

1. Increased reflux ratio always gives sharper separation, but there are many instances where the increase is insignificant.
2. The magnitude of the effect of reflux ratio $R$ in any given case depends upon the relative volatility $\alpha$ and the number of plates $n$, as well as $R$, with the order of importance generally being $\alpha$, $R$, $n$.
3. The effect of increasing $R$ is always proportionally greater at small values of $R$ than at larger values (assuming $\alpha$ and $n$ remain the same).
4. With a given value of $\alpha^n$, a small value of $\alpha$ results in reflux ratio changes having but a small effect on sharpness of separation at all reflux ratios, whereas a large value of $\alpha$ results in a marked effect for small reflux ratios with little effect for higher ones.
5. When $\alpha$ is small, $R$ has relatively little effect on sharpness of separation, regardless of the values of $\alpha^n$, $n$, and $R$, unless $n$ and $\alpha^n$ are made very large.
6. Increase in $n$ causes $R$ to have more effect (at low values of $R$).
7. With a given value of $R$ and $\alpha$, the effect of increasing $n$ is much more marked when $R$ is large than when it is small.

**Effect of Holdup.**   The principal effect of increasing holdup is to decrease sharpness of separation (page 22). A method for observing the effect of holdup consists of the comparison of a calculated distillation curve for a mixture in a column, assuming no holdup, with the actual curve obtained in a column of definite holdup. When this is done, it is found that the experimentally determined curve differs from the calculated curve very markedly when the holdup is more than 10 per cent of either of the components being separated. This figure, then, may be used to specify the maximum allowable holdup: the holdup of the column should not exceed in volume 10 per cent of the volume of any of the components being separated.

**Effect of Pressure Drop.**   An increase in pressure drop also increases the pressure on the still pot and thus increases the temperature of distillation. The importance of this factor will be discussed further in Chapter XIV.

### REFERENCE

1. Rose, A., *Ind. Eng. Chem.*, **33**, 684 (1941)

# XIII

## Operation of the Column

THE BASIC PRINCIPLES to be observed when operating a fractionating column are the same no matter what type column is used, namely, accurate temperature control, controlled throughput, and controlled reflux ratio. The operation of a Fenske column packed with glass helices, the construction of which is shown in Figure 46, will be described in detail as a means of illustrating the general practice required for good fractionation. The slight changes in technique required to operate different types of columns will be discussed later.

*Operation of a Heated Fenske Type Column.* The material to be fractionated is charged to the column pot. The column jacket is preheated by means of the winding to a suitable temperature, which may be 10–20 degrees below the boiling point of a charge boiling up to 150 C, or to a temperature 30–40 degrees below a higher boiling charge.

Heat is applied to the still pot and adjusted so that a steady reflux drops from the end of the cold finger condenser at the head. At the end of about five minutes' refluxing, column temperature adjustments are begun. The object is to hold the jacket temperature at approximately the temperature of the refluxing materials. If this is done, the jacket heating will furnish only enough heat to compensate for the heat lost from the system. In some cases it will be found that, even though the heat to the winding is increased somewhat, the temperature in the jacket does not increase. This means that the jacket is being heated by the refluxing liquid in the column. The voltage on the jacket winding should then be increased until the jacket temperature rises a little above that of the refluxing liquid. At this point it is certain that some heat is being supplied to the system. The jacket voltage can then be cut back slightly and the heat to the still pot is adjusted so as to maintain the desired rate of reflux at the head. In laboratory columns this rate can often be estimated by counting the drops of reflux from the condenser. For the column under consideration the rate was found to be about 120 drops per minute. After refluxing has continued for a short time, another final jacket adjustment is sometimes necessary.

Where separate means are provided for measuring temperature at the top and bottom of the column jacket, it will usually be necessary to maintain the temperature of the bottom thermometer about one degree above the temperature of the refluxing material when starting operation. The thermometer at the top of the jacket will then read the temperature of the material near the head of the column. This is because there is a temperature gradient up the column. After all adjustments have been made, the column should be allowed to operate under total reflux for a suitable period of time in order for equilibrium conditions to be established.

*Reflux Ratio.*   When equilibrium has been reached, the takeoff stopcock is adjusted for optimum efficiency so that the ratio of the material returned to the column to that taken off is equal to or a little greater than the number of theoretical plates in the column (see page 30). This reflux ratio can be determined closely enough for use in the laboratory by observing the ratio of the number of drops of condensate from the reflux pencil condenser to that of the number of drops of liquid being taken off.

*Floods During Operation.*   Flooding at the bottom usually occurs as the result of one of two things, assuming, of course, that the column is correctly constructed and packed: first, the rate of vaporization is too fast; or second, the column jacket is too cold. Flooding at the top of the column usually means that the column jacket is too hot.

In columns with removable packing it sometimes happens, through improper technique in adding the packing to the column or simply after a great deal of use, that areas of greater packing density develop. Flooding will be in evidence at these points, also, particularly at higher rates of throughput. In these cases nothing remains but to repack the column.

*Continuing the Fractionation.*   As the takeoff continues, gradual changes in the temperature adjustments will have to be made. Let us assume a charge of a mixture of two liquids boiling 10 degrees apart. After equilibrium is reached, we can picture the column as having only pure component $A$, the lower boiling component, refluxing at the head, with gradually increasing amounts of the second component being present as we progress down the column. Yet there is predominantly component $A$ in the column. Now, as we continue to take off pure $A$, the amount of the higher boiling component $B$ increases in the column until there is enough to cause an appreciable increase in boiling point of the mixture in the column. This will be evidenced by an increase in the temperature observed on a thermometer placed in the jacket against the lower part of the column. This means that more heat must be supplied to the jacket to avoid loss of heat from the column, since the temperature gradient from the column to the jacket is greater than when only component $A$ was determining the temperature. Therefore the jacket temperature is increased at this point.

Depending upon the relation between the heat loss of the column and the difference in boiling points between *A* and *B*, it may be necessary to have more or less of the column jacket at a temperature higher than the reflux during the time of transition from one pure product to a higher boiling component. In this case the rate of reflux may be the factor determining how much heat should be applied to the jacket, since the reflux rate should be held as constant as possible throughout the distillation.

The distinction between reflux rate and reflux ratio should be noted. *Reflux rate* is the quantity of material reaching the column head per unit of time. The term *reflux ratio*, as used here, is defined as the ratio of the amount of material returned to the column to that taken off as product. In many cases it may be an advantage to use a column head in which the amount of takeoff is constant. With this type of head, varying the reflux rate will automatically vary the reflux ratio since the same amount of product is taken off while the total amount of material refluxing is changing. In any case, as the jacket temperature is increased the amount of heat applied to the still is increased correspondingly.

**Special Cases.**    Occasionally it will be found that, with the jacket temperature set at the temperature at which the charged material should boil, no reflux will reach the top of the column. It is then necessary to operate with the jacket temperature above the head temperature. If this is not due to flooding or the transition from one pure component to another during the distillation, then there may be some peculiarity of column construction—the winding of the column heating element, the position of the thermometer with respect to the wall of the column, etc., which should be corrected. Each column must be studied separately to learn its operating eccentricities. Many of these difficulties of heat control are eliminated where a vacuum jacket surrounded by an auxiliary heater is used.

Occasionally, too, it will be found that no matter what temperature adjustments are resorted to, flooding will occur at the top of the column when enough heat is applied to give reflux. If the heat is decreased enough to prevent flooding no reflux is observed. In a heated column without a vacuum jacket this is usually caused by a large difference in boiling points between the two components, there being only a small quantity of the lower boiling component. When the jacket is heated enough to maintain a steady flow of material up and down the column, the packing may be heated to a temperature which is considerably above the boiling point of the low boiling material. As a result, this component vaporizes through the packing. It condenses at the head, but when it runs back into the column it is immediately vaporized again by the hot packing. Consequently, all this material is concentrated in the head just at the top portion and above the packing. For this situation the best procedure is to run very slowly, taking off the low boiling material with a very low reflux ratio. When there is practically none of this material left, the column is put on total reflux. The technique of intermittent takeoff may be used until the head temperature rises to the boiling point of the next pure component of the charge.

*Intermittent Takeoff.* This technique consists of keeping the column on total reflux for a specified period of time, then opening the takeoff stopcock and running off the material collected in the stopcock well, then returning to total reflux and repeating the process. This method has the advantage of assuring equilibrium and, usually, sharper separation may be obtained; that is, there is less intermediate fraction.

In a comparison of continuous against intermittent takeoff, Oldroyd and Goldblatt[1] used three different columns to distill α- and β-pinene. The columns used were a 1-inch by 4-foot vacuum-jacketed Podbielniak, a 1-inch by 7-foot column packed with $\frac{3}{16}$-inch Fenske helices (not vacuum-jacketed), and a Palkin type column with 45 one-inch plates spaced 2 inches apart. The basis for comparison of the two takeoff techniques was the amount of intermediate fraction obtained between cuts of α-and β-pinene of specified purity. A charge of 500 grams of a 50-50 weight per cent mixture of α- and β-pinene was distilled at 20 mm, where the α- and β-isomers boiled at 52.2 C and 59.7 C, respectively. The data of Table 38 were obtained at a reflux ratio of 100 to 1.

**TABLE 38**

| | *Grams of product between α- and β-pinene of indicated purity:* | | | |
| | *99.5%* | *99%* | *98%* | *95%* |
| --- | --- | --- | --- | --- |
| Podbielniak Column | | | | |
|   Uniform | 72 | 55 | 43 | 35 |
|   Intermittent | 52 | 37 | 27 | 23 |
|   Decrease | 20 | 18 | 16 | 12 |
| Fenske | | | | |
|   Uniform | 138 | 97 | 74 | 58 |
|   Intermittent | 121 | 95 | 73 | 56 |
|   Decrease | 17 | 2 | 1 | 2 |
| Palkin | | | | |
|   Uniform | 184 | 138 | 105 | 87 |
|   Intermittent | 171 | 130 | 103 | 72 |
|   Decrease | 13 | 8 | 2 | 15 |

Thus it is seen that an appreciably sharper separation is obtained by the use of intermittent takeoff. The data on page 43 also indicate this to be the case.

*Collection of Data.*  In Table 39 is given a sample of the data that should be collected during a fractionation. These data were taken from an actual fractionation of a mixture of 60 weight per cent toluene and 40 weight per cent carbon tetrachloride using the Fenske-type column previously described.

**TABLE 39**

| | | | | | Weight of charge = 100 grams | | | | | |
|---|---|---|---|---|---|---|---|---|---|---|
| Time | Frac-tion | Weight g | Cumu-lative weight g | $n^{20}D$ | Boiling point C | Temperature | | | Amp through jacket heater | Reflux ratio | Remarks |
| | | | | | | Bottom jacket | Top jacket | Still pot | | | |
| 12:00 | | | | | | 70 | 70 | 110 | 1.3 | | Atmospheric pressure = 734 mm |
| 12:10 | | | | | 77 | 77 | 76 | | 1.3 | | Refluxing |
| 12:15 | | | | | 77 | 82 | 76 | | 1.3 to 1.0 | | |
| 12:25 | | | | | 77 | 76 | 74 | 105 | 1.0 to 1.18 | | |
| 12:30 | | | | | 77 | 78 | 75 | | 1.18 | | |
| 12:50 | | | | | 77 | 78 | 75 | 109 | 1.18 | | Takeoff started |
| 1:00 | 1 | 2.1 | 2.1 | 1.4585 | 77 | 78 | 75 | 101 | 1.18 | | Atmospheric pressure = 734 mm |
| 1:20 | 2 | 5.7 | 7.8 | 1.4598 | 77 | 78 | 75 | | | 10/1 | |
| 1:40 | 3 | 5.3 | 13.1 | 1.4598 | 77 | 78 | 75 | | | | Increased pot heat |
| 2:00 | 4 | 7.2 | 20.3 | 1.4598 | 77 | 79 | 75 | 103 | | 10/1 | |
| 2:20 | 5 | 5.0 | 25.3 | 1.4598 | 77 | 82 | 75 | 103 | | | |
| 2:40 | 6 | 4.9 | 30.2 | 1.4603 | 77 | 87 | 76 | 104 | 1.18 to 1.3 | 10/1 | |
| 2:50 | 7 | 2.2 | 32.4 | 1.4618 | 80 | 88 | 79 | 108 | | | |
| 3:00 | 8 | 2.3 | 34.7 | 1.4658 | 94 | 91 | 85 | | 1.3 to 1.6 | 10/1 | |

**TABLE 39** (*Continued*)

| | | | | | | Temperature | | | | | |
|---|---|---|---|---|---|---|---|---|---|---|---|
| Time | Fraction | Weight g | Cumulative weight g | $n^{20}D$ | Boiling point C | Bottom jacket | Top jacket | Still pot | Amp through jacket heater | Reflux ratio | Remarks |
| 3:10 | 9 | 2.1 | 36.8 | 1.4795 | 104 | 100 | 98 | 115 | 1.6 to 2.0 | | |
| 3:20 | 10 | 1.8 | 38.6 | 1.4888 | 107.5 | 110 | 109 | | | 10/1 | |
| 3:30 | 11 | 1.8 | 40.4 | 1.4918 | 109 | 112 | 112 | 117 | 2.0 to 1.9 | | |
| 3:40 | 12 | 3.1 | 43.5 | 1.4950 | 110 | 111 | 111 | | | 10/1 | Atmospheric pressure = 734.2 mm |
| 3:50 | 13 | 3.1 | 46.6 | 1.4960 | 110 | 110 | 110 | 118 | | | |
| 4:00 | 14 | 3.0 | 49.6 | 1.4960 | 110 | 110 | 110 | | | 10/1 | |

The residue, pure toluene, is distilled over at a much lower reflux ratio and higher rate of throughput.

*Analysis of Data.* In this experiment the time period between 12:00 and 12:30 was consumed in establishing the correct temperature conditions. Any change in conditions made by the column operator such as increase in heat to the pot or jacket, change in atmospheric pressure, or change in reflux ratio, should be noted so that on analyzing the data it is at once apparent whether a change in system conditions resulted spontaneously or because of the operation adjustment.

It will be noted that at 2:00, fraction 4, the temperature at the bottom of the jacket had increased 1 degree without any change having been made in the heat input. This was the first indication that appreciable amounts of high boiling material were in the column. After 40 minutes the bottom temperature had risen further while the temperature at the top of the jacket had also begun to rise. The head temperature was still constant. At this point the heat input to the jacket was increased in order to compensate for the increased temperature. During the taking of the next fraction the head temperature also rose, indicating that part of the high boiling material had reached the top. Thus, by a simple observation of the column temperature it was possible to follow the charged material up the column and to have had ample warning of any changes that should be made to meet the changing conditions in the column.

A study of the refractive index and boiling point relationships showed that the index changed while the boiling point was still constant for fractions 5 and 6. Similarly, for fractions 12 and 13 the boiling point had reached that of toluene while the index still indicated some impurity. At fraction 5, where the index first showed signs of impurity in the product, the weight of the samples taken was decreased. This was done so that a number of points could be secured in order to draw a smooth analytical curve for the intermediate material.

Using the same charge as that illustrated here, two other fractionations were run, one at a reflux ratio of 3 to 1 and the other taking off the first 25 grams at a ratio of 10 to 1, and then continuing with the technique of intermittent takeoff at the same over-all reflux ratio. These curves are shown in Figure 22, page 43. The intermittent takeoff curves give an appreciably sharper separation. It is good practice, therefore, in running any fractionation to look for the signs of an approaching intermediate fraction and then either increase the reflux ratio or else use intermittent takeoff. Thus, in the routine operation of this column, it was found advisable to allow the column to operate on total reflux for about 10 minutes after the intermediate fraction approached the top of the column.

*Interpretation of Data.* The collected data are set up in some graphical form to make analysis easy. If the fraction can be analyzed easily as by refractive index or density, a plot of the per cent distilled versus the composition of the fraction can be drawn. However, in most fractionations encountered in the laboratory this is not possible. Therefore, the other alternative is to graph the per cent distilled versus the physical properties of the fractions, as for example, the boiling point, index of refraction, density, and the freezing or melting point. It cannot be emphasized too strongly that as many of these curves as conveniently possible should be drawn on one record sheet before attempting to draw any conclusions as to the purity of the fractions. It is the usual tendency simply to conclude that a material which gives a constant boiling point or even a small boiling range at the column head is pure material. This need not necessarily be true. As a matter of fact, it has been found[2] that even with the most careful fractionation, in the case of close-boiling hydrocarbon isomers, an impurity of several per cent of one of the isomers will have relatively little effect on the boiling point, refractive index, or density, but will normally affect the freezing point or spectroscopic analysis appreciably.

In any fractionation at least two physical properties of the fractions should be determined and, in the case of liquids, boiling point and index of refraction are the two most convenient. In the ordinary fractionation which has for its purpose the separation of materials from a chemical reaction mixture where the materials are of a dissimilar nature, a simultaneous plateau on both the composition-physical property curves usually indicates a relatively pure compound.

Figure 42 shows such a set of curves plotted from the data in Table 39.

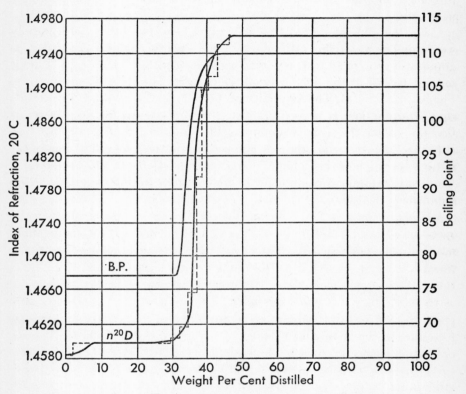

**Figure 42.** Data from Fractionation of Carbon Tetrachloride-Toluene

*Operation of Different Type Fenske Columns.* If the column used has a vacuum jacket, the column jacket adjustments are simplified or eliminated. If in conjunction with a vacuum jacket the column is also equipped with an electrically heated jacket, this latter jacket should ordinarily be kept at a temperature about 5 degrees below the temperature in the vacuum jacket.

If metal helices are used instead of glass, the efficiency of the column is increased considerably by preflooding the column to wet the packing before beginning operation. The still pot is heated strongly until the first flood appears at the bottom of the column. The heat is then maintained at such an intensity that the flood progresses slowly up the column. When all the packing has been wetted, the heat is removed and the liquid subsides. Care should be taken not to have a flood of such violence that the packing is disturbed.

*Metal Columns.*   In a metal column it is, of course, not possible to detect a flood by actually seeing the liquid in the column. The best indication of a flood in these columns is by observation of the pressure drop, that is, the difference in pressure between the top and bottom of the column. A flood in the column is usually accompanied by a very large increase in pressure drop as well as by a rapid fluctuation of the mercury in the manometer used to measure this drop.

*Operation of Other Type Columns.*   The temperature control of all columns described so far is essentially the same.

The Podbielniak, Stedman, and Lecky-Ewell columns should be preflooded to increase the efficiency. This increase in efficiency with preflooding is a characteristic of metal packings. A preliminary film of liquid on the packing is probably necessary in order to obtain uniform flow and distribution of reflux.

A study of Chapter XII will show the effect of the major variables on the operation of typical distillation columns. Adjustment of throughput, reflux ratio, etc. to obtain maximum efficiency as predicted by these data is necessary.

## REFERENCES

1. OLDROYD, D. M., and GOLDBLATT, L. A., *Ind. Eng. Chem.*, Anal. Ed., **18**, 761 (1946)
2. STREIFF, A. J., MURPHY, E. T., SEDLAK, V. A., WILLINGHAM, C. B., and ROSSINI, F. D., *J. Research Nat. Bur. of Standards*, **37**, 331 (1946)

# XIV

## *Vacuum Fractionation*

IN OPERATING a fractionating column under reduced pressure, it is necessary to observe a number of precautions not required at atmospheric pressure.

Under reduced pressure the vapor density is decreased considerably. In other words, the same weight of vapor in the column occupies much more space under reduced pressure than it does at atmospheric pressure. The greater the reduction in pressure, the greater will be the reduction in vapor density. We have seen before that the separating ability of a column depends to a large extent on the intimacy of contact between liquid reflux and rising vapor in the column. Under reduced pressure there will be less vapor by weight per unit volume of liquid, and consequently less contact. To remedy this, the vapor velocity or amount of throughput per unit time must be cut down. An arbitrary rule may be observed: the vapor velocity under vacuum should be an inverse square root function of that velocity which gives maximum efficiency at atmospheric pressure. For example, if the distillation pressure is $\frac{1}{25}$ atmosphere, the vapor velocity should not exceed 5 times the velocity used at atmospheric pressure. (See page 145 for calculation of vapor velocity.)

It should be emphasized that the pressure during distillation must be kept constant. A sudden decrease of a millimeter or two of mercury at low pressures will cause flooding in the column by greatly increasing the amount of material vaporizing. Similarly, an increase in pressure will cause a diminution or a complete cessation of reflux, destroying equilibrium conditions in the column. The lower the pressure, the greater will be the effect of a given change of pressure.

The importance of pressure drop through a system operating under reduced pressure is not generally appreciated. There is always some pressure drop in any fractionating system. Even with no vaporization from the still there is a difference in pressure at different parts of the system. The magnitude of this drop is determined primarily by the size of the tubes through which the system must be evacuated. A consideration of the process of evacuation will make this clear. When a system is being evacuated, pressure is reduced, not because the pump sucks the gas from the system but because the molecules of gas diffuse from the system. At low pressure the rate of diffusion of gases is quite rapid. However, the molecules must make their way out of the system by means of repeated collisions with the walls of the tubes between the point in the system under consideration and the pump. If the tubes are large, the molecules will be able to travel farther between collisions. However, if the tubes are quite small, it is conceivable that the gas would never find its way out, and so the pressure in the system would not be reduced sufficiently. It is always desirable, then, to have all the connections in a vacuum system as large as is practical.

When a material is being vaporized in the still pot, the difference in pressure between the pot and the pump becomes even greater because of the effect of the pressure required to push the material up the column through the packing.

The factors affecting the pressure drop under reduced pressure are apparent. As the amount of throughput increases, the pressure drop will increase. Similarly, for the same weight of throughput the pressure drop will decrease as the molecular weight increases. Temperature, pressure, free space in the column all affect the pressure drop through the system and should be taken into consideration before deciding on conditions for a fractionation under reduced pressure.

A rule for roughly estimating the temperature at which a compound will boil under a given pressure, if the boiling point at some other pressure is known, is as follows: the boiling point decreases 15 degrees every time the pressure is cut in half. For example, a compound boiling at 200 C at 760 mm would boil at 185 C at 380 mm, 170 C at 190 mm, 155 C at 95 mm, and so on. This is only a rough approximation. The error is usually in the direction to give a slightly higher approximated boiling point than is actually found. From this it will be seen how much greater is the effect of changing conditions at low pressures. For example, approximately the same change in boiling point is accomplished by going from 2 mm to 1 mm as is accomplished by going from 760 mm to 380 mm.

The effect of a given pressure drop through the system is much more evident at reduced pressure than it is at atmospheric. In an atmospheric pressure distillation the effect of a difference in pressure of 3 mm between the head and the still pot is inappreciable. However, the same difference may be present at diminished pressure. Then if the pressure recorded at the head of the column is 1 mm, the pressure of the liquid boiling in the flask is 4 mm, and the boiling points will differ as much as 30 degrees.

A column operating under reduced pressure is much more susceptible to flooding than it is at higher pressures. In distillations where the pressure is kept absolutely constant, this is principally because of the increased vapor velocity which tends to carry slugs of liquid up through the column.

The joint of the pot to the column base should be sealed or inspected carefully for leaks. A leak at any place below the top of the column packing causes great difficulty, because it cuts down enormously on the amount of throughput. If a stream of air is passing up through the column, it acts in two ways to destroy proper fractionating conditions. It acts as an air lift, carrying up liquid and usually causing flooding at the head. For this reason it is never advisable, unless absolutely necessary, to try to prevent bumping by the method of drawing air through a capillary tube extending below the surface of the liquid in the pot with the other end exposed to the atmosphere. The author has found the ordinary physicians' wooden applicator to be one of the most efficient methods of preventing bumping, both at atmospheric pressure and under vacuum. These sticks are inserted with one end resting on the bottom of the flask and the other extending up into the neck of the flask. About two of these sticks act as a very efficient ebullator. If it is necessary to use a controlled leak to prevent bumping, the smallest possible amount of air should be admitted.

Any air in the system acts further as a third component (see Chapter XX) causing codistillation at an appreciably reduced boiling point. It is always reduced somewhat by an amount proportional to the amount of air passing through the system.

The commercially available ground glass joint is usually satisfactory for vacuum fractional distillations (see page 116). It has been determined that normally these joints will hold a vacuum of about $10^{-4}$ mm of mercury. To eliminate completely the possibility of leaks, the mercury sealed joints may be resorted to. If the mercury in the seal is replaced by a heavy nonvolatile oil such as Apieson oil, a pressure as low as $10^{-8}$ mm of mercury may be held. Such pressures are required only in molecular distillation. The spherical joint is becoming more and more useful in the construction of glass equipment. It allows considerably more freedom of movement of parts, and consequently allows a system to be set up entirely free from strains with a minimum of care.

An exceptionally good stopcock[1] for use under vacuum is that shown in Figure 43. The well *A* may be filled with mercury or a nonvolatile oil, thus completely eliminating any possibility of leaks at the stopcock. This Newman type stopcock is particularly suitable for use as a takeoff valve for fractionating column heads since the takeoff rate may be observed at the drip point *B*.

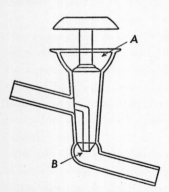

**Figure 43.** Stopcock for Use under High Vacuum

A typical arrangement of the apparatus for a vacuum fractionation is shown diagrammatically in Figure 44. All connections should be as large in inside diameter and as short as is practical. The number of stopcocks in the system should be reduced to a minimum and, where used, should have as large a bore as is possible. Capillary stopcocks should not be used. Besides cutting down tremendously on the speed of evacuation of the system, they also intro-

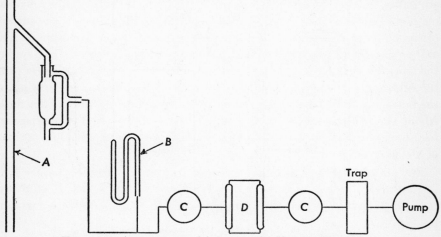

**Figure 44.** Arrangement of Apparatus for Vacuum Distillation

duce an appreciable pressure drop. For example, a 1.5 mm ID stopcock with a total capillary length of 13 cm will increase the pressure of a pump pulling against a dead-end manometer from 1 mm to a little over 2 mm. The manometer $B$ is placed close to the column system in order to record as closely as possible the actual pressure of distillation. The manometer should never be placed between the manostat and the pump since a false reading would always be given.

The surge tank $C$ may be 2 one-liter flasks placed in the line, one on each side of the pressure regulator $D$. The purpose of these flasks is to minimize changes in pressure in the line by allowing this change to spend itself in work against the comparatively large volume occupied by the flasks.

A word concerning the care of vacuum pumps might be in order. An oil pump, such as the Hi-Vac type, should *always* be protected by a sulfuric acid trap, a caustic trap, and a cold trap placed in such a way in the line that all vapors pass in succession through them before reaching the pump. The pressure which a vacuum pump can reach is limited by the vapor pressure of the oil. Consequently, if lower boiling vapors are allowed to pass into the pump and dissolve in the oil, the efficiency of the pump will be greatly impaired.

A desirable system of traps is shown in Figure 45. The sulfuric acid and lime traps are present not only to prevent low boiling compounds from being carried through the line, but also to take out any corrosive materials before they reach the metal parts of the pump. A suitable cold trap may consist of two concentric tubes as shown in Figure 45. The inner tube should extend to within about 1.5-2 inches of the bottom of the outer tube. If it is any

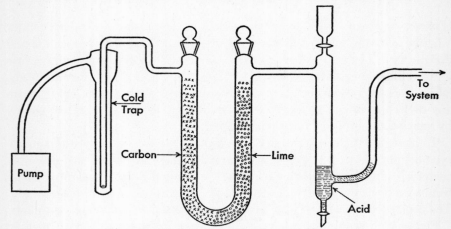

**Figure 45.** Trap System for Vacuum Distillation

closer to the bottom than this, there is the chance that its lower end will be submerged in any small quantity of material trapped. The whole cold trap assembly is surrounded by a dry ice bath in a Dewar flask. The volume of acid in the acid trap should be small enough to just cover the tube leading to the system. If the trap is too full, there is danger of acid being sucked back into the system.

An oil pump should always be operated at its highest capacity. For example, if a pressure of 10 mm is desired, it is never permissible to use a pump capable of pulling 1 micron and then bleed air into the system to raise the pressure. Instead, a manostat of the type shown in Figure 85 or in Figure 86 should be used. Air should never be pulled through the pump. It dissolves in the oil, raising the vapor pressure and lowering the efficiency.

In general, then, fractionations under reduced pressure can be carried out just as practically as those at atmospheric pressure, provided that a few added precautions are taken, and that the right equipment is available. It should be remembered that reducing the pressure always reduces the efficiency of fractionation, except in those cases where the vapor pressure curves of the materials being separated show an abnormal difference when the pressure is reduced.

### REFERENCE

1. NEWMAN, M. S., *Ind. Eng. Chem.*, Anal. Ed., **14**, 902 (1942)

# CHAPTER

# XV

## Construction of Columns

HAVING SELECTED A COLUMN on the basis of the principles outlined in Chapter VI, the following additional variables are usually considered in the actual design: type of head, reflux control, condenser, jacket, and temperature measurement and control. In this chapter a number of different heads, jackets, etc., are discussed. It is usually quite possible and practical to set up any desired combination of these variables with any given packing, simply by varying the proper dimensions.

To illustrate the construction of the usual laboratory column, the Fenske-type column shown in Figure 46 will be described in detail. The assembly comprises a heating jacket surrounding the column proper, separated therefrom by a dead air space, and surrounded in turn by a separate outer jacket. The construction and assembly of these various units is described as follows.

Figure 47 is exactly the same type of column, and illustrates the changes in dimensions that should be made as the size of the column is changed.

*Winding the Heating Jacket.* The pairs of holes $X$ and $Y$, blown in the inner jacket $D$, approximately 0.5 cm from each end, are about 0.3 cm in diameter, the distance between the holes in each pair being about 1 cm. One end of the heating element (#20 nichrome wire, 0.63 ohms per foot, 0.032 inch in diameter) $A$ is threaded through the holes $X$ to act as an anchor. Enough wire is left to run down through the inside of the jacket. This end is drawn taut and anchored by threading through one of the holes $Y$, and is finally led off to the line. The jacket is then wound with about 10-12 feet of the wire, spacing the windings to use the desired amount of wire. The end of the wire $B$ is anchored through the other hole $Y$, and serves as the second lead to the line. The winding is insulated to some extent from the bare glass by means of three strips of about 0.7 cm width asbestos tape (cloth or paper, although cloth is more satisfactory) placed lengthwise along the outer surface of the heating jacket and equidistant apart around the jacket.

Any suitable resistance wire or tape may be substituted for that specified, depending on the heat requirements. The winding recommended above will go to at least 300 C. In any of these windings a variable resistance is placed in the line with the heating jackets. This resistance should be capable of regulating input from about 0.1 to 7 amperes.

111

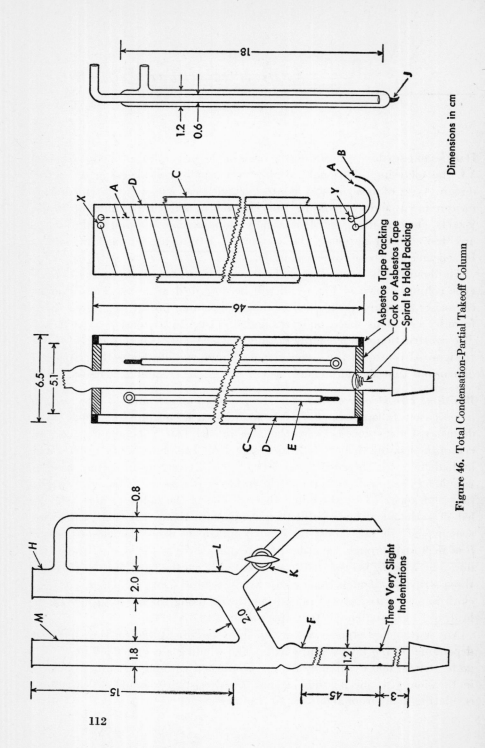

Dimensions in cm

Asbestos Tape Packing
Cork or Asbestos Tape
Spiral to Hold Packing

Three Very Slight
Indentations

Figure 46. Total Condensation-Partial Takeoff Column

112

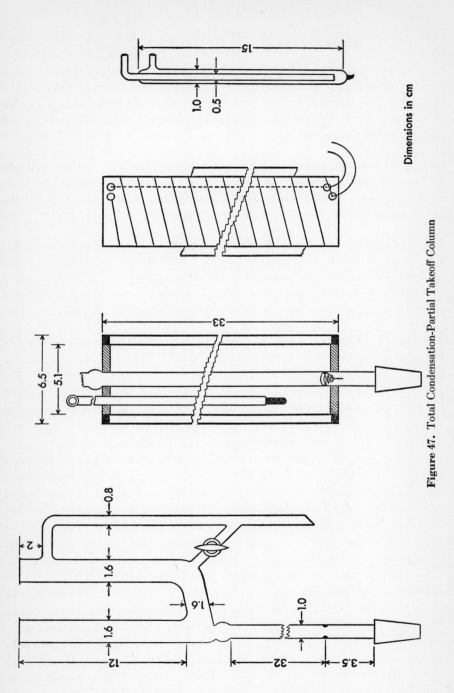

Dimensions in cm

Figure 47. Total Condensation-Partial Takeoff Column

***Jacket Assembly.***  The large outer jacket *C* is placed around the wound inner jacket *D*. Asbestos tape is wound around the inner jacket at the top and bottom until a snug fit is obtained. If necessary, the tape can be stuffed into the space between the concentric tubes by means of a knife or spatula. The two tubes should form one unit and there should be no sliding motion of the one tube inside the other. If this happens, the seals of tape have not been made snug enough.

***Jacket Thermometer.***  The thermometers *E* in the dead air space inside the heating jacket are attached to the column proper by asbestos tape. They should be placed in such positions that they can be read easily, while at the same time leaving the column itself clearly visible.

***Assembly of Column Inside Jacket.***  Just as the inner jacket and outer jacket were sealed with asbestos tape, so the space between the column proper and the inner jacket is sealed. It is sometimes satisfactory to use a slice of a large cork drilled to accommodate the column, which fits snugly into the inner jacket. At high temperatures, however, there is danger of charring the cork.

***Packing the Column with Helices.***  The small glass spiral is inserted through the top of the column. A spiral is used to hold the packing because it gives a maximum of free space. It is supported on three very slight indentations placed equidistant apart around the column. It should be emphasized that these indentations should be as small as possible. Likewise, the diameter

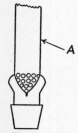

**Figure 48**
Packing Support

of the rod forming the spiral is as small as is practical, possibly one millimeter or a little more.

A second method[1] of supporting the helices is shown in Figure 48. The tube *A*, of the same diameter as the column, is pulled down to a cone shaped tip. Holes just small enough to support the packing are blown in the lower end. The sum of the areas of the holes blown should be at least equal to the free space area of the column, and preferably should be considerably more. A ground joint is sealed on as shown, and the whole is attached to the column.

The helices are dropped into the column through the thermometer well in such a way that no "bunching" takes place. If the helices are not separated before packing, areas of tight and loose distribution in the column will occur, causing channeling or flooding during distillation. It is advisable to add a bottom layer of two- or three-turn helices as a foundation between the packing support and the first single turn helices. Hall and Jonach[2] recommend disengaging sections above and below the packing to prevent flooding. In a column

11 mm ID and 560 mm long, for example, the column tube is expanded to 15 mm ID for distances of 50 mm immediately above and below the packed section.

A convenient method of adding the helices is as follows. A large funnel is placed in the thermometer well. Across the top of the funnel is placed a shallow box, in the center of which is drilled a hole about 1 cm in diameter. A small quantity of helices are poured into the box. By means of a glass rod pulled out to a point and fire polished, the helices are separated and pushed through the hole in the box, through the funnel, and into the column. Helices of more or less than a single turn are discarded. Packing is added to the height of the bottom of the bulb $F$.

Some method must be used to obtain an even distribution of helices through the column. In the case of metal helices, the packing should be tamped firmly and evenly by means of a rod as the helices are added to the column. For glass helices tamping is not very practical because of the fragility of the helices. Therefore, the outside of the column should be tapped constantly as the packing is added. The importance of obtaining a uniformly packed column should be strongly emphasized. Hall and Jonach state that, in the same column, it is possible to obtain theoretical plate values varying from 20 to 95, depending on the packing job. In a column 11 mm by 560 mm packed with $\frac{3}{64}$-inch stainless steel helices which normally gave 70 theoretical plates, the value dropped to 45 plates when the packing was introduced without tamping.

Willingham (quoted in reference 2) suggests the use of a wire screen for separating the helices. Hall and Jonach[2] use a wire screen placed over an ordinary 6-inch funnel to insert helices into their columns. A tamping rod passes through the screen and extends down into the column, and is kept in continuous motion during the addition of the packing.

***Reflux Condenser, or Cold Finger.*** The condenser is inserted into the well $H$, and held by means of a rubber stopper or standard taper joint. The drip point $J$ is adjusted so that the drops fall into the takeoff well $K$. Care should be taken to maintain sufficient clearance between the sides of the well and of the condenser so that the condensate drops off the end of the condenser instead of running down the sides of the well. The bottom of the condenser should be at about the level $L$ in the well.

***Head Thermometer.*** The head thermometer is inserted into the well $M$, and held by means of a rubber stopper or standard taper joint. The bulb should be in such a position that the vapors come into intimate contact with it as they pass up into the condenser well.

*Insulation.* A thick layer of asbestos cement is added to the column and head above and below the jacket. At the top, the cement is placed around both the column and the head from the top of the jacket, around the thermometer bulb, around the tube connecting the thermometer well and the condenser well, and around both wells for a length of about 6 cm toward the top. The takeoff line is left uncovered and the condenser well is bared just at and below the drip point of the condenser so that the condensate may be observed and the drops counted.

*Column Heads.* Column heads may be divided into two general types: total condensation-variable takeoff, and partial condensation-variable takeoff. Variations of these types have been developed to control reflux ratio automatically or semiautomatically, or to facilitate the removal of distillate. It is quite common practice to attach the column head to the column proper by means of a standard taper joint. However, Coulson[3] gives a word of caution about this practice since it gives another place for the escape of vapor when operating at atmospheric pressure. Under actual test conditions he found that an ordinary commercial joint in one case allowed the escape of 2 ml of benzene per hour when refluxing at the rate of 500 ml per hour. Therefore, special precautions must be taken to minimize leaks at this point by eliminating the joint or using proper lubrication.

*Whitmore-Lux Head.* For most laboratory needs, the total condensation-partial takeoff column head of Whitmore and Lux[4] is quite satisfactory (Figure 49). It can be made a permanent part of the column proper as in Figure 46, it admits of any reflux ratio adjustment with a minimum of effort, the construction is simple, and the observation of temperature and reflux is convenient and accurate. The vapors rising through the column $A$ pass over the thermometer $B$, and are condensed at the cold finger $C$. The condensate runs down over the small well $D$. Takeoff is regulated by the stopcock $E$.

*Turk-Matuszak Head.* Turk and Matuszak[5] have simplified the head described above by combining the condenser and thermometer wells into one chamber (Figure 50). In such a head it is necessary to have a drip point $A$, from which the condensate flows in such a way as to be counted as drops. It is also well to have a number of small vapor holes around the sides of the drip point. In smaller columns the holes are quite necessary. Their purpose is to prevent the flooding caused by condensate covering the main passage of the drip point when the rising vapor forces the liquid back up into the head. One other important point should be mentioned in connection with this head, namely, that the distance $h$ between the takeoff $B$ and the bottom

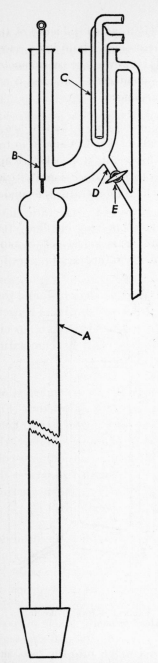

**Figure 49.** Whitmore-Lux Head

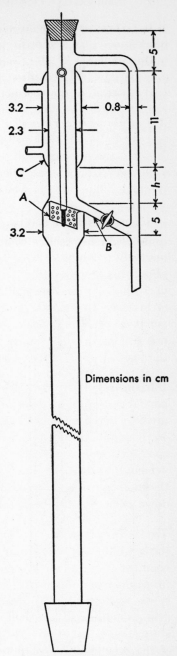

Dimensions in cm

**Figure 50.** Turk-Matuszak
Head

117

of the condenser $C$ should be at least 5 cm. This is to avoid influence of the condenser on the temperature reading. If the thermometer bulb is too close to the condenser, a false reading will be obtained. However, the thermometer may be safely placed through the middle of the condenser if at least 5 cm of the bottom of the thermometer is below the condenser.

***Adjustable Plug Takeoff Valve.***  The principal objection to the two heads described above is that a stopcock is used to regulate takeoff. Aside from the fact that the product might be contaminated by lubricant, stopcocks are apt to be very troublesome when the effort is made to reproduce some setting at a high reflux ratio, or when used at reasonably high temperatures or under vacuum.

Simons[6] has developed two column heads without stopcocks. The first (Figure 51) uses a ground plug $A$ with a groove ground on the surface of the plug in the direction of its length to a depth of 1 mm. By adjusting the plug by

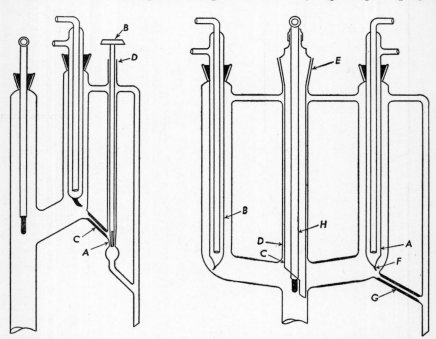

**Figure 51.**  Adjustable Plug
Takeoff Head (Simons)

**Figure 52.**  Vapor Partition Takeoff
Head (Simons)

means of the handle $B$, liquid flows from the takeoff well $C$ into the receiver. No lubricant is added to this plug since the liquid condensate acts as the lubricating agent. For vacuum fractionation and distillation requiring the elimination of air, a small piece of rubber tubing is placed below the plug handle *B*, and over the jacket *D*.

*Vapor Partition Takeoff.* The second Simons' head is an effective, easily constructed, and easily operated piece of apparatus (Figure 52). It is a device for the partitioning of hot vapors between two condensers. The material condensing on one condenser *A* is removed as distillate, while the condensate from the other condenser *B* is returned to the column. Thus, by regulating the amount of vapor supplied to each condenser, the reflux ratio is determined. The valve stem *C* is a piece of glass tubing that makes a close, sliding fit with the jacket *D*, without grinding. The lower end is ground on a taper as shown and the long end covers completely the inlet to one condenser while allowing vapor to rise to the other. A ground joint at *E* permits the valve stem to be rotated. This valve stem does not make a completely gastight seal. However,

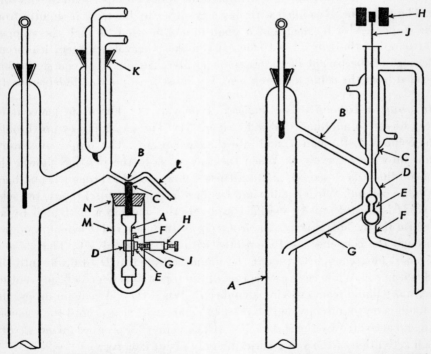

**Figure 53.** Mercury Takeoff Valve (Bush-Schwartz)

**Figure 54.** Automatic "Dumbbell" Takeoff Valve (Ferguson)

practically total reflux can be assured by sealing off as much vapor as possible from the condenser *A*, then rotating *A* so that any small quantity of condensation dropping from the drip point *F* will not flow into the takeoff trap *G*.

The thermometer *H* extends down through the inside of the valve stem and is in direct contact with the vapors, no matter what the setting of *C*.

***Mercury Takeoff Valve.*** Bush and Schwartz[7] have developed a very simple mercury valve (Figure 53) which operates quite satisfactorily at reasonably high temperatures and at pressures as low as 1 mm. It consists simply of a rubber tube *A* filled with mercury, the mercury reaching into a small trap *B* in the column outlet line and capable of being raised or lowered to regulate the size of the opening in the takeoff line. A heavy walled pressure tubing *A* (3 by 6 mm) plugged at one end is slipped over the Y stem *C* of the takeoff line and sealed with collodion. The steel collar *D* (1 cm wide) fitted with nut *E* is slipped on. The steel plate *F* (8 mm wide) is put in place and the side arm tube adjusted to take the screw *G*. The nut *H* is adjusted and the screw *G* is connected with the nut *E* through the side arm and the rubber tube *J*. The valve is filled with mercury through the standard taper joint *K* and tube *L*. The test tube *M* is filled with mercury either by lowering it slightly from the stopper *N* or by means of a small funnel inserted through the stopper. Surrounding the tube *A* with mercury makes the valve system leakproof. Because of the weight of the assembled valve, it cannot, of course, be suspended from the column takeoff arm, but must be supported independently.

***Automatic Takeoff.*** The *dumbbell* type valve of Ferguson[8] lends itself very nicely to automatic takeoff (Figure 54). The vapor passes up through the column *A*, through *B*, and into the condenser *C*. The liquid condensate runs into the reservoir *D*. When the valve *E* is in the position shown, the takeoff line *F* is closed off, and condensate flows over *E*, through *G*, and back into the column. When equilibrium has been reached at total reflux, the solenoid *H* is turned on. At specified intervals the solenoid is activated by an electric timer. This attracts the iron core in the glass rod *J* extending down through the condenser and connected with the glass valve *E*. The valve *E* is raised long enough to permit the liquid collected in *D* to drain into the takeoff line *F*. While the valve is raised, the top of *D* is sealed off, preventing any more liquid from entering chamber *D*. When the valve again drops, the column is on total reflux and no product can be withdrawn until the solenoid is again activated by the electric timer. The volume of product taken off with each activation of the valve varies by only about 0.05 cc.

One of the best of the many special column heads developed is that of Willingham and Rossini,[9] Figure 55. One advantage of this design is the provision which has been made to measure the accurate temperature of the liquid-vapor equilibrium at the head. Space is provided for a 25-ohm platinum resistance thermometer. The thermometer extends well down inside the jacketed portion of the column proper. An indication of the accuracy of the readings obtained from such a thermometer is given by the fact that, with a platinum resistance thermometer and with a controlled pressure, the temperature readings taken hourly showed normal variations of not more than ± 0.01 C for periods up to 200 hours when a pure compound was distilled.[9] The disadvantage of this head lies in the fact that it has a relatively large volume and requires more height than the ordinary head. Figure 56 is an assembly drawing of the head, thermometer, and valve control.

The well A (Figures 55 and 56) holding the platinum resistance thermometer B extends to the top of the packed section C. Vapors rising through D come into contact with the thermometer well over a relatively long portion of its length before rising into the condensing section, thus assuring accurate temperature readings. The apron E, extending part way around the tube, diverts the flow of reflux away from the wall of the column toward the thermometer well. The valve F is ground glass, operated by means of the control

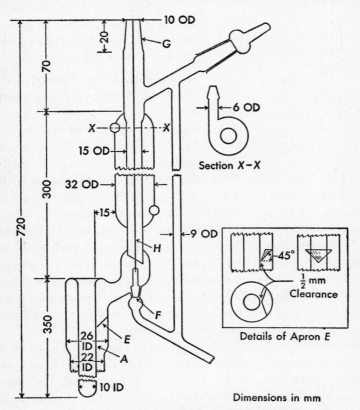

Dimensions in mm

**Figure 55.** Willingham-Rossini Column Head

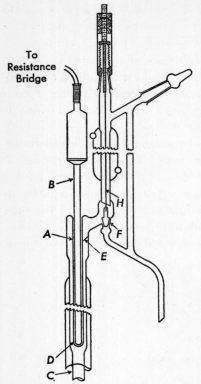

**Figure 56.** Assembly of Column
and Valve Control

shown in Figure 57. *G* is a standard taper joint which takes the joint *J* of Figure 57.

The control[11] shown in Figure 57 deserves special mention since it enables a very delicate control of the valve setting without resorting to the usual packing glands which cause trouble when operated under reduced pressure. The metal stem *A* attached to the tungsten wire *H* of Figures 55 and 56 is moved up or down by means of the knurled nut *B*. The metallic bellows *C* within the housing *D* is folded and unfolded as *A* moves up and down without any rotary motion. *E* is a lock nut, held stationary by the screws *F*. The bellows is hard soldered to the brass pieces at *G* so as to hold a high vacuum. *J* is a standard taper joint which attaches at *G*, Figure 55.

***Solenoid-Operated Takeoffs.*** The head designed by Bartleson, Conrad, and Fay,[12] Figure 58, makes use of one of the simplest of the solenoid-operated takeoffs. The valve consists of a steel ball *A* enclosed in glass. The glass seat *B* forms a tight seal for total reflux. When the electromagnet *C* is operated the ball is pulled up to position *D*, allowing for total takeoff. Upon release, the ball again seals off the takeoff line. By connecting the magnet to a timer, any desired automatic intermittent takeoff may be obtained. An indentation *E* is blown in the side of the column to allow for closer approach of the magnet. A thermometer is inserted at *F*, while *G* is the drip tip of a condenser.

Any of the types of condenser systems previously described for other heads may be used here. The chief advantage of this type of head is its simplicity, since the valve may be operated under reduced pressure without having any physical connection between the inside and outside of the column.

Another automatic takeoff head[13] is shown in Figure 59. The timer *A* actuates the electromagnet *B*, which in turn attracts the metal drip point *C*, holding it in position over the takeoff cup *D* until the desired amount of material has been taken off. When the electromagnetic circuit is broken, the drip point returns to the position shown, putting the column essentially on

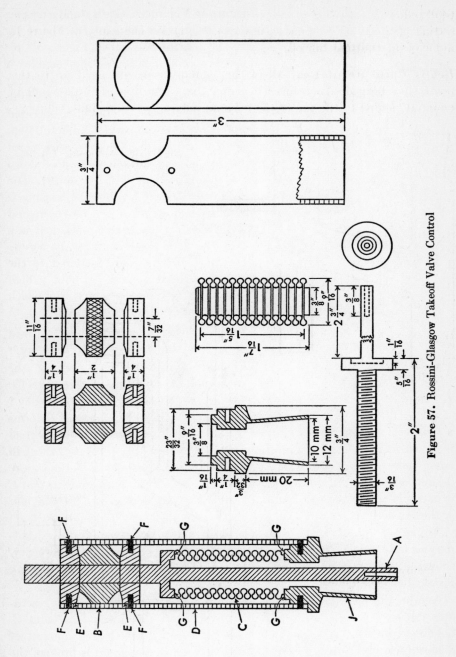

Figure 57. Rossini-Glasgow Takeoff Valve Control

total reflux. Total reflux is assured by the use of the stopcock *E*. By proper setting of the timer, the distillation can be run automatically by the technique of intermittent takeoff.

*Reflux Ratio Regulator.* All of the column heads discussed up to this point have been designed in such a way that regardless of the amount of material coming to the top of the column, only a certain definite volume is

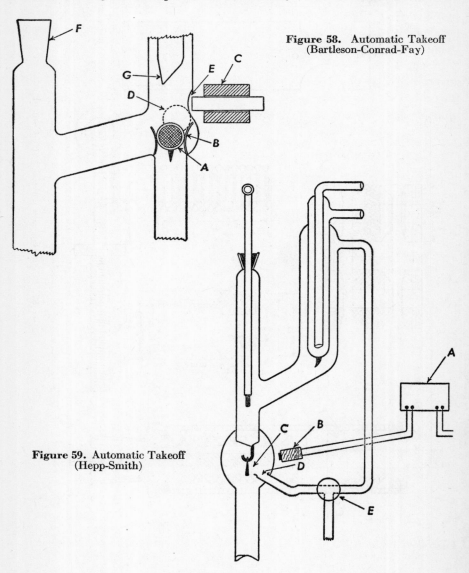

Figure 58. Automatic Takeoff
(Bartleson-Conrad-Fay)

Figure 59. Automatic Takeoff
(Hepp-Smith)

taken off. For example, if the stopcock or other takeoff device is set to take off 10 cc per hour, essentially the same volume will come off whether there are 15 cc or 100 cc of reflux at the head. Thus, if the rate of boiling in the pot is changed, the reflux ratio is changed, since a different volume of total reflux is obtained, but the same volume of distillate is being taken off. In other words, the reflux ratio varies with the rate of distillation.

Bruun has developed two heads with reflux ratio regulators which maintain a constant ratio regardless of the rate of reflux. These are based on the principle that the volume of flow through a capillary is inversely proportional to the length.

In Figure 60 a simple head[14] is shown, in which $R$ and $D$ are capillaries governing the flow of reflux and distillate respectively. The vapors rise through the column $A$, thence through $B$, and are condensed in $C$. A liquid head builds up in $E$, depending on the lengths of $R$ and $D$. The reflux ratio is determined

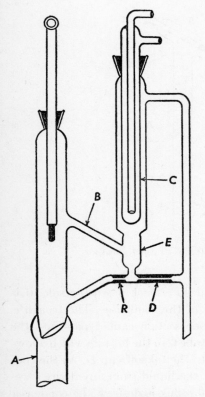

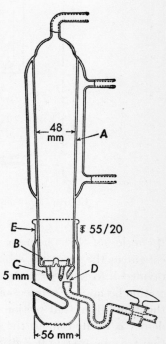

Figure 60. Bruun Reflux Ratio Regulator, Capillary Control

Figure 61. Berg Constant Reflux Ratio Regulator

by dividing the length of capillary $D$ by the length of capillary $R$. The rate of flow through either capillary may be increased by heating that capillary, since the rate of flow is also determined by the temperature. For example, if the lengths of the capillaries are 2 cm and 20 cm for $R$ and $D$, respectively, giving a reflux ratio of 10 to 1, and a ratio of 20 to 1 is desired, it will be necessary to heat $R$, causing a more rapid flow through $R$ while $D$ remains constant. Similarly, the ratio may be decreased by heating $D$.

A very simple and effective constant reflux regulator head is that designed by Berg,[15] Figure 61. The vapor rises through the column and condenses on

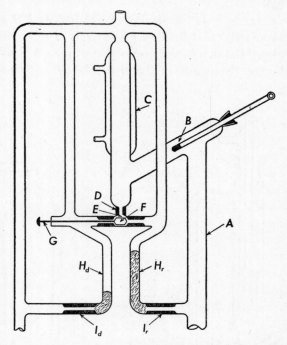

**Figure 62.** Bruun Direct-Reading Reflux Ratio Indicator

the inside of the condenser $A$. As the liquid flows back down the side, it is caught in the trough $B$ around the bottom of the condenser. The trough is divided into sections so that liquid from one section cannot pass into the section beside it. Each section has an outlet tube $C$ in the bottom which allows the liquid from that section to be directed to the takeoff cup $D$. As the condenser is rotated about the ground joint $E$, the liquid from any desired section may be taken off continuously. If total reflux is desired, the condenser is turned so that all the reflux is directed away from $D$. The peripheral length of any trough section compared with the total peripheral length determines the reflux ratio. For example, if one trough occupies one half of the total circumference, or 180 degrees, the ratio will be 1 to 1. If the trough occupies 60 degrees of circumference, the ratio will be 5 to 1; for 30 degrees it will be 11 to 1. The number of troughs will be limited by the circumference of the condenser. Care should be taken to make the trough deep enough and of large enough capacity so that the total liquid will flow through the downspout, preventing overflow from the smallest trough. The system must be kept perfectly vertical so that the volume of liquid flowing down the sides of the condenser will be equal at all points. The regulator should be calibrated before use, since the ratios calculated will probably be slightly in error because of the difficulty in getting accurate measurements of trough lengths. An advantage of this regulator is that it may be used for heterogeneous distillates, thus making possible the azeotropic distillation of mixtures which separate into two liquid phases at the condensation temperature.

***Direct-Reading Reflux Ratio Indicator.***  A second and more complicated direct-reading reflux regulating head designed by Bruun[16] is shown in Figure 62. This is an excellent regulator for use in distillations where holdup in the head of the column is not an important factor. The vapors rise through the column $A$, through the thermometer well $B$, and into the condenser $C$. The liquid passes down through the capillary $D$, which holds back uncondensed vapors, into the dividing chamber $E$. By means of a cylindrical metal plunger $F$, movable horizontally by means of a micrometric screw $G$, the flow from the dividing chamber $E$ may be carefully controlled. The capillary tubes $I_d$ and $I_r$ are identical in size and length. Therefore, the amount of liquid flowing through them will be directly proportional to the hydrostatic heads $H_d$ and $H_r$, the numerical values of which may be read from the calibrated scale. The reflux ratio is found by dividing $H_r$ by $H_d$. An increase or decrease in reflux ratio is obtained by turning the micrometric control screw $G$ to the left or right, respectively. When $G$ and $F$ are at the extreme left, the column is on total reflux.

In order to preserve constancy of flow through $I_r$ and $I_d$, it is necessary that both lines be at the same temperature. A commercial head of this type in which the capillaries are immersed in a heating box is available. In this head, also, the condenser $C$ and its system are bent back at an angle to the column in order to conserve head space. A capillary 0.9 mm by 100 mm with a hydrostatic head of 60 mm corresponds to a rate of 12 ml per min of a liquid like benzene. For greater rate of flow the capillaries may be made shorter, or the height of $H_d$ and $H_r$ increased above 60 mm. For flows of benzene up to 50 ml per min, a capillary tube of 1.0 mm by 50 mm will produce a hydro-static head of about 60 mm. It is important that the tubes $I_d$ and $I_r$ be identical in size and be perfectly horizontal.

*Partial Condensation Head.* All the column heads described so far have been of the total condensation-partial takeoff type. This type of column is usually much more satisfactory and requires less attention than any other type. However, when solids are being fractionated, the partial condensation type is better. In this type of column the amount of vapors condensing is regulated by control of the condenser temperature. Part of the vapors are condensed while the remainder pass from the system. In this way it is possible to keep a solid above its melting point in the column system. There is no stopcock involved in the takeoff, so this part of the system can also be heated to prevent solidification of the distillate.

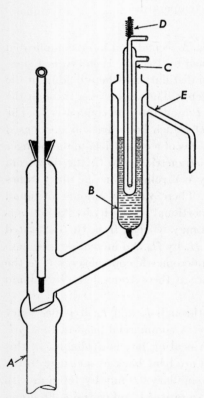

**Figure 63.** Partial Condensation Head (Whitmore-Nash-Laughlin)

Whitmore, Nash, and Laughlin[17] have developed a partial condensation column of the type shown in Figure 63. The vapors rise through the column $A$. $B$ is a fixed well filled with some high boiling liquid such as glycerine. $C$ is a cold finger which can be raised or lowered in the glycerine by means of a screw $D$. The temperature of the glycerine is regulated by raising or lowering the cold finger. The temperature is held at such a place that a very small amount of uncondensed vapors pass through $E$, which may be wound with a heating element if desired. The reflux ratio may be determined as usual by counting the drops from the end of the glycerine condenser.

A column head possessing many of the advantages of a total condensation column, yet permitting the removal of the product in the vapor state and condensation in an external condenser, has been developed by Arthur and Nickolls.[18] They objected to the fact that, in the ordinary head, the material in the stopcock well is constantly being diluted with condensate during attainment of equilibrium, so that the first sample off has some impurities in it. They developed the apparatus shown in Figure 64. The thermometer well $A$ is offset to avoid disturbance from the condenser or condensate. The vapors rising from the column are condensed at $B$. A small amount of liquid is caught by the slanted bridging tube $C$, and flows through the thermometer well to help prevent accumulation of dead vapors, while vapor also rises around $D$. The stopcock tube $E$ is slanted slightly upward to prevent liquid from collecting in it. The whole head is insulated to maintain vapors below the condenser.

The column[19] of Figure 65 also eliminates the small amount of static liquid at the head. When on total reflux, the liquid flows continuously through $ABC$ and back to the column. When takeoff is desired, the three-way stopcock $B$ can be operated for intermittent or continuous distillation.

A convenient tool for a preliminary separation of materials difficult to distill is the immersion still head of Bailey,[20] Figure 66. Tarry and resinous materials which tend to froth or bump have been distilled successfully. The line $A$ acts as both a vacuum line and a distillate line. As a drop of liquid collects on the end of the condenser $B$, it is forced up through $A$ by the pressure drop, and is collected in the receiver. The temperature of the condenser is regulated so as to maintain a fluid distillate. The pressure drop caused by lifting the material through $A$ is of the order of 1 mm of mercury. This apparatus, of course, does not give any high degree of fractionation, but it is useful for preliminary distillations of solids or other refractory materials before final fractionation.

*Condensers.* The choice of a condenser for a total condensation column lies between the sealed-in condenser of Figure 50 and the cold finger of Figure 49. Ordinarily, the cold finger is used when it is desired to be able to count the drops of reflux at the head or to direct the reflux from the end of the finger into the takeoff well. There is no great difference in

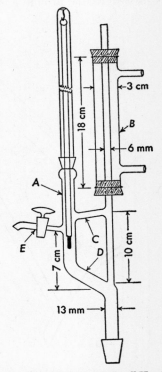

**Figure 64.** Vapor Takeoff Head
(Arthur-Nickolls)

the condensing efficiency of the two types. The use of either is dictated by the use to which it is to be put, or by the skill of the glassblower.

With the sealed-in condenser, a drip point somewhere lower in the column is usually necessary. This type does save space, permitting a single well for the thermometer and condenser. With a packed column in which the column and the head are not separable, a drip point detached from the condenser sometimes complicates removal of packing through the top. In the partial takeoff column, the cold finger condenser is used exclusively. The condensate can be observed from the drip point on the condenser relatively close to the takeoff, which facilitates finer adjustment by giving a rapid idea of the amount of distillate at the head of the column at any time.

*Temperature Control.* As mentioned before, the temperature of the area surrounding the column is controlled by means of various types of jackets. When the jacket is of the electrically heated type, a #20 nichrome wire having 0.63 ohm per foot resistance is a convenient size to use. With 10-12 feet of this wire wound around a 51-cm tubing over a diameter of 46 cm, a tempera-

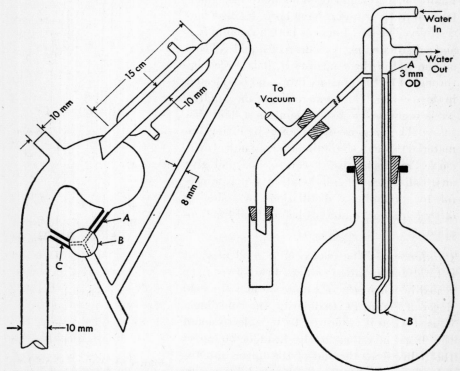

**Figure 65.** Continuous Reflux Flow Head (Lecky-Ewell)

**Figure 66.** Apparatus for Preliminary Distillation of Tarry Materials (Bailey)

ture range of 70-300 degrees is possible with an external resistance capable of passing 110 volts and 0 to 8 amperes.

*Heating the Still.* The still may be heated by means of a free flame or electric heater, an oil, sand, metal, or air bath, or by the heated jacket developed by Morey. An oil, sand, or metal bath gives a steady, uniform heat. However, it has one disadvantage in that it does not respond quickly to changes of applied heat. If the column starts to flood, the temperature at the pot cannot be reduced immediately without removing the bath completely.

Probably the best method of heating the still pot is by means of the jacket of Morey.[21] This consists of an asbestos or glass cover in which are placed heating coils, and which fits snugly around the flask, completely enclosing it. The heating coils are controlled by means of a rheostat. These heaters are made in different sizes to fit all sizes of flasks, and may be obtained commercially.

For columns whose pressure drops are appreciable, the apparatus shown in Figure 67 can be used to control rate of throughput automatically. As we have seen, the pressure drop increases as the throughput increases. In Figure 67 the U-tube manometer is attached to the pot. A permanent

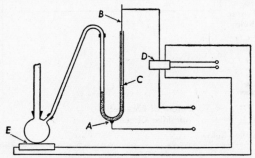

**Figure 67.** Automatic Heat Input Control

contact *A* is sealed into the bottom. The contact *B* is movable up and down The material in the pot is brought to boiling and adjusted to the proper throughput. The contact *B* is then lowered until it is just barely above the surface of the mercury in the manometer arm. If the throughput increases, the mercury in the side arm *C* will rise, making contact with *B*. This will close the circuit through the relay, which will in turn shut off the heater *E*. With the heater off for a short time, violence of boiling will decrease, the pressure drop will also decrease, and the mercury in *C* will fall, breaking the relay contact and turning on the pot heater again. This process is repeated throughout the course of the run, an extremely constant throughput being maintained.

To increase the sensitivity of this device and make its use possible with columns of small pressure drop, the mercury in the manometer may be replaced by a lighter material to amplify the manometer movement by change in pressure. A mixture of dibutyl phthalate and 6 per cent aqueous sodium chloride has been used successfully.[22] The phthalate is placed in the manometer arm nearer the column, while the aqueous solution is placed in the arm containing the contact B. For this arrangement the permanent contact A should be introduced into the side of the arm C nearer the lower end of contact B in order to assure its being in contact with the aqueous solution at all times.

The system using salt water in one arm is applicable only to operation at atmospheric pressure, since at low pressure the water would volatilize. Hall and Palkin[23] have reported a heat input control which uses a low vapor pressure mineral oil as the manometer liquid. Change in the height of the oil

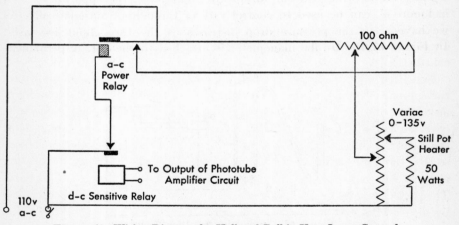

**Figure 68.** Wiring Diagram for Hall and Palkin Heat Input Control

indicating change in pressure drop through the column, actuates a photoelectric relay which controls heat input to the still. The oil used (Nujol) had a density of 0.862. A change in pressure of 15.7 mm of oil corresponds to a change of 1 mm of mercury. A box containing the light source and the photocell is so arranged that it can be moved to any height along the oil-filled manostat tube. Any convenient support may be used. It is desirable to have a micrometer screw for the final precise adjustment of height. The photocell is connected to the system, which contains a two-stage alternating-current-operated photoamplifier relay circuit, which operates a small sensitive relay. The relay wiring diagram[24] is shown in Figure 68.

To operate this control, the approximate rate of reflux desired is obtained by the use of the Variac to the still pot. The box is then moved along the tube until the relay is actuated, indicating that the meniscus of the manometer liquid has been reached. In this setup the circuit is opened when there is no oil interposed between the source of light and the cell. When the oil does move into the beam, it acts as a cylindrical lens to give a line image, thus actuating the cell. A very slight change in pressure drop will result in the opening or closing of the circuit, thus resulting in a very close regulation of column throughput.

*Column Jackets.* There are several variations of heating jackets for fractionating columns. A vacuum jacket operating at 100 per cent efficiency is the theoretically perfect solution. Since no heat is added or lost through a vacuum, the column is automatically adiabatic. However, ordinary vacuum jackets are not effective at temperatures much above 125 C, and if the column is being operated under reduced pressure, the effectiveness is even further impaired. Moreover, great care must be taken in the construction of a vacuum jacket. For a jacket much over three feet long, it is necessary to have a bellows effect along a small length in order to allow for thermal expansion and contraction.

One of the most practical and convenient column jackets is that shown on the column in Figure 46. It is very simple to construct, consisting merely of an inner tube on which the heating element is wound and an outer tube covering this wound tube and further insulating it from the air. The annular space between the column proper and the inside tube should be large enough so that the temperature in the column is not affected directly by the heating element, but rather is controlled by the annular space acting as an air bath. The jacket temperature can be controlled to at least one degree variation by means of a rheostat in series or parallel with the winding.

For columns up to about three feet in length, a single heating section is usually considered sufficient. A twelve-foot column is divided into three or four heating sections, while longer columns are usually wound in about four-foot sections.

A combination of a vacuum jacket around the column proper, the vacuum jacket itself being covered with the heating element jacket described above, has been used effectively. With this combination jacket, a very fine control of the heating coil is not necessary. It is only necessary to hold the air bath temperature within five or ten degrees of the temperature inside the vacuum jacket. Thus, the temperature gradient through the vacuum jacket is effectively reduced, and the jacket acts just as if a low boiling liquid were being distilled. However, the difficulties mentioned above in constructing a vacuum jacket make this type of control inconvenient for ordinary laboratory practice, at least in the longer columns.

Instead of using an air jacket, the temperature surrounding the column may be controlled by circulating heated liquid through the jacket. However, this method is not entirely satisfactory, since the temperature of the column cannot be measured. The jacket temperature must be held at the temperature of the head, and no indication of the progress of new fractions up the column is possible. Morton[25] has used this type of jacket, but he has also left an air space between the column proper and the circulating liquid so that temperature in this space can be measured and controlled.

Ordinary commercial lagging or insulation may also be used. The usual procedure is to wind a layer of insulating material ¼ to 1 inch thick, depending on the diameter of the column, then wind the heating elements around the insulation, and finally cover the elements with lagging. Thermocouples are placed against the column and in the insulation between the heating element and the column to measure heat flow. When the temperatures are the same, the column is being operated properly. This is the most dependable way of insuring adiabatic conditions (except for a vacuum jacket) since the flow of heat through the insulation is not as variable as it is through the air jacket. This method has the disadvantage of not allowing observation of the column packing during operation.

A somewhat more complicated method of controlling the jacket temperature is by means of a differential thermocouple. The hot junction is placed against the column, while the cold junction is placed between the heating element and the column and is separated from both by a layer of insulation. The heating current is then adjusted to a zero reading on a differential thermocouple galvanometer, indicating no temperature difference between the column and the point of location of the cold junction. Change in the heat input can be governed automatically by this setup, so that an entire fractionation can be run without ever having to adjust the temperature manually.

# REFERENCES

1. Long, J. R., *Ind. Eng. Chem.*, Anal. Ed., **17,** 197 (1945)
2. Hall, H. J., and Jonach, F. L., *Proc. Am. Petroleum Inst.*, **26,** [III], 48 (1946)
3. Coulson, E. A., *J. Soc. Chem. Ind.*, **64,** 101 (1945)
4. Whitmore, F. C., and Lux, A. R., *J. Am. Chem. Soc.*, **54,** 3451 (1932)
5. Turk, A., and Matuszak, A., *Ind. Eng. Chem.*, Anal. Ed., **14,** 72 (1942)
6. Simons, J. H., *ibid.*, **10,** 29 (1938)
7. Bush, M. T., and Schwartz, A. M., *ibid.*, **4,** 142 (1932)
8. Ferguson, B., Jr., *ibid.*, **14,** 493 (1942)
9. Willingham, C. B., and Rossini, F. D., *J. Research Nat. Bur. Standards*, **33,** 383 (1944)
10. Willingham, C. B., and Rossini, F. D., *Unpublished*, quoted in reference 9.
11. Rossini, F. D., and Glasgow, A. R., Jr., *J. Research Nat. Bur. Standards*, **23,** 509 (1939)
12. Bartleson, J. D., Conrad, A. L., and Fay, P. S., *Ind. Eng. Chem.*, Anal. Ed., **18,** 724 (1946)
13. Hepp, H. J., and Smith, D. E., *ibid.*, **17,** 579 (1945)
14. Bruun, J. H., *ibid.*, **2,** 187 (1930)
15. Berg, L., *ibid.*, **18,** 54 (1946)
16. Bruun, J. H., *ibid.*, **7,** 359 (1935)
17. Laughlin, K. C., Nash, C. W., and Whitmore, F. C., *J. Am. Chem. Soc.*, **56,** 1395 (1934)
18. Arthur, P., and Nickolls, C. L., *Ind. Eng. Chem.*, Anal. Ed., **13,** 356 (1941)
19. Lecky, H. S., and Ewell, R. H., *ibid.*, **12,** 544 (1940)
20. Bailey, A. J., *ibid.*, **14,** 71 (1942)
21. Morey, G. H., *ibid.*, **10,** 531 (1938)
22. Selker, M. L., Burk, R. E., and Lankelma, H. P., *ibid.*, **12,** 352 (1940)
23. Hall, S. A., and Palkin, S., *ibid.*, **14,** 652 (1942)
24. Shepard, F. H., and Schrader, H. J., *Electronics*, **9,** 36 (1936)
25. Morton, A. A., *Laboratory Technique in Organic Chemistry*, New York, McGraw-Hill Book Co., 1938

# XVI

*Testing the Column*

To EVALUATE the characteristics of a fractionating column, it is advisable to determine the number of theoretical plates, the operating holdup, the optimum throughput, the pressure drop, and, if the column is electrically heated, the amount of heat which must be supplied to the jacket to obtain maximum efficiency.

The literature contains several methods of indicating column efficiency which were introduced before the practice of expressing efficiency in terms of theoretical plates became common.

Peters[1] first used the formula

$$y = \frac{x}{k + (1 - k)x} \tag{1}$$

where

$x$ = concentration of more volatile component in liquid
$y$ = concentration of same component in vapor
$k$ = ratio of surface tension of less volatile component to that of more volatile.

The method of Hill and Ferris[2] has been mentioned earlier (see page 59). Neither of the methods mentioned above actually gives a good general method for comparing the separating ability of columns. The introduction of the method of determining theoretical plates gave, for the first time, a fairly sound basis for comparing columns of different types and sizes.

*To Determine Plates.* As we have seen, when a liquid is vaporized, the vapor is richer in the more volatile component. At a given boiling point when the liquid is in equilibrium with the vapor, the enrichment of the vapor is equivalent to that obtained by one theoretically perfect distillation or to one theoretical plate. Both a graphical method and an algebraic method for determining plates will be illustrated here.

To obtain the necessary experimental data for the column under observation, the following procedure is followed. The column is cleaned thoroughly and dried, drying being accomplished usually by refluxing a low boiling solvent such as acetone or alcohol through the packing and then pulling or blowing dry air through the system. The column is inspected very carefully for leaks, particularly if the determination is being made on a column which has 50 or more theoretical plates. Coulson[3] has given examples of errors introduced by leakage of vapors. For example, with a throughput of 500 ml per hour, with a loss of 2 ml per hour, the reflux ratio would be 250/1 instead of 500/0 (or infinite reflux). If the plates are to be calculated on the basis of the Fenske equation, no loss can be tolerated. If a finite reflux ratio such as 250/1 is known, then the Smoker equation must be used to obtain an analytical solution of the problem. As examples, for an $\alpha$ of 1.07 and a still and head composition of 0.1313 and 0.8471, respectively, for the lighter component, Fenske's equation gives 47.6 theoretical plates assuming total reflux, while Smoker's equation gives 52.5. If the column has a greater separating capacity, giving, for example, 0.0559 and 0.8471 as the pot and head compositions for the same mixture, Fenske's equation, assuming no loss, gives 67.1 theoretical plates while Smoker's equation with a reflux ratio of 250/1 gives 98.0 plates.

If the column jacket temperature is electrically controlled, it is heated almost to the boiling point of the test mixture. The mixture is brought to refluxing. After 0.25 hours, about 1 or 2 cc of distillate is drawn off in order to remove any low boiling impurities. Final adjustments of the rate of reflux and jacket temperature are made, according to the procedure given on page 97.

It is rather difficult to give any general rule for the period of time required for a particular column to reach equilibrium. The time required for attainment of equilibrium is a function largely of the holdup, throughput, and difficulty of separation involved, so that this time will vary not only for different columns but for the same column under different operating conditions. For example, a column 70 cm by 0.8 cm packed with $\frac{3}{32}$-inch stainless steel helices and having 27 theoretical plates will reach equilibrium in less than three hours, while a column 366 cm by 2.5 cm with the same kind of packing requires 24 to 36 hours to reach equilibrium with the same test mixture. The approach to equilibrium can be followed by following the change in properties of very small samples taken from the head of the column.

Coulson[3] has developed a very rough method of estimating the order of magnitude of the time required for a column to come to equilibrium as follows:

$$T_E = \left(\frac{H}{V} \frac{1}{x_s[\alpha/\{1 + (\alpha - 1)x_s\} - 1]}\right) \left[\frac{\log\, [1 + (\alpha^n - 1)\alpha x_s]/[1 + (\alpha - 1)x_s]}{n \log \alpha} - \left(\frac{\alpha x_s}{1 + (\alpha - 1)x_s}\right)\right] \quad (2)$$

where $T_E$ = time in hours to reach equilibrium
$\quad$ $H$ = operating holdup, moles
$\quad$ $V$ = throughput, moles per hour
$\quad$ $x_s$ = mole fraction of lower boiling component in still charge
$\quad$ $\alpha$ = relative volatility
$\quad$ $n$ = number of theoretical plates

When $x_s$ and $\alpha$ are small, and where $n$ is greater than 50, the above expression is approximately equal to

$$T_E = \frac{H}{V} \Big/ (1 + \log x_s / n \log \alpha) / x_s (\alpha - 1) \tag{3}$$

The derivation of these equations is based on the following reasoning: While the column is coming to equilibrium, the net amount of lower boiling material entering the column hourly will be $(V x_b - O x_s)$ moles, where $V$ and $O$ are the rates of boil-up and reflux at the base of the column in moles per hour, and $x_b$ is the mole fraction of lighter component at the bottom of the column. At total reflux, $V$ is equal to $O$, so that

$$V x_b - O x_s = V(x_b - x_s) \tag{4}$$

Now, with the column operating, it still contains $H x_b$ moles of the lighter component as holdup, where

$$x_b = \frac{\alpha x_s}{1 + (\alpha - 1) x_s} \tag{5}$$

At equilibrium, the gradient will be from $x_t$ at the top of the column to $x_b$ at the bottom. The total amount of light component held up in the column will be

$$\int_{l=0}^{l=L} x_l \frac{H}{L} \, dl \tag{6}$$

where $x_l$ is the mole fraction of lighter component at a distance $l$ from the bottom of the column, and $L$ is the total length of the column. $x_l$ is related to $x_b$ by the Fenske equation and by equation (5).

On integrating, the expression for the total moles of lower boiling component held up $M_L$ is

$$M_L = \frac{H[\log\{1 + (\alpha^n - 1) x_b\}]}{n \log \alpha} \tag{7}$$

If $M_L$ is the total moles of lower boiling material held up, and $H$ is the total holdup, then the expression

$$\frac{[\log\{1 + (\alpha^n - 1) x_b\}]}{n \log \alpha} \tag{8}$$

is the true mean mole fraction $x_m$ of the lighter component in the column contents at equilibrium.

During the period when the column is coming to equilibrium, the net amount of lighter component entering during any period will be $(Vx_b - Ox_s)$ moles, where $V$ and $O$ are the boil-up and reflux at the column foot, $V$ being equal to $O$ at total reflux so that $(Vx_b - Ox_s) = V(x_b - x_s)$.

If it is assumed that the reflux returning to the still is in equilibrium with the vapors of the composition given by equation (5), it will have the composition $x_s$. If it is also assumed that the still charge is large compared to the total holdup, the time required to reach equilibrium will be approximately equal to the ratio of the moles transferred to the rate of transfer, or

$$T_E = \frac{H(x_m - x_b)}{V(x_b - x_s)} \tag{9}$$

since $x_s$ can vary only slightly. Eliminating $x_b$ and $x_m$, equation (2) is obtained.

Coulson has applied his method of estimating to the data published for a number of different types of columns. The columns considered are those listed in Table 40.

**TABLE 40**

| Column | Type of packing | Reference |
|---|---|---|
| 1 | Stedman #112 | 4 |
| 2 | Stedman #112 | |
| 3 | $\frac{3}{32}$-inch single turn wire helices | 5 |
| 4 | $\frac{3}{32}$-inch single turn wire helices | |
| 5 | Lecky-Ewell spiral screen | 6 |
| 6 | $\frac{1}{16}$-inch single turn wire helices | 5 |
| 7 | $\frac{1}{16}$-inch single turn wire helices | |
| 8 | $\frac{1}{8}$-inch single turn glass helices | 5 |
| 9 | $\frac{1}{8}$-inch single turn glass helices | |
| 10 | Podbielniak, 20 gauge wire, 7 turns per inch | |

Coulson's results are given in Table 41.

**TABLE 41**

| Column | Diameter cm | Length cm | Throughput, $V$ ml/hr | Total holdup $H$, ml | Charge to still ml | Ratio $H/V$ | Time required for equilibrium $T_E$ hours |
|---|---|---|---|---|---|---|---|
| 1 | 2.5 | 62.5 | 150 | 9.5 | 190 | 0.0633 | 3.1 |
| 2 | 2.5 | 127 | 1080 | 75 | 1500 | 0.0695 | 3.4 |
| 3 | 2.54 | 95 | 506.7 | 60 | 1200 | 0.1184 | 5.8 |
| 4 | 2.54 | 150 | 3040 | 170 | 3400 | 0.0559 | 2.7 |
| 5 | 1.7 | 91.5 | 400 | 15 | 300 | 0.0375 | 1.8 |
| 6 | 2.54 | 85 | 1013 | 80 | 1600 | 0.079 | 3.9 |
| 7 | 2.54 | 125 | 3040 | 165 | 3300 | 0.0543 | 2.7 |
| 8 | 1.0 | 195 | 151.1 | 35 | 700 | 0.2228 | 10.9 |
| 9 | 1.0 | 195 | 471.3 | 38.5 | 770 | 0.0817 | 4.0 |
| 10 | 0.45 | 470 | 159.1 | 14.5 | 290 | 0.0911 | 4.5 |

In the above calculations a charge to the still was taken as 20 times the operating holdup.

In Table 41 the data are based on a column of the type described necessary to give 50 theoretical plates with an $\alpha$ of 1.07. If, now, the calculations are based on 100 plates, the results shown in Table 42 are obtained, it being assumed that the length, the total holdup, still charge, and ratio of $H/V$ are also doubled. The $T_E$ of Table 41 are included for comparison.

**TABLE 42**

| Column | 50 $T_E$ Plates | 100 $T_E$ Plates |
|---|---|---|
| 1 | 3.1 | 11.4 |
| 2 | 3.4 | 12.5 |
| 3 | 5.8 | 21.3 |
| 4 | 2.7 | 10.1 |
| 5 | 1.8 | 6.8 |
| 6 | 3.9 | 14.2 |
| 7 | 2.7 | 9.8 |
| 8 | 10.9 | 40.2 |
| 9 | 4.0 | 14.7 |
| 10 | 4.5 | 16.4 |

From these results it is seen that doubling the length, holdup, and theoretical plates of a column results in approximately a fourfold increase in the time required to reach equilibrium.

Berg and James[7] have developed more exact equations for calculating the time required for a column to come to equilibrium. The derivations of these equations are based on material transfer rates across liquid-vapor interfaces. The assumptions made in deriving the formulas are

1. The holdup of material in the reflux condenser and return system of the fractionating column is negligible.
2. A variable term in the basic time-composition equation is considered constant,

$$\frac{1 + Y}{1 + X} = \alpha$$

where $Y$ is the ratio of the mole fraction of lower boiling component to mole fraction of higher boiling component in vapor, and $X$ is the ratio of mole fraction of lower boiling component to mole fraction of higher boiling component in the liquid.

3. The vapor holdup in the column is negligible compared to that of the liquid.

The first of these equations is

$$\frac{1 - \dfrac{Y_o}{(x_w)(\alpha^{n+1})}}{1 - 1/\alpha^n} = \alpha^{-(\phi)\frac{(nL)}{H}\left(\frac{a-1}{a^n}\right)t} \tag{10}$$

where $X_w$ = ratio of mole fraction of lower boiling component to mole fraction of higher boiling component in still

$Y_o$ = ratio of mole fraction of lower boiling component to mole fraction of higher boiling component in reflux

$L$ = rate of reflux flow in column, lb moles per hr

$H$ = column holdup, lb moles of liquid

$n$ = number of theoretical plates

$t$ = time in hours

$\phi$ = function of $n\ln\alpha$

The values of $\phi$ as determined for various values of $n\ln\alpha$ are listed in Table 43 and are shown graphically in Figure 69.

**TABLE 43**

| $n\ln\alpha$ | $\phi$ |
|---|---|
| 0.4 | 19.5 |
| 0.6 | 10.9 |
| 0.8 | 7.10 |
| 1.0 | 4.63 |
| 1.2 | 3.64 |
| 1.4 | 2.89 |
| 1.6 | 2.48 |
| 1.8 | 2.17 |
| 2.0 | 1.92 |
| 2.6 | 1.49 |
| 3.2 | 1.32 |
| 4.0 | 1.16 |
| 5.0 | 1.07 |

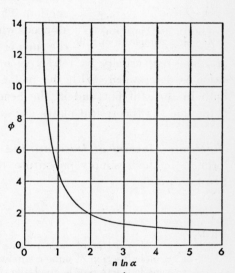

**Figure 69.** Factor $\phi$ as Employed in Equation (10)

As can be seen in Figure 69, as $n\ln\alpha$ approaches 6, or as $\alpha^n$ approaches 400, $\phi$, as well as $(1 - 1/\alpha^n)$ becomes equal to 1. In that case equation (10) becomes

$$1 - \frac{Y_o}{X_w \alpha^{n+1}} = \alpha^{-\left(\frac{nL}{H}\right)\left(\frac{\alpha-1}{\alpha^n}\right)t} \tag{11}$$

Where both $\alpha$ and $n$ are large, equations (10) and (11) may become difficult to handle. Equation (11) in these cases may be reduced to

$$\frac{Y_o}{X_w} = \left(\frac{nL}{H}\right)(\alpha - 1)(\alpha\ln\alpha)t \tag{12}$$

Of the above three equations, (10) is the most accurate, and is used with systems where $\alpha$ is small.

When equilibrium has been attained and with the column operating, small samples are withdrawn from the head and from the still. These are withdrawn simultaneously or within as short a time as possible in order to determine the enrichment from the still pot to the head at any instant. The still sample may be obtained by means of an apparatus such as that shown in Figure 70.

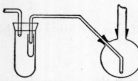

**Figure 70.** Apparatus for Obtaining Sample from Still

A tube extends below the surface of the boiling charge. The portion of the tube outside the still is bent so that a siphon can be started either by the pressure drop in the column or by a slight suction. This line is closed by a pinch clamp or stopcock when not in use. The first sample through the tube is discarded. The head and still samples are analyzed, usually by refractive index, and the mole per cent composition is determined. With the molar composition of the materials known both in the still pot and in the head at any one time, it is possible to determine the theoretical plates necessary to give that separation.

*Algebraic Method of Determining Plates.*  To determine plates by the formula method, simply substitute the above determined values in the Fenske formula:

$$\frac{x_A}{y_A} = \alpha^{(n-1)} \frac{x_B}{y_B} \tag{13}$$

where
$x_A$ = mole fraction of more volatile component at head
$x_B$ = mole fraction of same component in still
$y_A$ = mole fraction of less volatile component at head
$y_B$ = mole fraction of same component in the still
$\alpha$ = relative volatility (defined as the ratio of the vapor pressures at the boiling point)
$n$ = number of theoretical plates.

In this method it is necessary to know, besides the values experimentally determined, only the value of $\alpha$.

*To Determine Plates by the Graphical Method.*  For the graphical method, it is necessary to know the vapor-liquid equilibrium data for the system under consideration. Such data may be determined by means of the apparatus described in Chapter XIX, although a number of satisfactory binary mixtures have already been studied for use as test mixtures.

To use this method, the $x = y$ diagram (Figure 10, page 14) for the system is drawn, that is, the mole per cent of the more volatile material in the liquid,

$x$, is drawn as the abscissa while the mole per cent of the same component in the vapor $y$, is the ordinate. Since the determination is to be run under total reflux, the operating line (page 14) corresponds to a straight line diagonal equal to the formula $x = y$.

The remaining data necessary for measuring the theoretical plates of the column are the mole percentages of the more volatile material in the still pot and at the head, which we have obtained above. These points are plotted on the $x = y$ diagonal. For example, if the percentages are 25 in the pot and 75 at the head, the curve would be that shown in Figure 71.

$ABC$ is the liquid-vapor curve, $D$ is 75 mole per cent, and $E$ is 25 mole per cent. Starting at the top of the curve at point $D$, a series of steps is drawn between the equilibrium

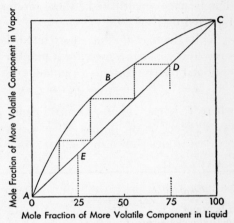

**Figure 71.** Determination of Theoretical Plates

curve and the $x = y$ diagonal, from the point $D$ to $E$. By this process of working the McCabe-Thiele diagram backwards, the number of theoretical plates in the column is determined as equal to the number of horizontal steps on the graph.

## Choosing a Test Mixture to Determine Theoretical Plates.

A test mixture to be used in determining theoretical plates should meet at least the following specifications:

1. The vapor liquid equilibrium data and/or the relative volatility should be known.
2. Molar composition of different proportions should be readily analyzed (by refractive index or density).
3. The mixture should obey Raoult's law as closely as possible.
4. The mixture should not be separable to give a pure component at the head because, in that case, an infinite number of plates would be given by the formula or graphic method.

Two mixtures are used quite extensively: (1) carbon tetrachloride-benzene with a boiling point difference of 3.4 degrees, used for the determination of plates up to about 30, and (2), $n$-heptane-methylcyclohexane with a boiling point difference of 2.4 degrees, used for columns up to about 125 plates. Data for these mixtures are given at the end of this chapter. In addition to the mixtures mentioned above, two others have been suggested[8] for testing columns having 200 or more theoretical plates. These are 2,3,4-trimethylpentane–2,3,3-trimethylpentane, and 2,5-dimethylhexane–2,4-dimethylhexane. The relative volatilities of these mixtures as well as a number of others are reported on page 39.

Willingham, *et al.*,[9] have correlated the experimentally determined temperatures and vapor pressures for a number of hydrocarbons, and constants were obtained for the Antoine equation,

$$\log P = A - B/(C + t) \tag{14}$$

where $P$ is the vapor pressure in mm and $t$ is the temperature in degrees centigrade. For the hydrocarbons suggested as test compounds in this chapter, the values shown in Table 44 for constants $A$, $B$, and $C$ were found.

**TABLE 44**

| Compounds | A | Constants B | C |
|---|---|---|---|
| *n*-heptane | 6.90342 | 1268.636 | 216.951 |
| methylcyclohexane | 6.82689 | 1272.864 | 221.630 |
| 2,2,4-trimethylpentane | 6.81189 | 1257.840 | 220.735 |
| 2,3,4-trimethylpentane | 6.85396 | 1315.084 | 217.526 |
| 2,3,3-trimethylpentane | 6.84353 | 1328.046 | 220.375 |
| 2,4-dimethylhexane | 6.85306 | 1287.876 | 214.790 |
| 2,5-dimethylhexane | 6.85984 | 1287.274 | 214.412 |

To use the constants in the Antoine equation, the temperature of operation is determined and the constants for the individual components are substituted in the equation to determine the vapor pressure of the component at that temperature. The ratio of the vapor pressures of the components at the operating temperature is the relative volatility.

Willingham and Rossini[8] have reduced the relationship between number of plates, temperature, and composition to the following formulas:

For *n*-heptane and methylcyclohexane, in the range 96.5 to 101.5 C,

$$n + 1 = [32.15 - 0.34(t - 99)] \log [(N_A/N_B)_{head}/(N_A/N_B)_{pot}] \tag{15}$$

For 2,2,4-trimethylpentane and methylcyclohexane in the range 97 to 101.5 C,

$$n + 1 = [48.07 + 0.13(t - 100)] \log [(N_A/N_B)_{head}/(N_A/N_B)_{pot}] \tag{16}$$

For 2,3,4-trimethylpentane and 2,3,3-trimethylpentane in the range 111.5 to 115 C,

$$n + 1 = [64.95 - 0.36(t - 114)] \log [(N_A/N_B)_{head}/(N_A/N_B)_{pot}] \tag{17}$$

For 2,5-dimethylhexane and 2,4-dimethylhexane in the range 107 to 110 C,

$$n + 1 = [250.5 - 1.7(t - 109)] \log [(N_A/N_B)_{head}/(N_A/N_B)_{pot}] \tag{18}$$

In these equations $N$ is the mole fraction and $t$ is the mean temperature.

In using the graphical method for determining plates, it is advisable to work in the center portion of the curve at its widest point. As the composition approaches the intersection of the $x = y$ curve and the vapor-liquid equilibrium curve, the distance between these two curves decreases, making it increasingly difficult to draw steps in this region. When it is necessary to work in these composition ranges the curve should be enlarged.

**Determining Theoretical Plates Under Reduced Pressure.** Several test mixtures have been suggested for determining the theoretical plates in columns operating under low pressure. Bishop[10] recommended either tri-*m*-cresyl phosphate–tri-*p*-cresyl phosphate, or dioctylphthalate–di-(butoxyethyl) phthalate. However, the analytical methods used require large samples and are not accurate. Hickman[11] used di-(2-ethylhexyl) phthalate–dibenzyl phthalate. This system is limited because of its high relative volatility to studies of columns having only two or three theoretical plates. Williams[12] has used di-*n*-butyl phthalate–di-*n*-butyl azelate to study columns of as high as 30 theoretical plates. The phthalate ester boils at 150 C at 1 mm, and the azelate ester boils at 155 C. The mixture does not depart appreciably from ideality, and the components differ sufficiently in refractive index so that this property may be used as a method of analysis. The data necessary for construction of the refractive index-composition curve and the vapor-liquid equilibrium curve are given at the end of this chapter.

**Vapor Velocity.** The vapor velocity may be expressed either as unit weight per unit time of material reaching the top of the column, or as unit distance per unit time. These are usually expressed in units of cubic centimeters per hour or feet per second for laboratory columns.

To determine the vapor velocity in feet per second, the following formula is used:

$$V = \frac{(T)(359)(P_1)(T_2)}{(M)(P_2)(T_1)(0.785)(d^2)} \tag{19}$$

where
$T$ = total throughput (reflux + takeoff) in pounds per second
$M$ = average molecular weight of the refluxing material
$P_1$ = 760 mm of mercury
$P_2$ = pressure of distillation in millimeters of mercury
$T_1$ = 273 C
$T_2$ = absolute temperature of distillation (273 C + boiling point)
$d$ = inside diameter of column in feet.

The amount of throughput may be determined in two ways: first, by direct measurement of the condensate in a calibrated cup at the column head or base; and second, by a heat balance at the condenser head of the column. In the second method, the quantity of condenser water and the inlet and outlet temperatures of the condenser water are measured over a period of time. From the heat of condensation of the refluxing liquid and the amount of heat picked up by the condenser water, it is possible to calculate the quantity of material condensing at the head.

***Vapor Velocity Under Diminished Pressure.*** When fractionating under reduced pressure, the efficiency of the column is decreased considerably because of the increased vapor velocity. An arbitrary rule has been set up to govern the selection of a vapor velocity to be used under vacuum: the vapor velocity under vacuum should be regulated so that it is related to the velocity used at atmospheric pressure by an inverse square root function of the fractional atmospheric pressure used. For example, if a pressure of 30.4 mm, or $\frac{1}{25}$ atmosphere, is used the vapor velocity should not exceed the inverse of the square root of $\frac{1}{25}$, or 5 times the velocity used under similar conditions at atmospheric pressure.

***Determination of Operating Holdup.*** Holdup is defined as the amount of charged material in the system above the liquid level in the still when the column is at operating conditions. To determine this holdup, a carefully weighed portion of some nonvolatile, soluble material (stearic acid is satisfactory) is added to a carefully weighed charge of test mixture. The system is brought to equilibrium operating conditions. A sample of liquid is withdrawn from the still, the sample is weighed, evaporated to dryness, the residue weighed, and from the increase in concentration of solids the operating holdup of the column is calculated.

For example, suppose 20 grams of stearic acid is dissolved in 180 grams of test mixture. The original concentration by weight, then, is 10 per cent acid. If, now, under operating conditions a 20 gram sample is withdrawn and evaporated, leaving a residue of 2.5 grams, the concentration of acid has increased to 12.5 per cent. This means that from the original 180 grams only 160 grams remain in the still mixed with the 20 grams of stearic acid to give a concentration of 12.5 per cent acid. The remainder of the original test mixture is holdup. Therefore, the holdup of this column under consideration is 180 minus 160, or 20 grams. The holdup can be expressed in volume if the specific gravity is known. Care must be exercised in removing the sample from the still so as not to lose any of the hot material. Such loss would introduce a very appreciable error.

The operating holdup may also be determined by actually drawing off and measuring the charge material above the pot. The device of Collins and

Lantz,[18] Figure 72, is a convenient apparatus for doing this. Reflux flows down through the annular space $A$, through the stopcock $B$, to the still pot $C$. The operating holdup is determined by shutting off the heat input to the pot while simultaneously closing stopcock $B$. The material draining into $A$, representing the operating holdup, is drawn off through $D$, cooled, and measured. It should be emphasized that, in order to use this method, the heat input to the

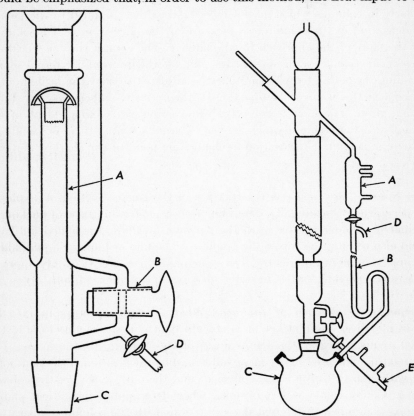

**Figure 72.** Apparatus for Determining Heat Loss and Operating Holdup (Collins-Lantz)

**Figure 73.** Apparatus for Testing Column under Operating Conditions (Collins-Lantz)

pot must be by such a means as to give an immediate response when it is turned off. The internal bare wire electric heater recommended by Collins and Lantz is quite satisfactory. The usual heating mantle or oil bath is not satisfactory since there is an appreciable lag between the time when the heat is shut off and the time when boiling in the pot stops. Such a time lag would serve to give a figure representing a considerably higher holdup than is actually the case.

***Determination of Heat Loss.*** The apparatus shown in Figure 72 may also be used advantageously in determining the amount of heat lost through the column. If the column is operated so that there is just a trace of reflux at the head, the amount of material collected in *A*, Figure 72, over a period of time is approximately the amount of material which condenses in the column.

It is important to know this heat loss or column condensation factor, particularly in columns which do not have external heat applied to the jacket. Condensation in the column is a measure of the effectiveness of insulation, and therefore of the approach to adiabaticity. The greater the condensation, the less effective is the insulation. In columns which have an external source of column heat, the temperature may be adjusted so that the heat input is the same as the heat loss, so that there is theoretically no heat loss or column condensation. The heat loss for the same materials is independent of the throughput. For columns which are not externally heated there is usually an increase in column condensation as the boiling point of the charged material increases.

***Free Space.*** Free space is that portion of the packed section of a column not occupied by packing. To determine free space for any type of packing, a graduated cylinder is filled with the packing, and liquid is added until the liquid also reaches the top of the graduate. The unit volume of liquid added per unit volume packing is the free space of the packing. It is only approximate, since packing settles in different ways in different columns.

***Temperature Control of Jackets.*** When adiabaticity is maintained by means of a heated air jacket, it is not always the best practice to hold the jacket temperature at the temperature of the refluxing test mixture. The temperature indicated is, of course, influenced by the position of the thermometer with respect to the heating element and the outside wall of the column proper. Consequently it is advisable, when determining theoretical plates, to make a number of different determinations with the column temperature held both above and below the temperature of the refluxing material to determine the optimum operating characteristics of the column.

The sidewall condensation, as mentioned before, is an indication of the efficiency of jacket heating or insulation. Goldsbarry and Askevold[14] have made a study of the column condensation in a 1-inch by 48-inch column packed with $\frac{1}{8}$-inch glass helices when various temperature differentials between jacket and head temperature were held. With *n*-heptane–methylcyclohexane refluxing, and a temperature differential of 0 degrees, the condensation rate was 620 cc per hour. With the column jacket 17 degrees below the head temperature, the condensation rate was 1050 cc per hour, while with a differential of 27 degrees the condensation rate was 1400 cc per hour.

*Pressure Drop.*  Pressure drop is defined as the difference in pressure between any two points in a system under consideration. In fractionation work it is usually considered as the increase in pressure between the head and the still pot.

For atmospheric distillations, the difference in pressure between the pot and head may be read simply by attaching an open arm manometer to the side of the pot. Under reduced pressure any two manometers may be attached to the pot and the head, or the pot and head may be connected to the two arms of a manometer. The difference in readings of the manometers or the arms will be the pressure drop.

*Testing Under Operating Conditions.*  All of the above described tests are run while operating the column at total reflux. Ordinarily this gives an accurate indication of the comparative values of two columns. However, the efficiency of a column usually drops off rapidly under operating conditions so that a column which gives, for example, 100 theoretical plates at total reflux will give possibly 75 or even 50 when product is being taken off at a finite and practical reflux ratio. The reason for this is clear from a consideration of the mechanism of fractional distillation. If, for example, there are 220 cc. of liquid condensing at the head of a column under total reflux, all this material is utilized in scrubbing other rising vapors. If, now, a reflux ratio of ten to one is started, then 20 cc. of distillate will be taken off, leaving only 200 cc. of reflux washing upcoming vapors. Furthermore, equilibrium conditions up through the column will be changed, with the net result that the separating ability of the column will be decreased.

Collins and Lantz[13] have used the setup shown in Figure 73 to evaluate the operating characteristics of a fractionating column under operating conditions. The column is brought to equilibrium under total reflux just as described previously. Takeoff at the desired rate and ratio is started. The overhead product passes through the jacketed receiver *A* and down through the distillate return line *B* to the distilling pot *C*. In effect, the column is then being operated as a continuous still, the distillate being returned to the pot as feed. When determinations of plate values are desired, samples are taken at *D* and *E*, and the calculations made as described previously through the McCabe-Thiele diagram or by the Fenske equation.

*Vapor Liquid Equilibrium for n-Heptane–Methylcyclohexane*

**TABLE 45**

KNOWN MIXTURE

| Mole fraction n-heptane | $n^{20}D$ |
|---|---|
| 0.0000 | 1.4232 |
| 0.0787 | 1.4200 |
| 0.1638 | 1.4165 |
| 0.2486 | 1.4135 |
| 0.3376 | 1.4100 |
| 0.4126 | 1.4075 |
| 0.5186 | 1.4036 |
| 0.6056 | 1.4004 |
| 0.6993 | 1.3970 |
| 0.7942 | 1.3942 |
| 0.9338 | 1.3899 |
| 1.0000 | 1.3878 |

**TABLE 46**

MOLE FRACTION n-HEPTANE IN:

| Liquid | Vapor | Liquid | Vapor |
|---|---|---|---|
| 0.0310 | 0.0350 | 0.5590 | 0.5780 |
| 0.0580 | 0.0620 | 0.5990 | 0.6180 |
| 0.0950 | 0.1030 | 0.6470 | 0.6660 |
| 0.1330 | 0.1430 | 0.7090 | 0.7280 |
| 0.1800 | 0.1920 | 0.7560 | 0.7710 |
| 0.2160 | 0.2290 | 0.7960 | 0.8100 |
| 0.2715 | 0.2890 | 0.8430 | 0.8535 |
| 0.3170 | 0.3330 | 0.8790 | 0.8900 |
| 0.3630 | 0.3810 | 0.9060 | 0.9130 |
| 0.4010 | 0.4200 | 0.9310 | 0.9400 |
| 0.4560 | 0.4750 | 0.9540 | 0.9625 |
| 0.5010 | 0.5210 | 0.9800 | 0.9860 |

Willingham and Rossini[8] have reduced the data to the following formula:

$$n_D \text{ (mixture)} - n_D \text{ (n-heptane)} = 0.0306N + 0.0048N^2, \qquad (20)$$

where $n_D$ is the refractive index at 25 C, and $N$ is the mole fraction of methylcyclohexane in the mixture. Similarly, for 2,2,4-trimethylpentane and methylcyclohexane at 25 C,

$$n_D \text{ (mixture)} - n_D(2,2,4\text{-trimethylpentane}) = 0.0244N + 0.0072N^2, \quad (21)$$

where $n_D$ is the index of refraction, and $N$ is the mole fraction of methylcyclohexane in the mixture. These equations reproduce the experimentally observed values of refractive index within $\pm$ 0.0001.

*Vapor Liquid Equilibrium for Benzene-Carbon Tetrachloride*

**TABLE 47**

KNOWN MIXTURE

| Mole fraction CCl$_4$ | $n^{25}D$ |
|---|---|
| 16.873 | 1.4942 |
| 31.954 | 1.4903 |
| 43.419 | 1.4867 |
| 55.495 | 1.4823 |
| 64.704 | 1.4785 |
| 71.042 | 1.4756 |
| 79.671 | 1.4711 |
| 87.639 | 1.4663 |
| 93.504 | 1.4623 |

**TABLE 48**

MOLE FRACTION CARBON TETRACHLORIDE IN:

| Liquid | Vapor |
|---|---|
| 5.07 | 6.82 |
| 11.70 | 14.57 |
| 17.72 | 21.26 |
| 25.25 | 29.22 |
| 29.47 | 33.65 |
| 39.59 | 43.85 |
| 56.00 | 58.60 |
| 67.37 | 69.26 |
| 76.58 | 77.83 |

Since the vapor liquid curve of the above system is somewhat irregular near the pure components portion of the curve, concentrations of test mixture should be chosen so that only the middle portion of the curve is used. Determinations of plate values above about 25 plates are likely to be quite erroneous.

*Vapor-Liquid Equilibrium for Di-n-butyl Phthalate–Di-n-butyl Azelate at 1.00 mm of Mercury*

**TABLE 49**

| KNOWN MIXTURE | |
| --- | --- |
| Mole fraction di-n-butyl phthalate | $n^{20}D$ |
| 0.0000 | 1.4404 |
| 0.0490 | 1.4424 |
| 0.1522 | 1.4471 |
| 0.2520 | 1.4518 |
| 0.3503 | 1.4566 |
| 0.4499 | 1.4616 |
| 0.5503 | 1.4669 |
| 0.6502 | 1.4722 |
| 0.7496 | 1.4778 |
| 0.8489 | 1.4836 |
| 0.8993 | 1.4866 |
| 0.9512 | 1.4898 |
| 1.0000 | 1.4928 |

**TABLE 50**

| MOLE FRACTION DI-n-BUTYL PHTHALATE IN: | |
| --- | --- |
| Liquid | Vapor |
| 0.0000 | 0.000 |
| 0.0490 | 0.071 |
| 0.1522 | 0.195 |
| 0.2520 | 0.310 |
| 0.3503 | 0.409 |
| 0.4499 | 0.508 |
| 0.5503 | 0.606 |
| 0.6502 | 0.697 |
| 0.7496 | 0.785 |
| 0.8489 | 0.870 |
| 0.8993 | 0.913 |
| 0.9512 | 0.957 |
| 1.0000 | 1.000 |

## REFERENCES

1. PETERS, W. A., JR., *Ind. Eng. Chem.*, **15,** 402 (1923); **16,** 1126 (1924)
2. HILL, J. B., and FERRIS, S. W., *ibid.*, **19,** 379 (1927)
3. COULSON, E. A., *J. Soc. Chem. Ind.*, **64,** 101 (1945)
4. BRAGG, L. B., *Ind. Eng. Chem.*, Anal. Ed., **11,** 283 (1939)
5. WHITMORE, F. C., et al., *J. Am. Chem. Soc.*, **62,** 795 (1940)
6. FAY, J. W. J., *Ann. Repts. Chem. Soc.*, 223 (1943)
7. BERG, C., and JAMES, I. J., *Chem. Eng. Progress*, **44,** 307 (1948)
8. WILLINGHAM, C. B., and ROSSINI, F. D., *J. Research Nat. Bur. Standards*, **37,** 15 (1946)
9. WILLINGHAM, C. B., TAYLOR, W. J., PIGNOCCO, J. M., and ROSSINI, F. D., *ibid.*, **35,** 219 (1945)
10. BISHOP, C. A., *Ph. D. Thesis U. of Pittsburgh*, 1942
11. HICKMAN, K. C. D., *J. Am. Chem. Soc.*, **52,** 4714 (1930)
12. WILLIAMS, F. E., *Ind. Eng. Chem.*, **39,** 779 (1947)
13. COLLINS, F. C., and LANTZ, V., *Ind. Eng. Chem.*, Anal. Ed., **18,** 673 (1946)
14. GOLDSBARRY, A. W., and ASKEVOLD, R. J., *Proc. Am. Petroleum Inst.*, **26,** [III], 18 (1946)

# XVII

*Accessory Equipment*

IN THIS CHAPTER will be discussed those pieces of equipment, aside from the column itself, necessary to run a fractional distillation under certain specific conditions.

*Fraction Cutters.* When operating a column at atmospheric pressure, a fraction cutter is a convenient piece of apparatus to use for collecting and transferring distillate fractions. However, when operating under reduced pressure a fraction cutter is a necessity, since it permits the taking of a number of cuts and the changing of cut receivers without varying the pressure on the column.

Figures 74 and 75 show two simple fraction cutters which may be used for all-purpose fractionation work. To use the cutter of Figure 74 under reduced pressure, the following procedure is used. The vial $A$, in which the sample is finally to be collected, is placed inside the large test tube $B$, and the whole is attached to the bottom of the fraction cutter as shown. When collecting the sample, stopcocks $C$ and $D$ are in the position shown, while $E$ is turned through 90 degrees. To remove the sample, turn stopcock $E$ to the position shown to allow the sample to run into vial $A$. Then close $E$. Turn stopcock $D$ through 180 degrees, allowing the pressure in the vial $A$ and test tube $B$ to reach atmospheric pressure through the vent $F$. Remove the vial, replacing it with a new one. Replace the vial and test tube. Turn stopcock $C$ through 90 degrees to shut off the column from the rest of the system. Turn stopcock $D$ through 180 degrees to evacuate $A$ and $B$ again.

When the operating pressure has been reached, turn $C$ through 90 degrees to bring the column back into the pump system. The above process is repeated for each fraction taken.

When evacuating $A$ and $B$ after taking a fraction, it is necessary to shut off the column from the rest of the system in order to maintain a constant pressure in the column. If the column were left in the system, the pressure in the column would rise as soon as the unevacuated system $B$ was added to the column system. If the column pressure cannot be maintained with $C$ closed off from the vacuum pump, it is satisfactory to leave $C$ open and evacuate $B$ by means of a separate pump attached at $F$. When the desired pressure is reached, $D$ is turned through 180 degrees, and operation is continued as before.

The fraction cutter of Figure 75[1] has the advantage of having only two stopcocks. To operate this fraction cutter, attach $A$ and $B$ as before. When operating, stopcock $C$ is in the position shown in Figure 75, while $D$ is turned through 90 degrees. When a sample has been collected in the fraction cutter,

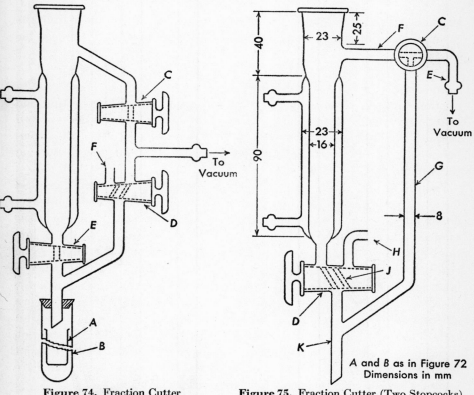

**Figure 74.** Fraction Cutter (Three Stopcocks)

**Figure 75.** Fraction Cutter (Two Stopcocks) (Towne-Young-Eby)

$D$ is turned to the position shown and the sample is collected in $A$. Stopcock $C$ is then turned through 180 degrees, leaving the system $EF$ open to the vacuum pump, and closing off $G$. Stopcock $D$ is then turned through 180 degrees, allowing $A$ and $B$ to reach atmospheric pressure through the system $HJK$, which is open to the air. $B$ and $A$ are removed, and $A$ is replaced by a new vial. Stopcock $D$ is turned through 90 degrees. Stopcock $C$ is turned through 90 degrees clockwise (90 degrees counterclockwise of position drawn), thus shutting off the column through line $F$, and evacuating $A$ and $B$ through

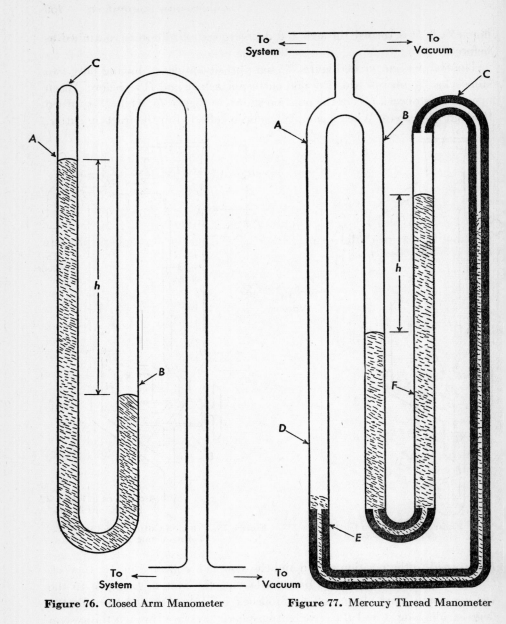

**Figure 76.** Closed Arm Manometer       **Figure 77.** Mercury Thread Manometer

line *EG*. If it is desired, *A* and *B* can be evacuated by means of a separate pump at *H*, as explained above. When the pressure in *A* and *B* reaches the operating pressure, stopcock *C* is turned to the position shown and fractionation is continued.

*Manometers.*     Manometers, or pressure gauges, are used to measure the pressure at which a fractionation is being run. There are three different types of manometers available. The first consists simply of a tube longer than 760 mm in height, one end of which is inserted into a container filled with mercury. The upper end of the tube is then connected to the vacuum system. The height to which the mercury rises in the tube is the difference between the atmospheric pressure and the pressure in the system. To obtain the system pressure, subtract the height of the mercury in the tube from the atmospheric pressure as determined by means of a standard barometer.

Much more satisfactory than the above are the closed arm or U-type manometers. One side of the U-tube is filled with mercury, while the other is attached to the vacuum system. As the pressure is lowered, mercury is drawn down from the arm *A*, Figure 76, and rises in the arm *B*. The pressure is observed by direct reading of the distance *h*, the difference in height of the mercury or other material in the arms *A* and *B*. The upper pressure limit which can be observed on these manometers is determined by the distance between the level of the mercury in arm *B* and the point *C*, the top of arm *A*. This distance is measured, of course, when the system is at atmospheric pressure. Thus, if a pressure range from atmospheric pressure on down is desired, the distance must be 760 mm if the manometer is filled with mercury. If the highest pressure desired is only 100 mm, then the height can be reduced to 100 mm.

The mercury in these manometers may be replaced by some other liquid such as concentrated sulfuric acid or butyl phthalate, which have very low vapor pressures. Since these materials have a much lower density than mercury, the sensitivity of the gauge is increased. Naturally, suitable corrections in the height of the manometer must be made to account for the difference in density between mercury and these lighter liquids.

The most conveniently constructed and easily filled manometer is that shown in Figure 77. The two arms *A* and *B* are left open until the required amount of mercury has been added. The thread of mercury through the capillary *C* may be connected by tilting the manometer. The tubes *A* and *B* are then connected to a single outlet. The pressure is read as the distance *h*. When the manometer in Figure 77 is filled for use, the mercury should extend in a continuous column from *D* down through capillary *E*, up over capillary

*C*, down through *F*, and up part way into *B*. When a vacuum is pulled on the system, the mercury breaks at *C*. Mercury falls in tube *F* and rises in tube *B*. The pressure of the system is the height *h*.

At pressures below about 1 mm of mercury, the McLeod gauge, Figure 78, is used. The volume of the capillaries *A* and *B*, and of the bulb *C*, are known. The gauge is attached to the system at *D*. When the mercury bulb *E* is lowered, mercury falls from the whole manometer to the point *F*, allowing the bulb *C* and the capillary *A* to come to the pressure of the system. The bulb *E* is then raised, trapping the gases in *C*. The bulb is raised until the mercury in *B* is level with the top of capillary *A*. The difference between the mercury level in *A* and *B* gives the additional pressure $P_2$ in millimeters, of

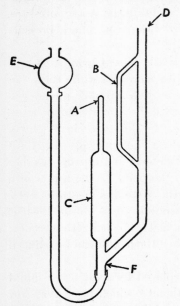

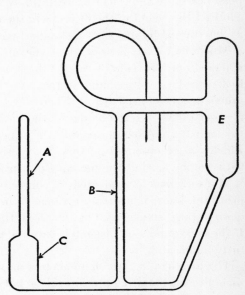

Figure 78. McLeod Gauge          Figure 79. Modified McLeod Gauge

volume $V_2$ of compressed gas in capillary *B*. The volume $V_1$ before compression is the total volume of bulb *C* and capillary *A* above the point *F*. The pressure of the system is then calculated from Boyle's law:

$$\frac{V_1}{V_2} = \frac{P_1 + P_2}{P_1} \qquad (1)$$

Ordinarily, the manometer is calibrated at different pressures and a direct reading scale is attached between *A* and *B*.

Figure 79 is a more convenient modification of the McLeod gauge. The pressures are calculated or read in the same way as was done for the ordinary

McLeod gauge. Rotating the whole gauge through 90 degrees displaces all
the mercury into $E$, which takes the place of lowering the mercury bulb $E$
of Figure 78.

For pressures from about 0.05 to 2 or 3 mm of
mercury, that is, pressures between the sensitivities
of the ordinary manometer and the McLeod gauge,
the manometer shown in Figure 80 is useful. Olive
oil or some other oil which has been subjected to
prolonged evacuation at 100 C is used instead of
mercury. The oil is introduced at $S$, filling $R_1$ and
$B$ to the level $AA'$. Additional oil is added to $R_2$.
The volume of $R_2$ is equal, approximately, to that
of the tube $C$. The system is attached at $S$. The
whole manometer can be rotated through 90 degrees.
The pressure of the system is determined from

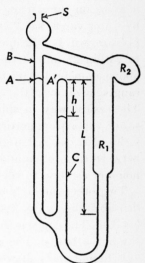

$$p = \frac{h^2}{(L - h)r} \qquad (2)$$

where $p$ = mm of mercury
    $h$ = mm
    $L$ = mm
    $r$ = ratio of density of mercury to that of the
        oil used.

**Figure 80.** Modified
McLeod Gauge

A discussion of the possible errors encountered in using a McLeod or modified McLeod gauge is appropriate at this point. Figure 78 will be used as the
gauge under discussion.

The pressure $P_2$ is a factor of the volume of compressed rarefied gas trapped
in $C$. The higher the pressure, the more gas. As the vacuum increases, or pressure decreases, the volume of gas will become smaller. The McLeod gauge
operates on the assumption that the gases trapped in $C$ are *noncondensable*.
If the gases in $C$ condense, serious errors will be introduced. It is obvious that
a given weight of liquid will occupy considerably less volume than the same
weight of material in the gaseous state. Therefore, if the gas collected in $C$
condenses under the pressure applied as the mercury is raised against it, the
apparent volume of rarefied gas will be considerably smaller than is actually
the case, and a fictitiously low pressure reading will be recorded.

Flosdorf[2] gives a very striking illustration of the error introduced by water
vapor in a system, the pressure of which is being recorded by a McLeod type
gauge. He compares two gauges of the same scale length, one having a range
of 0-5000 microns, the other recording 0-700 microns. At 24 C the vapor
pressure of water is 22 mm. Therefore, if the pressure on the vapor is 22 mm

or more, the vapor will condense to liquid, allowing the mercury to move up in the capillary to a point 22 mm from the top. On the scales used, this recorded a pressure of about 100 microns for the wide-range gauge, and 11 microns on the narrow-range gauge. Now, if the pressure is caused largely by water vapor, say 250 microns, with only about 2 microns of air, the total pressure will be 252 microns. However, in both gauges the mercury will rise to within 22 mm of the top of the capillary, indicating the pressure given above, namely, 100 microns for the wide-range and 11 microns for the narrow-range gauge, even though in both cases the actual pressure is 252 microns. The easiest way to eliminate these errors is, of course, by preventing the water vapor from getting into the gauge. This can be done most easily by a series of traps, including a chemical absorption trap and a cold trap placed between the system and the gauge. However, it is advisable to have the manometer as close to the source of the distilling material as possible.

Two other methods are available for correcting the error caused by condensable gases. The first is by flushing the gauge with air before a reading is taken. The gauge is shut off from the rest of the system and air is admitted through a T-tube. The gauge is then evacuated and again shut off from the system and air is allowed to enter. By repeating this sequence several times, the water vapor will be flushed out. This method is not applicable at very high vacuums. A second method is to heat the gauge to a point where the vapor will no longer condense at the pressure attained. Again, this method does not work at highest vacuum.

A new gauge may also give a pressure reading which is in error because of a flow of noncondensable gases from the glass used in its construction. In this case a fictitiously high reading will be obtained because, besides the gases actually in the system trapped in $C$, molecules coming from the glass will increase this volume, giving an apparent pressure higher than is actually the case. This can be corrected only by attaching the gauge to a pump and evacuating it at as low a pressure as possible for several days at a somewhat elevated temperature.

If it is absolutely necessary to know that the reading obtained on a system is correct, a convenient method of corroborating readings is to use two gauges of different scale ranges. The readings will agree if no complicating factors are introduced.

*Boiling Point Apparatus.* It is sometimes not satisfactory to take the refluxing temperature of the material in a column as the true boiling point. Therefore, some piece of equipment designed to measure not only the boiling point of a pure compound, but the slight boiling range of a mixture should be available to take the boiling points or ranges of the cuts obtained from such a fractionating column.

Quiggle, Tongberg, and Fenske[3] have reported a modified Cottrell apparatus which is satisfactory for most purposes, both for atmospheric and reduced pressure boiling points. The apparatus, Figure 81, is heated by means of a double winding of asbestos-covered chromel wire. In the middle of the heated portion is wound a short length of #28 chromel wire closely wound and covering a length of 5-6 mm. Connected in series with this is the main winding consisting of #20 wire. The fine winding provides a hot spot which avoids initial bumping. It is well, also, to etch the inside surface of the inner tube of the heated section. A variable resistance is used to control the amount of heat applied. Tubes *A* and *B* are concentric tubes, open at the top and bottom, and joined together by a short piece of 7-mm tubing at *C*. It is also advisable to further center this part of the apparatus by three indentations in the top of the outside tube. The outer tube *A* rests on the edge of the main portion of the apparatus as shown. A number of file marks are made around the bottom edge of *A* in order to permit circulation. The inner tube *B* does not touch the main portion of the apparatus. It may be centered by the indentations at *D*.

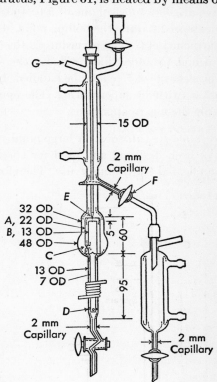

Figure 81. Modified Cottrell Boiling Point Apparatus (Quiggle-Tongberg-Fenske)

Dimensions in mm

When the liquid starts to boil, a mixture of boiling liquid and vapor rises in the annular space between *A* and *B*. The liquid from the very outside circulates to the inside through *C*. The mixture of liquid and vapor impinges in a steady stream on the thermometer or thermocouple at *E*. The liquid portion of the stream striking the thermocouple falls into the inner tube. The reflux from the condenser runs into the main portion of the apparatus outside the annular space, and thence passes to the inside tube. The cooled liquid in this tube descends to the bottom and out into the annular space into the heated space. The cycle is then repeated. The charged material is allowed to reflux until equilibrium is reached, usually 15 to 20 minutes. The temperature is read and a definite portion of liquid is taken off through $F$. Equilibrium is again obtained, the temperature observed, and another portion removed.

This apparatus as described takes a charge of 40 to 50 cc. The designers have distilled to a volume of 5 to 10 cc with no evidence of superheating. If it is desired to take the boiling point at reduced pressure, the vacuum system is attached at $G$. The procedure is the same as at atmospheric pressure. Willard and Crabtree[4] have reduced the size of the boiling point apparatus so that a charge of 5 cc may be handled. In this apparatus it is possible to distill to 2 cc without superheating. The operation and construction are the same as for the macro apparatus.

*Pressure Regulators.* A large number of pressure regulators, or manostats, have been designed and used for specific purposes. Many of these are too complicated for ordinary use. Therefore only a few of the simpler types,

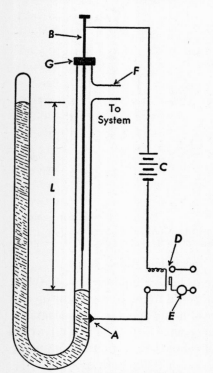

**Figure 82.** Pressure Regulator Controlling Operation by Vacuum Pump (Cox)

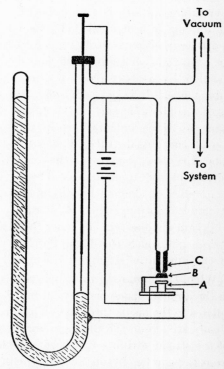

**Figure 83.** Pressure Regulator Operating on Controlled Leak Principle

easily operated and constructed, will be described here. All the manostats mentioned below have been tested and found to operate quite satisfactorily as described.

Possibly the simplest manostat is that shown in Figure 82. An ordinary closed arm manometer is equipped with a permanent sealed-in contact $A$ and an adjustable contact $B$, connected in series with a battery $C$ and a relay $D$. The armature of the relay is connected to the pump motor $E$. When a vacuum is pulled at $F$, the mercury rises in the manometer arm until it makes contact with the lower end of $B$, thus closing the circuit which actuates the relay, stopping the motor. When the system pressure rises, the mercury falls, the circuit is broken, and the pump starts pumping, continuing until the mercury again rises to make contact with $B$. Naturally, the pump used with this manostat must not allow air or oil to suck back into the system when it is not operating. Cox[5] reports that with a reasonably tight system this manostat will hold 15 mm with the pump operating less than 1 per cent of the time. This regulator should hold to $\pm$ 0.1 mm.

The sealed-in contact $A$ should be made of tungsten. This material, which may be salvaged from the filaments of high-voltage electric light bulbs, makes a tight, nonleaking seal with glass. The adjustable contact $B$ may be made of copper or brass. If possible, it should have a platinum wire tip. This tip helps cut down the corrosion at the surface of the mercury. The adjustable contact enters the manometer through a packing gland $G$. This gland must be constructed to hold a vacuum of 1 mm. It may be made from a standard high-pressure joint. Part of the joint fits tightly over the open end of the manometer and is sealed on with collodion or shellac. The packing is inserted and the top portion tightened down around the rod $B$.

The dimensions of the manometer depend on the range of operation desired. The length $L$ is the maximum pressure that can be held during operations. For example, if the pressure range desired is 1 mm to 200 mm, length $L$ should be 200 mm. The chief disadvantage of this type of manostat lies in the wear it gives the pump unless the system is very tight.

A second manostat using a manometer with an adjustable contact is shown in Figure 83. The same type of electric circuit as in Figure 82 is used. When the circuit is closed, the buzzer $A$ is activated. As the rubber-sealed arm $B$ pulls away from the end of the capillary $C$, air enters the system, the pressure rises, the mercury drops in the manometer, and the circuit is opened. When this happens, the buzzer arm $B$ again presses against the end of the capillary, sealing it off from the atmosphere. The pump pulls the pressure down again, the mercury rises, closing the contact, and the process is repeated. With this manostat the pump runs continuously. The contacts and the packing gland are the same as those described above. The buzzer used may be a telegraph or doorbell buzzer.

In Figure 84 the same method of controlling a leak in the system is used as that of Figure 83. The buzzer *A* and the capillary *B* are the same. However, the manometer used is slightly different.[6] The element *C* is in constant contact with the mercury. Stopcock *E* is left open during the evacuation of the system. When the pressure is within a millimeter of that desired, stopcock *E* is closed, thus making the arms *F* and *G* an effective manometer. As evacua-

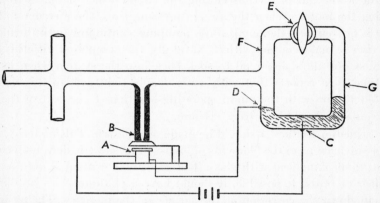

**Figure 84.** Pressure Regulator Operating on Controlled Leak Principle (McConnell)

tion continues the mercury rises in arm *F* until contact is made with *D*. The circuit is closed, the buzzer arm pulls away from the capillary, air enters the system, the pressure is raised, and the contact at *D* is broken. The same cycle takes place as described above and the pressure is held constant. If the whole manostat is mounted so that it can be rotated slightly, a finer control of the choice of pressure is obtained.

Manostats which operate on the principle of a controlled leak should not be used when an oil pump is the source of vacuum. The steady stream of air flowing through the system dissolves in the oil, reducing to a considerable extent the efficiency of the pump.

The electrically operated manostats described above all possess the same inherent disadvantage, namely, that fouling of the mercury at the point of contact occurs, and the contact sticks open or closed. Even when platinum electrodes are used and a condenser is placed across the line to reduce sparking, the surface of the mercury becomes dirty. If the manostat can be filled with sulfuric acid instead of mercury this difficulty is eliminated.

A more sensitive type of manostat which can be used over any desired pressure range is that of Williams,[7] Figure 85. The liquid in the manostat consists of an upper layer of dibutyl phthalate saturated with diethylene glycol, while the lower layer, in which is dissolved about 0.5 per cent sodium nitrite as a conductor, consists of diethylene glycol saturated with dibutyl phthalate. The contact points $A$ and $A'$ are connected to an electronic relay which activates a solenoid valve connecting the system to a 5-gallon pressure reservoir, held below the pressure of distillation.

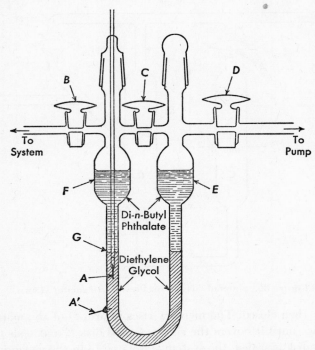

**Figure 85.** Sensitive Pressure Regulator Useable over Any Pressure Range (Williams)

To start operation, stopcocks $B$, $C$, and $D$ are open as shown in Figure 85. As the pressure approaches that desired, stopcock $C$ is closed, that is, turned through 90 degrees. This causes the liquid to rise in bulb $E$ and fall in bulb $F$ until the level $G$ falls below the contact $A$. As the pressure in the system rises or falls, circuit between the contacts is made or broken, activating the solenoid and keeping the pressure constant. Williams immersed the manostat proper in a constant temperature bath held at 25.0 C in order to minimize change in density or mutual solubilities of the manostatic liquids. With this setup he was able to hold the operating pressure constant to at least ± 0.01 mm of mercury.

There are still other types of manostats which do not employ an electric circuit but which act by means of a mercury seal. Figure 86 shows a very satisfactory example of this type designed by Lewis.[8] It can be used over almost any series of pressures, is easy to operate, and holds a given pressure to about ± 0.02 mm in the range of 5 to 70 mm. During operation, the stopcocks $A$ and $B$ are left open until the pressure approaches that desired. Both

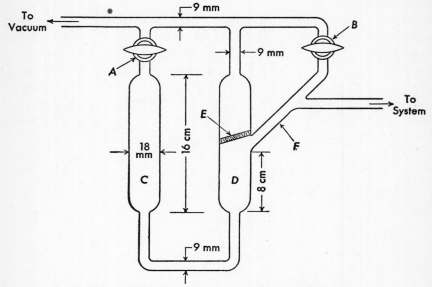

**Figure 86.** Sintered Glass Disk Pressure Regulator (Lewis)

$A$ and $B$ are then closed. The mercury rises in arm $D$ of the manostat, continuing to rise until it covers the sintered glass disk $E$ and seals off the arm $F$. When the disk is sealed, the system is isolated from the vacuum pump and the pressure of the system at the time the disk is sealed is the operating pressure which the manostat will hold.

The manostat acts on the principle that gas will pass through the sintered glass disk although mercury will not. If the pressure of the system rises slightly, the mercury in $D$ will be depressed, allowing the vacuum pump to act again on the system through the disk and $F$. The pressure in the system will be lowered, mercury will rise, sealing off $E$, and the desired pressure will be held. By repeating this cycle, a pressure varying by ± 0.2 mm can be maintained. Slight final adjustment of the operating pressure can be obtained by rotating the manostat to the left or right, left for lower pressure, right for higher pressure. When the distillation is finished, stopcock $A$ is opened first to avoid a rapid surge of mercury through the arm.

The disk $E$ should be set in the arm as close to the outlet $F$ as possible. The choice of the disk should be given some consideration. For a range of low pressures, a coarser disk should be used. With higher pressures a fine disk is satisfactory. It should be remembered that as the disk gets finer, the pressure drop across it becomes greater. In other words, a pump which pulls to 10 mm on the pump side of the disk might give a vacuum of only 20 or 30 mm on the system side. Thus, this disk would have a pressure drop of 10 to 20 mm. A coarse disk has only about 2 mm pressure drop. The author has found it advisable to use a coarse disk for all work. The vacuum source is then adjusted, either by means of a controlled leak in the system or by regulating the capacity of the pump, so that the low pressure side of the arm $D$ is about 10 mm lower than the desired operating pressure. If this is done, the mercury will not be pulled through the disk. If mercury does appear on the low vacuum side of the disk, it is because the pressure differential between

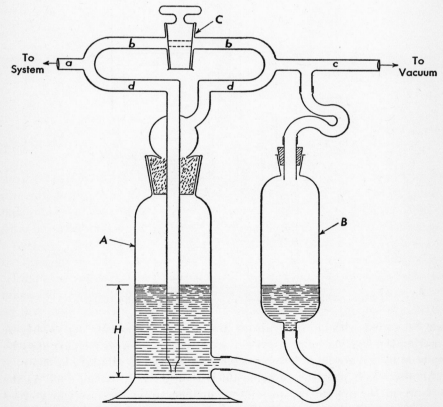

**Figure 87.** Mercury Resistance Pressure Regulator (Donahoe-Russel-Vander Werf)

the pump and the system is too great. When a controlled leak is used to lower the pressure on the low vacuum side, it should be inserted in the system near the pump before the trap, surge tank, and manometer (see Figure 44).

Another simple regulator[9] is shown in Figure 87. Mercury is placed in the tube $A$ and the leveling bulb $B$. The vacuum pump is started with the stopcock $C$ open, allowing the system to be evacuated through the path $a$, $b$, $c$. When the pressure approaches that desired, $C$ is closed, making the evacuation path $a$, $d$, $c$. The pressure of the system is determined by the height $H$ of the mercury in the tube, which is in turn regulated by raising or lowering the leveling bulb $B$. An advantage of this type of regulator is that the pressure

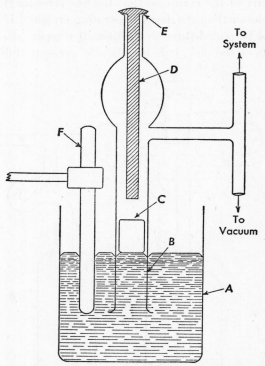

**Figure 88.** Mercury Float Type Pressure Regulator (Clark)

can be varied without interrupting the distillation, simply by raising or lowering the leveling bulb. If greater sensitivity is desired, mercury may be replaced by a material of lower specific gravity such as dibutyl phthalate.

Another easily constructed manostat is that of Clark,[10] Figure 88. As the pressure in the system becomes lower, mercury from the reservoir $A$ rises inside tube $B$, in turn raising the float $C$ to the point where it lifts the rod $D$.

As the top of D is unsealed at E, air enters the system, the pressure is increased, the mercury and float fall in B, and the system is resealed at E. The pressure is again pulled down and the above sequence of events is repeated. The valve seal at E is made by shaping the end of a glass rod into an ellipsoid, grinding off the top of tube B evenly, and then making a firm seal by grinding the two together with emery powder. The rod D should fit into the top of B snugly enough so that there is very little sideway motion, yet loosely enough so that it rises and falls easily from the pressure of the float. The valve seat should be wide enough to prevent leaking, and small enough so that the two surfaces do not stick together. The float C can be made from a hollow tube flattened on both ends. It, too, should not be allowed any appreciable side motion, otherwise the flat surface of the float might hit the rod D at different heights and thus give different pressures for the same mercury height. For

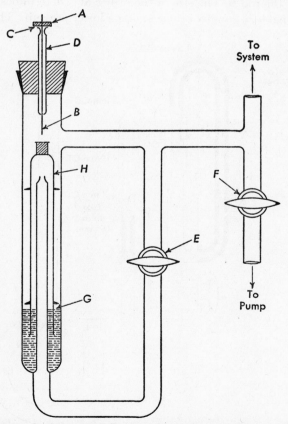

**Figure 89.** Cartesian Type Pressure Regulator with Valve on Outside
(Spadaro-Vix-Gastrock)

more sensitive adjustments the rod *F* may be raised or lowered into the mercury in order to raise or lower the height of mercury in *B* by smaller increments than can be done by raising or lowering *A*. Other materials besides mercury may also be used in this manostat.

A manostat of the Cartesian type[11] is shown in Figure 89. The valve consists of the adjustable rubber disk *A*, a rigid corrosion-resistant rod *B*, and the orifice *C*. The rod is free to move up and down through the tube *D*. The operation is similar to others described. Stopcock *E* is left open until the pressure is reduced to within about 10 mm of that desired, when it is closed, with stopcock *F* remaining partially open. Mercury rises in *G* until the tube *H* engages the rod *B*. As *H* raises *B*, the valve at *C* is opened, allowing air into the system. As the pressure is raised, *G* falls, the valve closes, and the pressure is again pulled down. Final close adjustment is made by raising or lowering the disk *A* on the rod *B*. The size of the orifice at *C* determines the minimum pressure attainable, a smaller orifice giving a lower pressure. This manometer

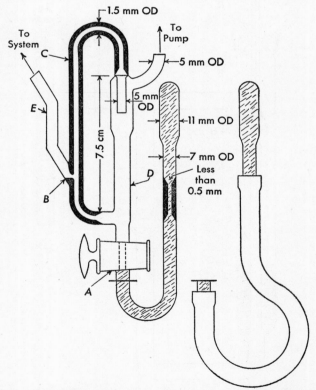

**Figure 90.** Circulating Mercury Pressure Regulator (Emerson-Woodward)

has the advantage over others of the Cartesian type of having the valve on the outside of the system where it can be replaced or repaired easily.

The manostat of Emerson and Woodward[12] also uses the principle of intermittent sealing off of the system from the pump by means of mercury, but by a different method. This apparatus is shown in Figure 90. The stopcock $A$ is closed during the initial evacuation. When the desired pressure is approached, the stopcock is opened slightly and mercury is allowed to rise almost to outlet $B$. When the vacuum is within 1 or 2 mm of that desired, mercury is allowed to seal off $B$ so that a globule of mercury circulates in the system $CD$. The side arm $E$ is used as a controlled bleed to maintain the capacity of the pump equal to about the capacity of the leak in the system. The circulation of the mercury in $CD$ is maintained constantly. When the distillation is finished and before the pump is shut off, the apparatus is rotated clockwise and stopcock $A$ is opened.

If the reservoir portion of the apparatus is connected to the stopcock by means of pressure tubing as shown, a wider range of pressures may be obtained by raising and lowering the bulb.

*Vacuum Pumps.*   Pressures as low as $20\mu$ (0.02 mm of mercury) are easily obtained with a simply built apparatus. The ordinary water aspirator pump is available in most laboratories. The pump will pull to a pressure of from 10 to 30 mm of mercury, depending on the temperature and rate of flow of the water aspirated. When a condensation pump such as is shown in Figure 91 is placed in series with a water pump, a pressure of 20 to $50\mu$ is practical. The mercury pump not only increases the range of pressure available, but also increases the capacity of the pumping tremendously. In the pump shown in Figure 91, the backing pump such as the water aspirator is attached at $A$. The system, with the same traps as for other pumps, is attached at $B$. The backing pump is turned on and the mercury in the condensation pump is started boiling. The mercury vapors rise through $C$, pass through the nozzle $D$, and are condensed. The gas from the system to be evacuated diffuses against the stream of mercury until it gets to the nozzle $D$. It is then carried out of the system by the flow of mercury vapor. In addition to the traps between the system and the mercury pump, an

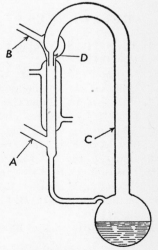

**Figure 91.** Mercury Vapor Condensation Pump

additional trap is placed between the latter and the water pump to prevent water from sucking back into the mercury.

Mercury is one of the best materials for use in the general laboratory condensation pump. It is thermally stable and is easily freed from vapors that might be pulled through. There are several other materials which can be used in a condensation pump and which, because of their lower vapor pressure, give a lower pressure than can be obtained with mercury. However, these organic materials are easily contaminated by vapors from the system.

Table 51 gives some of the materials that have been used, together with the lowest attainable pressure.

**TABLE 51**

| Compound | Boiling point at 1 mm | Lowest pressure mm of Hg at 25 C | |
|---|---|---|---|
| | | *Without trap* | *With ice-cold trap* |
| n-Butyl phthalate | 149 | $2 \times 10^{-4}$ | $2.0 \times 10^{-6}$ |
| n-Amyl phthalate (amoil) | 164 | $2.5 \times 10^{-5}$ | $5.0 \times 10^{-7}$ |
| n-Octyl phthalate | 211 | $5.0 \times 10^{-8}$ | $5.0 \times 10^{-8}$ |
| 2-Ethylhexyl phthalate (octoil) | 184 | $5.0 \times 10^{-7}$ | $5.0 \times 10^{-8}$ |

The commercial mechanical oil pump will pull to a pressure of about $0.3\mu$. The precautions discussed on page 109 should be observed to keep volatile material from dissolving in the oil. The pressure obtained is influenced to a large extent by any volatile material which exerts back pressure on the system.

## REFERENCES

1. TOWNE, R. S., YOUNG, E. E., and EBY, L. T., *Ind. Eng. Chem.*, Anal. Ed., **13,** 626 (1941)
2. FLOSDORF, E. W., *ibid.*, **17,** 198 (1945)
3. QUIGGLE, D., TONGBERG, C. D., and FENSKE, M. R., *ibid.*, **6,** 466 (1934)
4. WILLARD, M. L., and CRABTREE, D. E., *ibid.*, **8,** 79 (1936)
5. COX, H. L., *ibid.*, **1,** 7 (1929)
6. McCONNELL, C. W., *ibid.*, **7,** 4 (1935)
7. WILLIAMS, F. E., *Ind. Eng. Chem.*, **39,** 779 (1947)
8. LEWIS, F. M., *Ind. Eng. Chem.*, Anal. Ed., **13,** 418 (1941)
9. DONAHOE, H. B., RUSSELL, R. R., and VANDER WERF, C. A., *ibid.*, **18,** 156 (1946)
10. CLARK, W. S., *Science*, **103,** 145 (1946)
11. SPADARO, J. J., VIX, H. L. E., and GASTROCK, E. A., *Ind. Eng. Chem.*, Anal. Ed., **18,** 214 (1946)
12. EMERSON, R. L., and WOODWARD, R. B., *ibid.*, **9,** 347 (1937)

# XVIII

## *Special Columns*

IN THIS CHAPTER will be discussed four types of fractionating columns not easily classified in any of the groups considered up to this point. They are the pressure column, the low temperature column, the concentric tube column, and the reverse takeoff column.

*Pressure Column.* Just as it is sometimes convenient to carry out a fractionation under reduced pressure to decrease the boiling points of the components, so, too, it is sometimes advantageous to increase the pressure on the system above atmospheric pressure in order to increase the boiling points. By this means it is possible to fractionate, at room temperature or above, compounds which are normally gases at this temperature. This avoids the necessity of having a special low temperature condensing medium at the head, and overcomes the inconvenience of having to keep the whole system below room temperature.

A second reason sometimes used for distilling under superatmospheric pressure is to increase the vapor density and thus make scrubbing of the vapor with the refluxing liquid more efficient (pages 5 and 106). In this respect, however, there is another factor to be considered, and that is the distortion of the vapor-liquid equilibrium curve. If the shape of this curve remains the same at all pressures, then the effect of increasing pressure would always be to increase the efficiency of fractionation. However, when the curve is distorted it may change to make fractionation either easier or more difficult. For example, the system benzene-toluene has been studied[1] at various temperatures and pressures up to 280 C at 500 lb per sq in. The relative volatility was found to decrease,

**TABLE 52**

| Temperature C | $\alpha$ |
|---|---|
| 120 | 2.27 |
| 200 | 1.63 |
| 240 | 1.56 |
| 280 | 1.35 |

thus increasing the difficulty of separation.

Similarly, Fawcett[2] found that $\alpha$ for 2,2-dimethylpentane and 2,4-dimethylpentane decreased from 1.045 at 80 C to 1.013 at 200 C. However, values for 2,2-dimethylpentane and 2,2,3-trimethylbutane increased from 1.051 at 80 C to 1.068 at 200 C, and the system 2,4-dimethylpentane and 2,2,3-trimethylpentane, with boiling points differing by only 0.2 degree at atmospheric pressure, increased from $\alpha$ of 1.006 at 80 C to 1.055 at 200 C.

A column designed to operate above atmospheric pressure[3] is shown in Figure 92. The pressure is obtained from compressed air entering at $A$. A constant pressure is maintained by the valve $B$, which is filled with mercury. This valve is composed of a sealed glass bulb $C$, which is ground at $D$ to fit the seat $E$. By adjusting the height of the mercury in the leveling bulb $F$, the desired pressure is obtained on the base of the bulb $C$. When the pressure of the entering air exceeds the desired pressure, bulb $C$ is forced down, breaking the seal at $D$ and $E$. The air escapes to the atmosphere through $G$, thus lower-

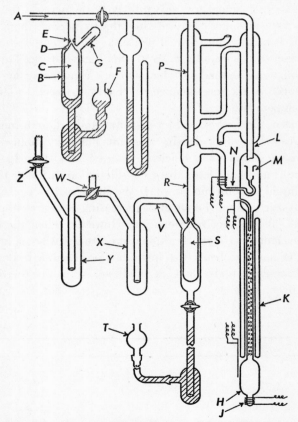

**Figure 92.** Superatmospheric Pressure Column (Simons)

ing the pressure and allowing the valve to be sealed off again. By this continuous opening and closing of the valve, a constant pressure is maintained on the system.

The material to be fractionated is charged into $H$. Heating is accomplished by means of the nichrome heater at $J$. The vapors pass up through the column $K$, packed with any desired packing, and are condensed at $L$. The reflux drops into cup $M$, which has a small hole in its side to permit the escape of liquid. Some of the liquid passes into the capillary $N$, where it is reboiled by means of the small nichrome heater wound around $N$. This revaporized material is again condensed at $P$ and this condensate passes down through $R$ and out through the valve $S$. This valve is similar to that described above and is opened and closed by lowering or raising the mercury bulb $T$. When the desired fraction has been allowed to run through valve $S$, most of it will run into $V$. However, some will remain above the mercury in $S$. When the valve $S$ is closed, valve $W$ is opened to the atmosphere. This reduces the pressure on the system below $S$ and the fraction vaporizes, being caught in the receiver $X$, cooled in liquid air or some other suitable medium. The receiver $Y$ may be used as a double trap, keeping valve $W$ closed and opening valve $Z$.

*Low Temperature Columns.* The design of the columns discussed previously usually requires some modification when materials are to be fractionated which are ordinarily gases at room temperature and atmospheric pressure. If the fractionation is to be carried out at atmospheric pressure, the first requirement is, of course, a means of cooling not only the reflux condensate at the head, but also the whole column in order to maintain adiabatic conditions. The Podbielniak commercially made column, vacuum jacketed, is satisfactory for most low temperature work.

A simplified low temperature column[4] is shown in Figure 93. The column $A$ may be packed with any desired packing material. To charge, tubes $B$ and $C$ are both open. The pot $D$, which may be of about 50-65 cc capacity, is cooled in liquid air or dry ice. The gas or liquid is admitted at $B$ or $C$ and condenses in the system. When charging is completed, tube $C$ is closed. The whole column is then placed in a vacuum flask and kept there during operation. Heating of the charge is accomplished by the small nichrome wire heater at $E$. The vapors pass the sealed-in thermocouple at $F$ and condense at the condenser $G$. This condenser consists of two concentric tubes, $H$ and $J$, sealed at the top. In the innermost tube is placed the cooling medium, which may be dry ice or liquid air. The condensed reflux flows down the column, coming into contact with rising vapors in the same way as in the higher temperature fractionation. When equilibrium has been reached, takeoff is through $C$. Tube $B$ is closed, $C$ is opened, and the condensate is collected in a suitable cooled receiver. When the proper sized fraction has been collected, $C$ is closed, $B$ is opened, and the column is again kept on total reflux. The next fraction is taken in a like manner. This column will take a charge as low as 5 cc and as high as 100 cc by varying the size of the pot.

The same type of column[5] with a somewhat different head design is shown in Figure 94. The condenser $A$ consists of two concentric tubes $B$ and $C$,

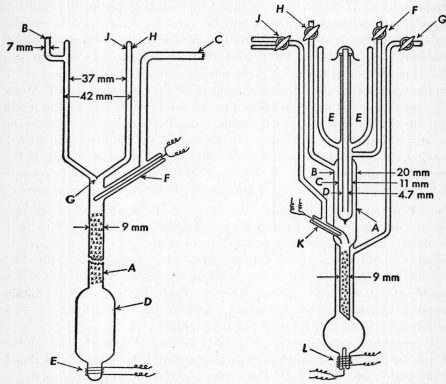

**Figure 93.** Simplified Low Temperature Column (Simons)

**Figure 94.** Low Temperature Column (Simons)

through the center of which passes a copper tube $D$. The bottom end of $D$ is roughened to allow free passage of air, while the top end of this tube is left open to the atmosphere. Liquid air or dry ice is placed in the reservoir $E$. Outlet $F$ is connected to a water pump and air is pulled through the condenser system. The air, cooled by passage over the cooling medium, also cools the condensing pin. The amount of cooling is regulated by the amount of air pulled through.

The column is operated the same as was the column in Figure 93. The gas is charged through $G$ with $H$ also open. Heat is then applied with $G$ closed and

*H* open. When equilibrium has been reached, the sample is taken off through *J* with *H* closed. The column is also immersed in a vacuum bottle for control of temperature. The temperature of the reflux material is read by the thermocouple *K*, while heating is accomplished by means of a protruding nipple *L*, wound with nichrome wire.

*Concentric Tube Columns.*  The concentric tube column depends for its efficiency on the washing action obtained between vapor and liquid when they pass up and down in the annular space between the tubes. The liquid forms a thin film on the surfaces of the tubes, allowing intimate contact with the uprising vapors.

There are several critical factors to be taken into account in the construction and use of this type of column. The tubes comprising the column must be uniform in size throughout their length so as to present a uniform annular space along the whole column. The tubes must not touch each other. If they do, channeling will occur from this point down through the column and the effectiveness of the column may be almost completely destroyed. The column must be mounted very accurately in vertical position also to avoid channeling. The advantages of this type of column lie in its low *H.E.T.P.* and in its low holdup when run quite slowly. However, takeoff is very slow, as is seen from the examples in Table 53.

Figure 95 shows a very small column[6] of the concentric tube type. The flask *A*, connected to the outer tube *B*, is of about 4-5 cc capacity. To the end of the cold finger *C* is attached a small cup *D* of approximately 0.2 cc capacity. The inner tube *E* consists of a very thin-walled tube sealed at both ends and drawn out at the bottom end as shown. This inner tube sits loosely in the outer tube and is centered accurately at top and bottom by the several very slight beads *F*, blown around the inner tube. A clearance of 1.5 mm is recommended between the inner and outer tubes.

The material to be fractionated, 0.5 to 2 cc, is charged through *G*. The material is brought to refluxing very slowly. The condensate runs down the cold finger and into the cup, overflowing down the annular space between the tubes. After a suitable time, the material in the cup is removed through *G* by means of a small pipette. The outlet *H* is for the use of reduced pressure if desired. The operating data for this column are given (column I in Table 53).

Hall and Palkin[7] have found it possible to increase the length of the column to almost anything desired by using small segments of tubing joined by special centering devices. Each inner segment is wound spirally with glass thread to distribute the reflux evenly over the surface. Column III, Table 53, is a column constructed in the above manner.

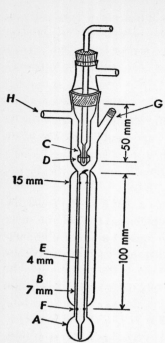

**Figure 95.** Craig Small-Scale Concentric Tube Column

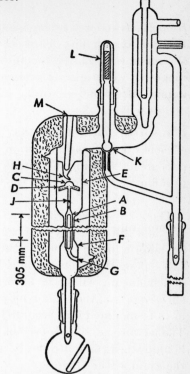

**Figure 96.** Reflux Partition Concentric Tube Column (Naragon-Lewis)

**TABLE 53**

| Column | Size of tubes | | Through-put | Holdup | Plates | Takeoff | Column length | Reference |
|---|---|---|---|---|---|---|---|---|
| | ID mm | OD mm | cc/hr | cc | | cc/hr | cm | |
| I | closed | 4 | | | | | | |
| | 7 | 9 | | 0.1 | 8 | 0.3-0.4 | | 6 |
| II* | closed | 4 | 110 | 5 | 85 | 0.163 | 142 | 8 |
| | 6 | 8 | | | | | | |
| | 10 | 12 | | | | | | |
| | 14 | 16 | | | | | | |
| III | closed | 10 | 70 | 11.7 | 110 | | 8 segments each 30 cm long | 7 |
| | 13 | 15 | 117 | 12.6 | 89 | | | |
| | | | 163 | 13.1 | 66 | | | |
| | | | 234 | 14.1 | 46 | | | |
| | | | 315 | 14.6 | 40 | | | |
| IV | closed | 3 | | | 64 | 0.1 | 31.5 | 9 |
| | 5 | 7 | | | | | | |

*Pressure drop, 0.25-0.28 mm of mercury

Naragon and Lewis[10] have improved the design of concentric tube columns by including a reflux distributor at the head of the column which partitions the reflux equally between the outer tube and the center tube. The column in Figure 96 consists of an inner tube $A$, 6.5 mm outside diameter, and an outside tube $B$, 8.0 mm inside diameter. The tube $A$ is drawn down at one end and sealed to an 8 mm ball $C$. To this ball are sealed troughs $D$, made by cutting 7 mm outside diameter glass tubing longitudinally, the troughs being tilted downward at a 15 degree angle. The ends of the troughs are cut at an angle of 30 degrees from the vertical and at right angles to the length. Slots 1 by 3 mm are cut into the ends of the troughs. The bottom of tube $A$ is drawn down to 2 mm outside diameter and left extended for 5 cm, with a small needle eye at the end. As an aid to exact centering in assembling the column, tube $A$ is wrapped at a 6-mm pitch with copper wire of approximately 0.75 mm outside diameter, making use of the needle eye and two projections sealed on below the ball $C$ to hold the ends of the wire. The tube $B$ is flared at the top and a piece of 25-mm outside diameter tube $E$ is sealed to it. The tube $A$, with the wire wrapping, is inserted through $E$ into $B$ so that a snug fit is obtained. The wire is loosened from the needle eye and cut back to the inner tube. The end of $A$ is pulled down to eliminate the needle eye and is bent over to the side. To the lower end of tube $B$ is sealed a piece of 18-mm outside diameter tube $F$. The bent end of $A$ is sealed to $F$ at $G$. The drip tip $H$ has a clearance of about 2 mm between the tip and the ball. The projections $J$ sealed to the inner tube are glass supports at angles of 180 degrees to each other. They are also sealed to the outer tube to hold the inner tube in place.

When the glass portion of the column is assembled, the copper wire is dissolved out with acid. The meniscus in the annular space is tested for flatness as a check on the uniformity of spacing by raising and lowering a leveling bulb which is connected to the bottom of the column and contains first water and then a hydrocarbon. The critical dimensions are the 2-mm clearance between $H$ and $C$, and the clearance between $A$ and $B$. A liquid contact between $H$ and $C$ results in the liquid reflux to the column being spread equally over the ball, with one-half flowing down the troughs to the outside wall while the remainder flows down the inside tube. The 1-mm clearance between the troughs and the wall provides a liquid contact there also. Takeoff is by means of the ground glass valve $K$ operated by means of the solenoid $L$. The temperature measuring device is inserted into the well $M$.

The operating characteristics of this column are given in Table 54. The theoretical plates were determined using a $n$-heptane-methylcyclohexane test mixture.

TABLE 54

| Throughput | | | |
| Drops per minute | Ml per hour | Theoretical plates | H.E.T.P. cm |
| --- | --- | --- | --- |
| 50 | 77 | 86 | 0.35 |
| 60 | 92 | 76.5 | 0.40 |
| 70 | 107 | 62.5 | 0.49 |
| 80 | 122 | 53 | 0.58 |

The operating holdup is estimated to be 1.0 to 1.5 ml. Except for the lower throughput rates, three to four hours are usually required to reach equilibrium.

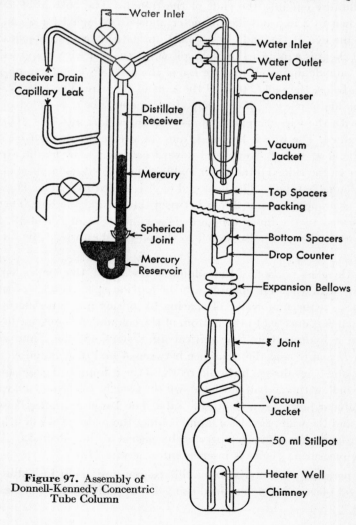

**Figure 97.** Assembly of
Donnell-Kennedy Concentric
Tube Column

The concentric tube column of Donnell and Kennedy[11] gives *H.E.T.P.* values which are among the lowest ever reported for any type of column. The assembly of this column is shown in Figure 97. The inner tube is held in place by the spacers located as shown. Placing the spacers outside the annular space prevents the collection of liquid on the lugs with resultant intermittent draining and bridging of the annular space. Uniform reflux distribution is obtained by providing a shallow depression on the closed top of the inner tube. The liquid overflows uniformly, thus giving an even flow around the annular space. The bottom of the inner tube is drawn down to a point and rests on the calibrated drop counter.

Details of the column, condenser, and distillate receiver are shown in Figure 98. The spacers are made from 1-mm rod, and are sealed radially, three around the 2-mm glass rod attached to the top of the inner tube, and three around the drawn out portion of the bottom of the inner tube. The spacers are ground to a sliding fit.

The uniformity of the annular space may be checked by attaching a leveling bulb, filled with water, to the bottom of the column by means of rubber tubing. The bulb is raised until the column is filled with water, and then lowered at the rate of about 10 cm per second while the meniscus is carefully observed. A number of different observations should be made, rotating the inner tube slightly between each in order to determine the position which gives the least deviation of the meniscus from the horizontal. Donnell and Kennedy have found that columns deviating from the horizontal by 20 mm to 30 mm for a 0.75 mm annular are satisfactory.

The reflux head, Figure 98 (b), consists of a cold finger condenser through which runs a 0.3 mm ID capillary. Reflux flowing from the condenser is directed to the end of the capillary by means of three glass prongs which extend from the lower end of the ground glass joint to the capillary. The capillary must be carefully centered above the exact center of the inner tube to insure uniform reflux distribution around the inner tube as the reflux drops from the end of the capillary. Distillate is removed intermittently by drawing up through the capillary part of the drop of reflux which collects on its end. The distillate receiver system (Figure 98 c) operates on the siphon principle. Mercury is forced up to the three-way stopcock 1, by water pressure through stopcock 2, which is then closed. The timer is then set to energize the solenoid intermittently, permitting the water to flow out the capillary tip. As the mercury level drops in the receiver, an amount of distillate equal to the amount of water discharged is drawn into the receiver. The cut is removed from the receiver by turning stopcock 1 to connect the receiver with the drain, then opening stopcock 2 to force the mercury up to stopcock 1, thus forcing the distillate

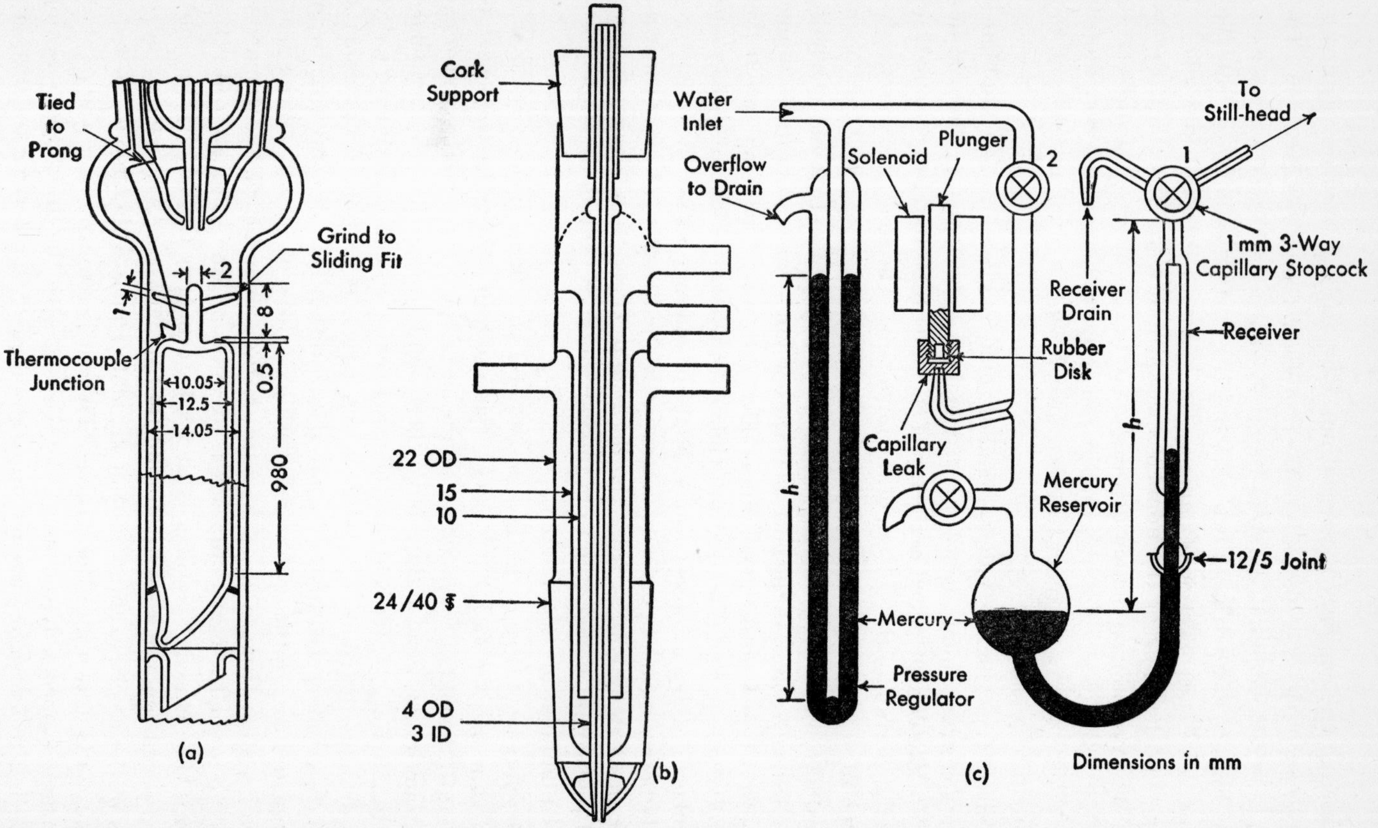

Figure 98. Details of Donnell-Kennedy Concentric Tube Column

180

out through the capillary receiver drain. The distillate receiver requires no calibration since it is made from precision bore tubing having a bore of 0.1406 inch. This corresponds to a volume of 0.100 ml per centimeter of length.

An improved head and takeoff system are shown in Figure 99. Liquid reflux flows through the tube $A$, and back down over the packing. The capillary tube $B$ is filled with liquid which is prevented from flowing into the receiver by means of the nitrogen pressure applied at $C$. The pressure is adjusted by means of the small bubbler. When the pressure is released intermittently by means of the timer operated solenoid, a small amount of distillate flows into the receiver.

Because of the fact that the boiling rate is low in this type of column, it is essential that the system be stable thermally. It may be either enclosed in a silvered vacuum jacket or an unsilvered jacket around which is wound an auxiliary heater.

If a ring of liquid forms between the base of the condenser and the column in the head shown in Figure 97, it may be eliminated by winding a heating coil around the ground glass joint in order to heat it above the reflux temperature. Care must be taken to locate the thermocouple in such a position that reflux does not flow down the wires to the packing, but drips from the capillary tip.

Table 55 gives the data obtained by Donnell and Kennedy on several of the columns described.

**TABLE 55**

| Reflux time (hours) | Boilup rate ml/hr | | Theoretical plates | H.E.T.P. mm |
|---|---|---|---|---|
| | Pot | Head | | |
| 4 | 55 | 16 | 96 | 7.7 |
| 24 | 67 | 16 | 111 | 6.6 |
| 24 | 97 | 8 | 103 | 7.1 |
| 6 | 127 | 16 | 114 | 6.5 |
| 6.5 | 134 | 16 | 93 | 7.9 |
| 15 | 185 | 16 | 82 | 9.0 |
| 22 | 44 | 37 | 104 | 7.1 |
| 27 | 73 | 104 | 86 | 8.6 |
| 18 | 111 | 44 | 107 | 6.9 |
| 24 | 113 | 16 | 100 | 7.4 |
| 8 | 153 | 19 | 79 | 9.4 |
| 10 | 231 | 19 | 84 | 8.8 |
| 48 | 100 | 54 | 123 | 8.0 |
| 13 | 124 | 32 | 127 | 7.8 |
| 10 | 186 | 21 | 93 | 10.6 |
| 15 | 270 | 250 | 46 | 21.5 |
| 10 | 270 | 250 | 46 | 21.5 |

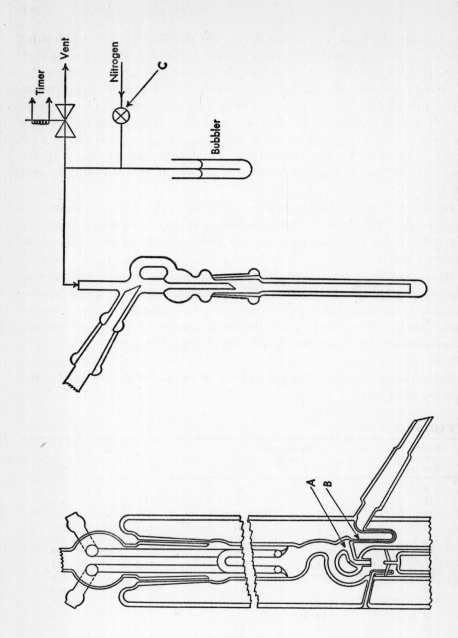

**Figure 99.** Improved Head and Takeoff System for Donnell-Kennedy Concentric Tube Column

*Reverse Takeoff Column.*  In the reverse takeoff or stripping column, the highest boiling material is taken off first. This type of column is quite useful when the material to be distilled contains only a small amount of the high boiling component. This latter component may be taken off, leaving the lower boiling material pure. It is used successfully with liquids that bump or foam, and with materials that are likely to decompose on prolonged heating.

Such a column[12] is shown in Figure 100. The material to be distilled is charged to the reservoir $A$ through the standard taper joint $B$, which accommodates a condenser. A resistance winding $C$ supplies heat to boil the charge and to insure agitation. The liquid is allowed to pass down through the column at a rate determined by the stopcock $D$. When the liquid reaches the vaporizer $E$, which is heated by bath $F$, it is vaporized, the lighter vapors ascending through the column to the condenser by way of the by-pass line $G$. The line $G$ is heated along its entire length by means of an electric winding. As heating continues, the lighter vapors concentrate in the reservoir. When takeoff is started, the heavy material is taken off at $H$. As the fractionation proceeds, the temperature of the distillation, measured by the thermocouple at $J$, becomes progressively lower until finally it reaches the temperature of the lowest boiling component at the end of the distillation.

The column fractionating section $K$, as well as the vaporizer $E$, are packed with $\frac{1}{8}$-inch glass helices or other suitable packing. When a column of this type is used as a stripping column, the holdup is appreciably higher than when it is used as a batch-distillation column.

A larger scale stripping column[13] is shown in Figure 101. The charge from the reservoir $A$ is fed by the proportioning pump $B$, as liquid to the preheater $C$. The liquid passes down through the column, through the sight glass $D$ and the line $E$, into the vaporizer $F$. Here it is completely vaporized, condensing in $G$. Some of the vapors enter the base of the column through $H$. The entire column is surrounded by a vacuum jacket and by magnesia pipe-lagging. Reaching the top of the column they pass through the preheater $C$, acting as the preheating material, into the cooler $J$, and finally return to the reservoir $A$. The higher boiling material is concentrated in $D$ and $E$, and can be removed through the valve $K$. $L$ and $M$ are sight glasses.

In a column of this type 43 feet high and $1\frac{5}{16}$ inches in diameter, packed with $\frac{1}{8}$-inch single turn rings of #26 nickel wire, Fenske obtained 108 plates with a throughput of 3 to 3.4 liters per hour and a pressure drop of 80 to 100 mm of mercury. When the same column was used as a batch-enriching column, that is, removing the more volatile material first at the top of the column, plate values of 94 to 122 were obtained at throughputs of 2.5-4.2 liters per hour, and 39-80 mm pressure drop.

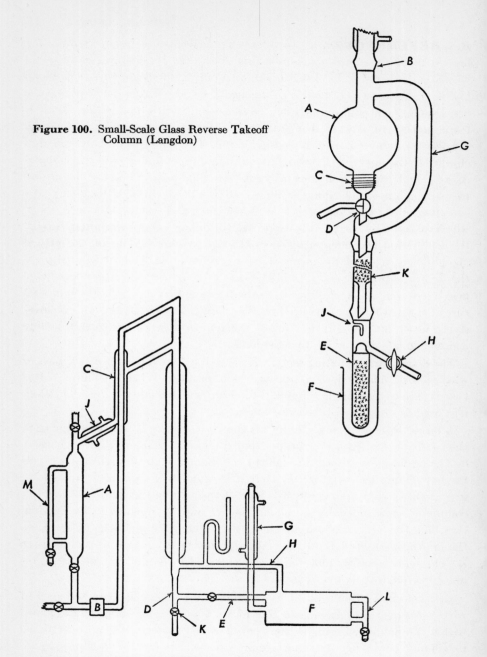

**Figure 100.** Small-Scale Glass Reverse Takeoff
Column (Langdon)

**Figure 101.** Large-Scale Reverse Takeoff Column (Fenske)

# REFERENCES

1. GRISWOLD, J., ANDRES, D., and KLEM, V., *Trans. Am. Inst. Chem. Engrs.*, **39**, 223 (1943)
2. FAWCETT, F. C., *Ind. Eng. Chem.*, **38**, 338 (1946)
3. SIMONS, J. H., *Ind. Eng. Chem.*, Anal. Ed., **10**, 30 (1938)
4. SIMONS, J. H., *ibid.*, **14**, 430 (1942)
5. SIMONS, J. H., *ibid.*, **10**, 648 (1938)
6. CRAIG, L. C., *ibid.*, **9**, 441 (1937)
7. HALL, S. A., and PALKIN, S., *ibid.*, **14**, 807 (1942)
8. SELKER, M. L., BURK, R. E., and LANKELMA, H. P., *ibid.*, **12**, 352 (1942)
9. NARAGON, E. A., BURK, R. E., and LANKELMA, H. P., *Ind. Eng. Chem.*, **34**, 356 (1942)
10. NARAGON, E. A., and LEWIS, C. J., *Ind. Eng. Chem.*, Anal. Ed., **18**, 448 (1946)
11. DONNELL, C. K., and KENNEDY, R. M., *Proc. Am. Petroleum Inst.*, **26**, [III], 23 (1946)
12. LANGDON, W. M., *Ind. Eng. Chem.*, Anal. Ed., **17**, 590 (1945)
13. FENSKE, M. R., *Ind. Eng. Chem.*, **28**, 644 (1936)

# XIX | *Vapor-Liquid Equilibrium Determinations*

To DESIGN A COLUMN for a specific purpose, or even to determine the number of theoretical plates in a given column, we have seen that it is necessary to know the vapor-liquid equilibrium data for the system being distilled. Since very few systems form ideal solutions so that the equilibrium data can be calculated from Raoult's law, it is necessary to have some means for determining these data for a binary mixture over the whole range of compositions. The complete equilibrium curve is drawn after a series of individual determinations have been made of the vapor in equilibrium with the liquid from which it was vaporized, the starting liquids being of varying compositions, from 100 mole per cent of the lower boiling to 100 mole per cent of the higher boiling component. The job of any vapor-liquid equilibrium still, then, is to give a sample of vapor condensed to a liquid which is in exact equilibrium with the sample liquid itself.

A number of methods have been used to determine vapor-liquid equilibrium. The first of these is the simple distillation of a very small sample of vapor from a flask containing a large quantity of liquid. This method can be inaccurate since some reflux almost always takes place. In addition, a relatively large sample of material is required. A second method[1] is to pass vapor of constant composition through a liquid until equilibrium is reached. This method is capable of refinement, but it is subject to considerable inaccuracy unless the correct, rather difficult operating technique is used (see page 191). A third method[2] consists of collecting and analyzing several successive fractions from a batch distillation and then extrapolating back to a point where zero distillate would be obtained. A fourth method, and by far the most satisfactory, is that developed by Othmer,[3,4] and consists in vaporizing a liquid, condensing the vapors, and then recirculating the condensate through the cycle until equilibrium has been obtained. This is done in a self-contained equilibrium still. Several requirements have to be satisfied to make such a still operate efficiently and without error. First, the liquid must be vaporized and condensed without allowing any reflux between the time of the first vaporization and the final condensation. Reflux would serve to give a vapor richer in the more volatile component than is actually the case in a true equilibrium. Second, entrainment of liquid in the vapor must be avoided.

Carrying over of unvaporized material will give an equilibrium value containing less than the actual amount of lower boiling component in the vapor. Third, the composition of the material in the still should remain constant. Fourth, no part of the apparatus should be superheated sufficiently to cause total instead of equilibrium vaporization, which would also give a value of vapor composition too low in the more volatile component. Fifth, the boiling solution should be completely homogeneous.

Various investigators have taken care of the above requirements in different ways. The following described equipment will illustrate the design and operation of equilibrium stills.

The first and one of the most satisfactory and simply operated equilibrium stills is that of Othmer,[3] Figure 102. In this model the vapors rising through $A$ are jacketed by vapors of the same boiling point in $B$. In this way reflux is eliminated, and the vapor passes into the condenser without being enriched above the point actually obtained by true equilibrium vaporization. The composition in the still is held constant by returning the distillate to the still through $F$. This recycling of the liquid, combined with the agitation caused by boiling, is probably sufficient to insure homogeneity of the still charge.

The operation of Othmer's apparatus, Figure 102, is as follows. The charge is heated to boiling by means of an internal heater. The vapor is allowed to rise in $B$ until it reaches the open stopper $C$, thus driving out all air and jacketing the inner tube $A$ with vapors. Stopper $C$ is then closed. The binary mixture

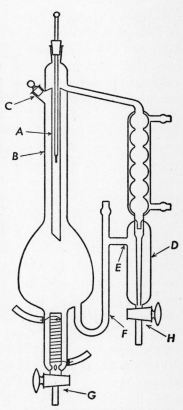

**Figure 102.** Othmer Original Vapor-Liquid Equilibrium Still

in the flask is then distilled over into the receiver $D$. As the depth of the distillate in $D$ reaches $E$, it overflows into the distilling flask through $F$. A constant rate of distillation is then maintained, the distilled liquid circulating down through the tube $F$, then back into the distilling flask. Usually, equilibrium is indicated when the temperature of the thermometer remains constant. To insure equilibrium, a volume of liquid equal to about three or four times the volume of *D* is distilled. Samples are then taken from *G* and *H* and are analyzed by some convenient method, usually refractive index or density. The sample from *G* is the liquid composition, while that from *H* is the vapor composition in equilibrium with it. The first few cubic centimeters from each stopcock are discarded. A second binary mixture of different composition is then put through the same process as above. In this way all the data necessary for the use discussed on page 13 may be collected.

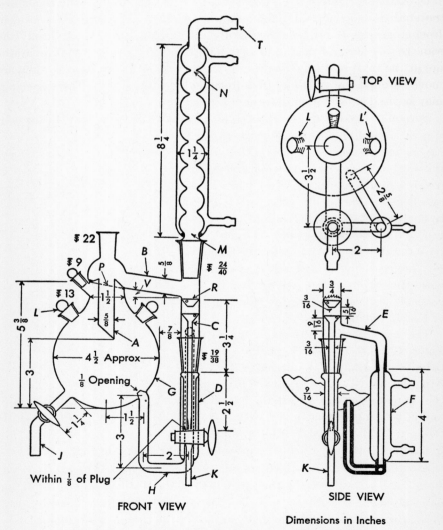

**Figure 103.** Othmer Refined Vapor-Liquid Equilibrium Still

Othmer[4] has improved this apparatus in order to cut down further on the possibility of condensation and reflux on the tube $A$ in Figure 103. The vapors pass up through $A$ and then through the tube $B$. Liquid and uncondensed vapors pass down through the inner funnel $C$, rising in the concentric receiver $D$ until they overflow through $E$ into the cooler $F$, from where they return to the boiler $G$ by way of tube $H$. The advantage of this arrangement lies in the fact that the distillate goes to the receiver at the boiling point, thus cutting down on the possibility of air being dissolved in the condensed material. Samples of liquid and vapor compositions, respectively, are taken from stopcocks $J$ and $K$. The operation of this apparatus is essentially the same as that described for Figure 102. The openings $L$ in the actual apparatus are at the front and back instead of on the sides as drawn, that is, they are moved around the still 90 degrees from the drawn positions. These openings may be used for charging the still or for purposes of cleaning.

Several constructional details should be noted. The opening $M$ in the con-

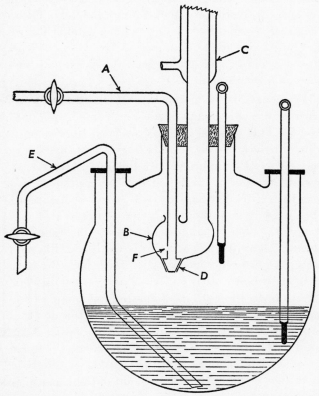

**Figure 104.** Vapor Liquid Equilibrium Still from Three-Necked Flask (Wiley-Harder)

denser is a maximum, while $N$, at the top of the condenser, decreases to $\frac{1}{4}$ inch in diameter. $P$ is a sloping shelf to direct any condensate into the receiver. The drop counter $R$ is as close to $C$ as possible. The line $B$ has the slope indicated by $V$. $T$ is the outlet to the atmosphere, or is the point of attachment of a vacuum system if one is desired.

The apparatus[5] shown in Figure 104 can be adapted to any size three-necked flask. The mixture is vaporized, the vapor passing through the opening at the top of cup $B$ and condensing in $C$. The cup $B$ is about 20 ml capacity and has the female portion of a standard taper joint attached to the bottom as shown. The tube $A$, adjusted vertically, is attached to the male portion of the joint which is sealed off at the bottom. The tube $A$ is raised, leaving the female joint opening in the bottom of the cup open. When a constant rate of reflux is obtained, $A$ is lowered until the joint is partly closed. The male portion is so regulated at $D$ as to maintain an opening just large enough to allow part of the reflux to drain out while maintaining a liquid level which nearly fills the cup. When equilibrium has been reached, as noted on the thermometer, tube $A$ is lowered to seal off the opening completely. Then the cup contains material of the composition of the vapor in equilibrium with the liquid in the flask. The vapor sample is drawn off by means of a slight vacuum through the small hole $F$, and out through $A$. The liquid sample is drawn out in the same manner through $E$.

Figure 105 is an example[6] of an apparatus designed to measure equilibrium by passing vapors through a liquid of constant composition until equilibrium has been reached. This type of still was designed to eliminate two possible errors in ordinary recycling stills, namely, the danger that the vapors leaving the liquid may not be in equilibrium with the liquid because (1) of vaporization from a small portion of the liquid the composition of which has been changed by ordinary distillation, or (2) of flash vaporization of the liquid condensate being returned to the still. It can be seen that in this type of still the vapor leaving the liquid is not generated from the liquid. The tube $A$ is a flash boiler heated above the boiling point of the liquid. Liquid from the condensate chamber $B$ flows under its own hydrostatic head through the capillary $C$, and into the flash boiler. It is vaporized and passes through the tube $D$, which extends close to the bottom of the residue chamber $E$. The vapors, which impinge on the thermocouple well $F$, pass up through the liquid in the residue chamber, through $G$, and into the condenser $H$, from where they return as liquid to the condensate chamber. The residue chamber $E$ is heated by a wound coil in such a manner that the heat loss is exactly balanced. The line $G$ is heated slightly above the boiling point of the vapor in order to eliminate condensation.

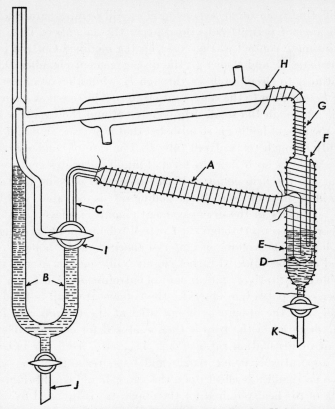

**Figure 105.** Apparatus for Determining Equilibrium by Passing Vapor through Liquid of Constant Composition (Jones-Schoenborn-Colburn)

Care must be used in adjusting the temperature of the residue chamber winding so as to balance heat loss exactly. If the temperature is too low, condensation will occur in the liquid and recirculation will stop. If it is too high, excessive vaporization to the condenser will occur and the flash boiler will be overloaded. The three-way stopcock $I$ acts as a vent to connect the residue chamber tube with the atmosphere prior to taking samples so that siphoning does not occur. The vapor equilibrium sample is taken off at $J$, while the liquid sample comes off at $K$.

The vapor-liquid equilibrium still designed by Gillespie[7] shown in Figure 106 does an effective job of preventing condensation of the vapors in the still while at the same time causing circulation of both vapors and liquid, and keeping entrainment at a minimum. The apparatus is based on the vapor recirculation principle but differs essentially from others of this type in that the boiling liquid is also circulated rapidly. The liquid is boiled in the boiler

*A*, but, differing from other vapor-liquid equilibrium apparatus, the vapor and liquid are not permitted to separate in this chamber. They are maintained in intimate contact as they pass up the modified Cottrell pump *B* to the thermometer *C*, and thence to the disengagement chamber *D*. In *D* the liquid continues to circulate down through *E*, while the vapor passes to the condenser *F*, and then to the condensate trap *G*. The overflow from *G* returns to the boiler through the small drip counter *H* and the capillary *J*. During operation the rate of boiling is so adjusted that a mixture of liquid and vapor rises steadily through the Cottrell tube *B*. The rate of condensate return to the boiler should be such that the level of liquid fluctuates gently just above the capillary in the drip counter. If the apparatus is being operated incorrectly, it will be quite obvious. If the boiling rate is too rapid, visible entrainment will take place in the disengagement chamber; uneven or slow boiling allows vapor to pass up through the Cottrell tube without carrying with it a stream of liquid. The volume of material charged to the boiler is somewhat critical and must be adjusted rather closely. Gillespie has used a simple test to determine quantitatively the amount of entrainment. The boiler is charged with 20 per cent potassium chloride, the condensate trap is filled with distilled water, and the apparatus is operated at the desired rate for several hours. The material in the trap is then analyzed for chloride. The per cent entrainment at distillation rates of 3.2, 5.5, and 7.5 ml per minute in the described apparatus is 0.005, 0.025, and 0.05, respectively, a rate which would have no significant effect upon the vapor-liquid equilibrium data.

The bulk of the heat required for the apparatus is supplied by an external heat source. However, the internal heater *K* is usually necessary to maintain a steady boiling rate. The apparatus in Figure 106 is constructed with a Cottrell tube 10 mm in outside diameter for systems under reduced pressure or 8 mm OD for atmospheric pressure.

The advantages of this equilibrium still may be understood more easily by referring to the graphic representation of the system as shown in Figure 107. The portion *A* represents conditions existing in the Cottrell tube, where liquid and vapor are in intimate contact with each other; point *B* represents the disengagement chamber, where the liquid and vapor are separated suddenly and completely in such a way that refluxing is impossible.

The still shown in Figure 108 was designed by Williams[8] especially for determining the vapor-liquid equilibrium of higher boiling materials under reduced pressure, and was used by him to collect the data on di-*n*-butyl phthalate–di-*n*-butyl azelate reported on page 151. The mixture to be studied is charged through the filling tip *A*, which is then sealed off to prevent leakage. The distilling material circulates through the condenser *B*, down through the

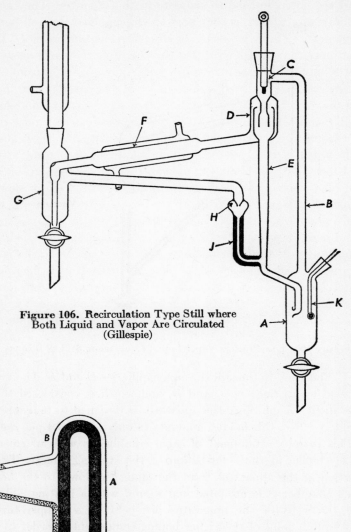

**Figure 106.** Recirculation Type Still where Both Liquid and Vapor Are Circulated (Gillespie)

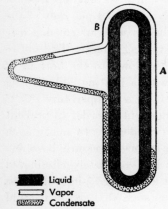

**Figure 107.** Schematic Representation of Vapor-Liquid Circulating System

■■■ Liquid
☐ Vapor
▨▨ Condensate

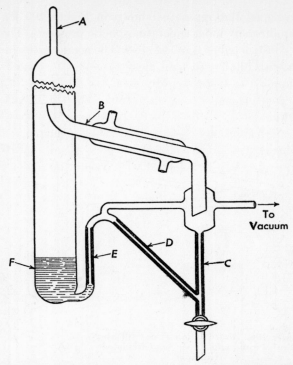

**Figure 108.** Low Pressure Vapor-Liquid Equilibrium Still (Williams)

capillary $C$, and back to the still through capillaries $D$ and $E$. The volume of material held up in the loop $C$ and $D$, and which is considered the vapor sample, is about 1.7 ml. Since the apparatus is designed to take a sample of approximately 50 cc, this holdup amounts to only about 3.4 per cent of the charge. This permits attainment of rapid equilibrium without causing any measurable change in the composition of the starting charge. The entire boiler portion of the apparatus from the filling tip down to the bottom of the boiling chamber $F$ is insulated and wound with a heating coil. During operation the walls of the apparatus are held at a temperature 15 C above the boiling point of the higher boiling component in order to prevent any refluxing of the vapors before reaching the condenser. In many such pieces of apparatus designed to be operated under reduced pressure, bumping has been a serious problem. However, Williams has completely eliminated bumping by introducing into the boiling chamber a mass of $\frac{3}{32}$-inch stainless steel helices. The volume of the helices used was such that, with a liquid charge of 50 ml, the top surface of the helices was covered to a depth of about 2 mm.

Othmer[9] developed the apparatus shown in Figure 109 for determining vapor-liquid equilibrium under superatmospheric pressures. The unit, welded throughout, is constructed of stainless steel. The condensate reservoir is fitted front and back with full length sight glasses to allow for visual control.

Pressure is applied to the system by means of a cylinder of nitrogen connected by a regulating valve to a surge tank. The surge tank (not shown) consists of a stainless steel tube 8 inches wide and 36 inches long made of ⅛-inch sheet, and capped by ½-inch heads. The principle of the operation of this apparatus is the same as that of the glass apparatus. However, some special techniques have to be followed when operating under pressure. The

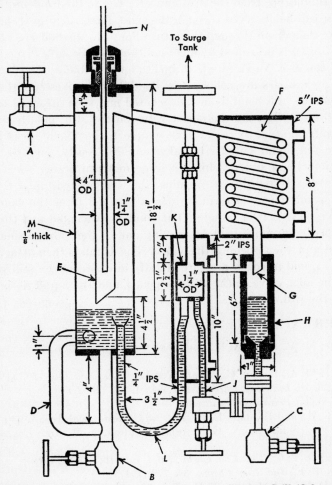

**Figure 109.** High Pressure Vapor-Liquid Equilibrium Still (Othmer)

charge, about 600 cc, is admitted through the vent valve *A*, with the liquid sample valve *B* closed, and the vapor sample valve *C* open. The valve *C* is closed and heating is started. Heating is accomplished by means of a Bunsen burner applied to the reboiler tube *D*. The desired pressure is obtained by the admission of nitrogen in slight excess over the pressure at which the determination is to be made. When circulation has been started the trapped air is vented off through valve *A*. The pressure is then reduced to that desired by bleeding off the excess from an exhaust valve on the back of the surge tank. Vapors generated in the boiler *M* pass through the inner tube *E* and into the condenser *F*. The condenser consists of seven 4-inch turns of ⅜-inch iron pipe size. The liquid drops from the drip indicator *G* into the condensate reservoir *H*, where it can be observed through the sight glass, then up through *J* into the trap *K*, then down through the return line *L* to the boiler. The temperature of the vapor is measured by means of the thermocouple extending to the bottom of the well *N*. The well, 16 inches long, is made of ⅜-inch OD, 16 U. S. Gauge. Samples are collected in bombs with valves on either end. To collect a sample, the bomb is first evacuated and then attached to the outlet valve *B* or *C*. Opening the outlet valve on the still and the inlet valve on the bomb allows a representative sample to be taken. It is important that vapor and liquid samples be taken simultaneously, since distillation is being continued and since flashing of some material occurs when the pressure is decreased slightly by opening the still system into the bombs. Material for subsequent determinations is charged from the same type of bomb as is used to collect samples. The bomb is evacuated and the material to be charged is drawn into it by placing one of the valve openings below the surface and then opening the valve. The bomb is then attached to the vent valve *A*, and nitrogen pressure slightly in excess of the still pressure is applied. The inlet valve to the still is opened, and the liquid flows from the bomb into the still.

## REFERENCES

1. ROSANOFF, M. A., LAMB, A. B., and BREITHUT, F. F., *J. Am. Chem. Soc.*, **31,** 448 (1909)
2. ROSANOFF, M. A., BACON, C. W., and WHITE, R. H., *ibid.*, **36,** 1893 (1914)
3. OTHMER, D. F., *Ind. Eng. Chem.*, Anal. Ed., **4,** 232 (1932)
4. OTHMER, D. F., *Private communication*
5. WILEY, R. M., and HARDER, E. H., *Ind. Eng. Chem.*, Anal. Ed., **7,** 349 (1935)
6. JONES, C. A., SCHOENBORN, E. M., and COLBURN, A. P., *Ind. Eng. Chem.*, **35,** 666 (1943)
7. GILLESPIE, D. T. C., *Ind. Eng. Chem.*, Anal. Ed., **18,** 575 (1946)
8. WILLIAMS, F. E., *Ind. Eng. Chem.*, **39,** 779 (1947)
9. OTHMER, D. F., and MORLEY, F. R., *ibid.*, **38,** 751 (1946)

# Azeotropic and Extractive Distillations

THE INTRODUCTION of a third component into a distillation charge in order to improve separation has not been generally used in small-scale laboratory work, except in the case of steam distillations. Ordinarily, it has required some investigation to discover what material will best facilitate separation, and such investigations have usually been carried out by trial and error. For laboratory distillations, such investigations are frequently not feasible where only one such distillation has to be run and where the amount of charge available is not large. However, if a number of the same type of fractionations are to be run, the results may be well worth the added work necessary for this method. In addition there are many mixtures which cannot be separated by physical means without resorting to either azeotropic or extractive distillation. The use of these two types of distillation has become very important in large-scale work, particularly in the petroleum industry.

As more and more data are collected on these techniques, it becomes increasingly evident that added component distillation, particularly of the azeotropic type, can be fitted to small-scale distillation.

*Azeotropic Distillation.* In azeotropic distillation the added material and one or more of the primary substances form a constant boiling mixture (C.B.M.) which results in a useful change in the relative volatility or ease of separating these substances. The two basic requirements for the use of an added component are: first, that it reduce the partial pressure of one of the original components more than it does the other; and second, that it be easily removed from the distillate. The solubility of the third component should be such that complete miscibility exists at the boiling point of the azeotrope. The closer the components come to being immiscible without actually separating into two liquid phases, the more effective will be the third component. This is reasonable since it follows that such a solution also will deviate greatly from Raoult's law, and it was noted previously that separation by azeotropic distillation was effected as a result of nonideality of the resulting solutions.

We have seen previously that the relative volatility $\alpha$ is a measure of the ease of separation of two components. Therefore, if the partial pressure of one component is reduced without the other being affected, the relative volatility will also be increased and the compounds will be more easily separated.

For an ideal solution, a solution obeying Raoult's law, the partial pressures $p_A$ and $p_B$ of components $A$ and $B$ are given by

$$p_A = MP_A$$
$$p_B = MP_B$$

where $M$ is the mole fraction of the component and $P$ is the vapor pressure of that component in the pure state. The total vapor pressure of an ideal solution of $A$ and $B$, therefore, is

$$P_T = p_A + p_B$$

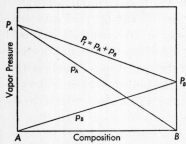

**Figure 110.** Vapor Pressure-Composition Diagram of Ideal System

as shown in Figure 110.

However, in most cases encountered under actual working conditions the solutions are not ideal. The vapor pressure curves are not straight lines, so that the equation $P_T = p_A + p_B$ is a line curving from $P_A$ to $P_B$. Figure 111 (a) shows the vapor pressure composition curve for a nonideal mixture which shows a positive deviation from Raoult's law, while Figure 111 (b) shows a nonideal system with a negative deviation.

When an azeotrope is formed, the temperature-composition curve has one of the two forms shown in Figure 7, page 7. The difference in enrichment from the liquid to vapor between the ideal solution and the azeotropes should be noted. Except at the maximum or minimum boiling points of the azeotropes, the spread between the liquid and vapor composition is large—considerably larger by comparison than the liquid-vapor composition spread of an ideal mixture having the same boiling difference. Consequently, the azeotrope may be separated from either pure component by a fractionating column

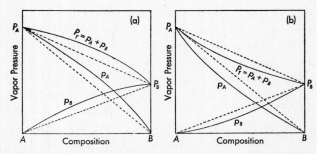

**Figure 111.** Vapor Pressure-Composition Diagram of Nonideal System

of much less efficiency than would be required to separate two pure components with the boiling point difference equal to that of the difference between the azeotrope and the pure component from which it is separated.

In an ideal solution each type of molecule acts as if there were no other type present, that is, there is no difference in the force of attraction between $A$ for $A$ and $A$ for $B$, no heat is evolved or absorbed, and there is no change in the internal energy or volume. Now, if any of the above conditions are not met, then the mixture is no longer ideal and an azeotropic mixture is possible. The formation of an azeotrope, then, might be said to be contingent upon nonideality. Knowing the causes of nonideality, it would then be possible to predict which classes of materials would form azeotropes with other classes.

Ewell, Harrison, and Berg[1] have presented an excellent correlation of the relationship between azeotrope formation and hydrogen bond formation. The idea of hydrogen bonding is well known, and has been definitely established by physical measurements. Briefly, it implies a coordinate type of bond existing between a hydrogen which is already attached to another atom, and a donor atom such as oxygen or nitrogen. For example, in esters of salicylic acid, a hydrogen bond is postulated thus:

Water is probably the most common example of hydrogen bonding, and the so-called abnormal behavior of water has been attributed to this effect.

Similarly, the hydrogen attached to a nitrogen, of which ammonia is the simplest example, can coordinate:

There is considerable difference in the strength of these coordinate bonds formed between hydrogen and other atoms, depending upon the type of compounds and the atoms between which the hydrogen is coordinating. For example, the bonding between a nitrogen and a hydrogen atom attached to oxygen is quite strong, while the bond between nitrogen and a hydrogen attached to another nitrogen is considered weak. On the basis of the strengths of the hydrogen bonds or the lack of formation of such bonds, organic liquids have been arranged[1] into five classifications:

CLASS I. Liquids capable of forming three-dimensional networks of strong hydrogen bonds—for example, water, glycol, glycerol, amino alcohols, hydroxyl amine, hydroxy acids, polyphenols, amides, etc. Compounds such as nitro methane and acetonitrile also form three-dimensional networks of hydrogen bonds, but the bonds are much weaker than those involving OH and NH groups. Therefore these compounds are placed in Class II.

CLASS II. Other liquids composed of molecules containing both active hydrogen atoms and donor atoms (oxygen, nitrogen, and fluorine)—for example, alcohols, acids, phenols, primary and secondary amines, oximes, nitro compounds with α-hydrogen atoms, nitriles with α-hydrogen atoms, ammonia, hydrazine, hydrogen fluoride, hydrogen cyanide, etc.

CLASS III. Liquids composed of molecules containing donor atoms but no active hydrogen atoms—for example, ethers, ketones, aldehydes, esters, tertiary amines (including pyridine type), nitro compounds and nitriles without α-hydrogen atoms, etc.

CLASS IV. Liquids composed of molecules containing active hydrogen atoms but no donor atoms. These are molecules having two or three chlorine atoms on the same carbon as a hydrogen atom, or one chlorine on the same carbon atom, and one or more chlorine atoms on adjacent carbon atoms, for example, $CHCl_3$, $CH_2Cl_2$, $CH_2Cl-CH_2Cl$, $CH_2Cl-CHCl-CH_2Cl$, etc.

CLASS V. All other liquids, that is, liquids having no hydrogen-bond forming capabilities, for example, hydrocarbons, carbon disulfide, sulfides, mercaptans, halohydrocarbons not in Class IV, nonmetallic elements such as iodine, phosphorus, sulfur, etc.

Based on this classification the summary of deviations from Raoult's law given by Ewell, Harrison, and Berg is as follows:

| Classes | Deviations from Raoult's law | Hydrogen bonding |
|---|---|---|
| I + V ⎱ II + V ⎰ | Always positive. I + V frequently limited solubilities. | H bonds broken only. |
| III + V | Always negative. | H bonds formed only. |
| I + IV ⎱ II + IV ⎰ | Always positive. I + IV frequently limited solubility. | H bonds both broken and formed, but dissociation of I or II liquid is more important effect. |

| I + I | | | |
|---|---|---|---|
| I + II | Usually positive. | H bonds both broken | |
| I + III | Very complicated groups. | and formed. | |
| II + II | Some negative deviations | | |
| II + III | give maximum azeotropes. | | |

| III + III | | |
|---|---|---|
| III + V | Quasi-ideal systems. | No H bonds involved. |
| IV + IV | Always positive or ideal. | |
| IV + V | Azeotropes, if any, will | |
| V + V | be minimum. | |

If a system showing a positive deviation from Raoult's law forms an azeotrope, it will be minimum boiling. An azeotrope from a system with a negative deviation will have a maximum boiling point. Systems showing a maximum boiling point are comparatively rare, Lecat[2] listing only about 250 of this type of azeotropes as compared with 3000 minimum boiling systems.

An interesting maximum boiling point azeotrope reported[3] is that of pentachlorethane and 1,3,5-trimethylbenzene. All other binary azeotropes studied in the series in which one component is a hydrocarbon are minimum boiling. The authors point out that the polarity of pentachlorethane is produced by introducing a C—H bond into a molecule that otherwise is composed of C—Cl bonds, rather than the usual method of introducing an —OH or C=O. This seems to be an exception to the summary above, which indicates that these two materials, one in Class IV and one in Class V, should exhibit minimum boiling points.

Besides hydrogen bonding, another physical property may be used in a very general sense to predict azeotrope formation, that is, the dipole moment. Substances of like polarity can be expected to form more nearly ideal solutions. The less the departure from ideality and the greater the similarity of structure of the components, the closer together must be the boiling points of the components if an azeotrope is to be formed. Materials deviating greatly from Raoult's law and being dissimilar in structure, such as ethanol and water, form azeotropes even though they are not particularly close boiling.

Mair, Glasgow, and Rossini[3] have investigated the separation of aromatic hydrocarbons, naphthenes, and paraffins by means of azeotropic distillation. They concluded (a) that aromatic hydrocarbons could be separated from naphthenes and paraffins very easily, (b) that naphthene hydrocarbons may be separated from paraffins with difficulty, this separation requiring several distillations through an efficient column, (c) that aromatic hydrocarbons of different degrees of "aromaticity," as for example an alkyl benzene, an alkyl tetrahydronaphthalene, and an alkyl naphthalene, may be separated with more or less difficulty depending on the mixture, and (d) that naphthene hydrocarbons having different numbers of naphthene rings in the molecule may be separated by several distillations. As examples of these separations, toluene boiling at 110.6 C was separated almost quantitatively from a 110-110.5 boiling mixture of paraffins and naphthenes from petroleum, using methyl cyanide, boiling point 82 C, as the azeotrope-forming material. When a 204-206 C boiling fraction of aromatic hydrocarbons from the kerosene portion of petroleum was distilled with diethylene glycol monomethylether at 217 mm of mercury, the mono-, di-, or tri-alkyl benzenes were separated from 1,2,3,4-tetramethyl benzene, and this latter compound in turn was separated from tetrahydronaphthalene.

If the boiling points and compositions of several azeotropes between one compound A and several other compounds are known, all of these latter compounds being in the same series, it is possible to approximate[2,4] the boiling point and composition of azeotropes of other compounds of the same series with the first material A. For example, suppose the data of Table 56 are known for azeotropes of compounds B, C, D, etc., with A:

**TABLE 56**

| Component | Boiling point of pure component | Boiling point of azeotrope with A | Mole % A in azeotrope |
|---|---|---|---|
| B | 115 C | 114 C | 10 |
| C | 130 C | 127 C | 20 |
| D | 140 C | 136 C | 31.5 |
| E | 155 C | | |
| F | 167 C | | |

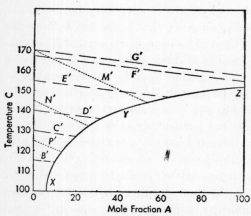

**Figure 112.** Prediction of Formation, Boiling Point, and Composition of Azeotrope

The curve XYZ in Figure 112 is drawn for the boiling point-composition of the azeotropes. The lines B', C', D' are then drawn from the boiling point of the pure component to the boiling point of the azeotrope. Now, suppose it is desired to know the boiling point of the azeotrope formed by compound E with A. A tie line having the same slope as B', C', and D' is drawn from the boiling point of pure E to the curve XYZ. The intersection of $E'$ and $XYZ$ will give the boiling point and composition of the azeotrope of $E$ with $A$, in this case 147 C, and containing 62.5 per cent $A$. It will be noticed that the tie line $F'$ does not intersect the azeotrope boiling point-composition curve. This indicates that no azeotrope is formed between $A$ and $F$.

Since each class of compounds, such as olefines, paraffins, naphthenes, etc., will show a different tie-line slope, the possibility of separating two compounds by azeotropic distillation may be roughly predicted. For example, in addition to the data in Table 56, those of Table 57 are known:

**TABLE 57**

| Component | Boiling point of pure component | Boiling point of azeotrope with A | Mole % A in azeotrope |
|---|---|---|---|
| G | 170 C | | |
| M | 170 C | | |
| N | 145 C | 133 C | 26 |
| P | 125 C | 120 C | 13 |

where $G$ is of the same class of materials as $B$, $C$, $D$, etc., and $M$, $N$, $P$ are in a different class from $B$, $C$, and $D$, but are themselves of the same class. Tie lines are drawn as described above. The tie line $G'$ does not intersect the curve so that no azeotrope of $A$ with $G$ is predicted. On the other hand, tie line $M'$ does intersect, so that from a study of Figure 112, it would be predicted that compounds $G$ and $M$, boiling at the same temperature, could be separated by azeotropic distillation with compound $A$, which would form a constant boiling mixture with $M$ but not with $G$.

It should be clearly understood that this is a very rough method of prediction and should not be used rigorously since the tie-line slopes in the same class of compounds do vary.

With some azeotrope-forming compounds, it is possible to depress the partial pressure of an organic liquid more than that of water. Absolute alcohol has been prepared[5] by the addition of ethyl ether. Under slight pressure the partial pressure of the ethyl alcohol is depressed far more than water, so that anhydrous alcohol is taken off at the bottom of the column. Mercuric chloride has the same effect,[6] water being taken off at the head of the column, leaving anhydrous alcohol as the residue. Glycerol[6] has the opposite effect, lowering the partial pressure of water more than alcohol so that absolute alcohol may be distilled.

Using *tert*-butanol, Tongberg and Johnson[7] separated benzene from *n*-hexane. Marschner and Cropper[4] have studied the behavior of benzene with ten nonaromatic hydrocarbons to discover the boiling range over which benzene forms azeotropes. They discovered C.B.M. formation of benzene with hydrocarbons the boiling points of which varied from 68 C to nearly 100 C. The boiling point spread of the naphthenes which form azeotropes with benzene and the boiling point lowering are smaller than those of the paraffins. This difference may be utilized to separate paraffins from naphthenes by azeotropic distillation with benzene. The azeotropic behavior of benzene is more pronounced the higher the hydrogen-carbon ratio of the second component.

Keyes and co-workers[8] studied the systems toluene-methylcyclohexane and benzene-cyclohexane. They used a number of compounds as third components, including acids, alcohols, ethers, ether-alcohols, ketones, amines, nitro-compounds, etc. Almost all types of polar compounds acted as effective separating components.

An increase or decrease in pressure usually affects the composition of an azeotrope, as well as the boiling point difference between the azeotrope and the pure component of the system. For example, in the system ethyl alcohol-ethyl acetate,[9] at 760 mm of mercury pressure the azeotrope with a composition of 30.93 per cent alcohol boils at 71.81 C, giving a boiling point difference with ethyl acetate of 5.34 degrees. At 77.4 mm, the azeotrope containing 15.95 per cent alcohol boils at 18.71 C, boiling point difference 2.3 C, while at 1775.5 mm the azeotrope contains 38.87 per cent alcohol, boils at 91.35 C, and shows a boiling point difference of 7.25 degrees.

It should not be assumed that a large deviation from Raoult's law necessitates the formation of an azeotrope. Toluene and methylcyclohexane,[10] for example, deviate greatly from ideality but do not form an azeotrope.

From a study of the above examples, the usefulness of azeotropic distillation is obvious. The separation of isomeric compounds of the same boiling point is a possibility. Hundreds of other examples of the utility of azeotrope formation are recorded in the literature. The few reported here will serve as some basis for consideration of the use of this important tool.

*Extractive Distillation.*   In extractive distillation, separation of two components is effected by the addition of a third component just as in azeotropic distillation. However, the foreign component in this case is relatively nonvolatile compared to the components to be separated. It acts as a preferential solvent for one of the components. It is usually introduced near the top of the column and flows down through the packing, washing the ascending vapors and absorbing one of the components preferentially. The temperature of the system is such that the liquid and vapor phases coexist. In other words, extractive distillation is fractional distillation in the presence of a solvent. The vapor pressure of the dissolved material is lowered, thus raising the relative volatility of the two-component mixture to be separated.

The use of extractive distillation in small-scale laboratory work is extremely limited. The same objection raised to the use of azeotropic distillation applies here, namely, the difficulty of determining definitely a suitable solvent when possibly only a single small volume distillation is to be run. In addition, the equipment involved is somewhat more complicated, involving as it does the necessity of having an additional inlet near the top of the column.

As an example of the effectiveness of extractive distillation, Benedict and Rubin[11] report the separation of a mixture of paraffins and toluene using phenol as a solvent. Without the solvent, $\alpha = 1$, giving no separation. On the addition of phenol, the $\alpha$ increases to 3.7, giving a boiling point difference of about 80 C.

Dicks and Carlson[12] have compared directly one instance of extractive distillation and ordinary fractional distillation by using the same column as a batch-enriching fractional distillation column and as an extractive distillation column. When a mixture consisting of about 10 mole per cent methylcyclohexane and 90 mole per cent toluene was distilled in the column studied, an average of 17.8 theoretical plates was obtained, giving a distillate consisting of 84-89 per cent methylcyclohexane. When the same column was used as an extractive distillation column, using aniline as a solvent, 100 per cent methylcyclohexane was recovered in the distillate. A study of the vapor pressure curve of the system toluene-methylcyclohexane shows that a separation to give more than 92 per cent methylcyclohexane in the distillate is extremely difficult. Therefore this is a case in which extractive distillation accomplishes very easily what would be impractical by ordinary fractional distillation.

The same authors used the same column to compare the separation of n-heptane-methylcyclohexane by the two techniques. With fractional distillation a value of 13.1 theoretical plates was obtained. The $\alpha$, reported previously, is 1.074 for the mixture. When n-heptane-methylcyclohexane was extractively distilled, using aniline as the solvent, a separation equivalent to that which would be obtained in a fractional distillation column of 51.9 theoretical plates was obtained. On the basis of the separation reported in a column of 13.1 theoretical plates, the $\alpha$ was raised from 1.074 to 1.30. Using a different concentration of aniline, Griswold, *et al.*,[13] report an increase of $\alpha$ from 1.074 to 1.47 for the same system.

This method was also applied to the separation of the constant boiling mixture cyclohexane-benzene. Using aniline, the azeotrope of 47 mole per cent cyclohexane was broken so as to give 100 per cent cyclohexane as distillate.

Buell and Boatright[14] have studied the separation of butadiene from a number of hydrocarbons, using furfural as the solvent at a pressure of 65 pounds per square inch, absolute. The relative volatility of the mixture of butadiene with the second component is given for normal distillation and for extractive distillation.

In Table 58 the plates required for the separation of the given mixture, both with and without the addition of furfural, are calculated by the Fenske equation based on 99 mole per cent of the more volatile component in the distillate and one per cent of the more volatile component in the residue.

**TABLE 58**

| Butadiene with | Normal | | With furfural | |
|---|---|---|---|---|
| | $\alpha$ | Plates required | $\alpha$ | Plates required |
| Isobutane | 1.209 | 35.1 | 2.614 | 9.6 |
| Isobutylene | 1.070 | 135.7 | 1.666 | 18.0 |
| 1-Butene | 1.046 | 204.7 | 1.718 | 17.0 |
| 1,3-Butadiene | | | | |
| *n*-Butane | 0.871 | 66.6 | 2.020 | 13.1 |
| 2-Butene (low-boiling isomer) | 0.843 | 53.9 | 1.190 | 52.9 |
| 2-Butene (high-boiling isomer) | 0.776 | 36.2 | 1.065 | 145.7 |

It can be seen from Table 58 that in all cases except the butenes improvement in separability is obtained. One other interesting thing should be noted. For *n*-butane and the 2-butenes, the addition of butadiene reverses the order of volatility. Normally, butadiene would be taken off either *n*-butane or the butenes as the more volatile component. However, the addition of butadiene causes the butane or the 2-butenes to be distilled as the more volatile component.

***Comparison of Azeotropic and Extractive Distillations.*** Fundamentally, both azeotropic and extractive distillations accomplish separation by producing deviations from ideality so that the difference between the volatilities of the compounds to be separated is increased. In extractive distillation, no constant boiling mixture is formed.

The choice of a solvent for extractive distillation is considerably wider than for azeotropic distillation. For the former case, the only conditions are that it preferentially lower the vapor pressure of one of the components more than the other, that it be less volatile than either of the components, and that it be miscible with the mixture throughout the total range of the operating conditions. For azeotropic distillation, the third component must have a boiling point reasonably close to that of the component with which it is to form the constant boiling mixture. In both cases it is, of course, important that the added component be easily separated from the desired product.

Azeotropic distillation is more convenient to use than extractive distillation. All of the solvent may be charged to the still-pot at the beginning of the distillation, and any batch-fractionating column can be used without further change. A relatively high solvent concentration is used for extractive distillation. However, if the solvent is easily separated from the product, this is not important from the point of view of energy consumption since the solvent is not taken over as distillate.

## REFERENCES

1. EWELL, R. H., HARRISON, J. M., and BERG, L., *Ind. Eng. Chem.*, **36**, 871 (1944)
2. LECAT, MAURICE, "L'azeotropism," Brussels, 1932
3. MAIR, B. J., GLASGOW, A. R., JR., and ROSSINI, F. D., *J. Research Nat. Bur. of Standards*, **27**, 39 (1941)
4. MARSCHNER, R. F., and CROPPER, W. P., *Ind. Eng. Chem.*, **38**, 262 (1946)
5. OTHMER, D. F., and WENTWORTH, T. D., *ibid.*, **32**, 1588 (1940)
6. MARILLER, C., and COUTANT, J., *Bull. Assoc. Chem. Sucr. Dist.*, **42**, 288 (1925)
7. TONGBERG, C. O., and JOHNSON, F., *Ind. Eng. Chem.*, **25**, 733 (1933)
8. UPDIKE, O. L., JR., LANGDON, W. M., and KEYES, D. B., *Trans. Am. Inst. Chem. Engrs.*, **41**, 717 (1945)
9. MERRIMAN, R. W., *J. Chem. Soc.*, **103**, 1801 (1913)
10. QUIGGLE, D., and FENSKE, M. R., *J. Am. Chem. Soc.*, **59**, 1829 (1937)
11. BENEDICT, M., and RUBIN, L. C., *Trans. Am. Inst. Chem. Engrs.*, **41**, 353 (1945)
12. DICKS, R. S., and CARLSON, C. S., *ibid.*, **41**, 789 (1945)
13. GRISWOLD, J., et al., *Ind. Eng. Chem.*, **38**, 65 (1946)
14. BUELL, C. K., and BOATRIGHT, R. G., *ibid.*, **39**, 695 (1947)

# X X I

*Micro and Semimicro Fractionation*

TRUE MICRO FRACTIONATION, that is, fractionation involving volumes of material approximating 0.01-0.05 cc, is one of the most difficult micro processes to develop. This might be concluded from the very nature of the fractionation mechanism as we have discussed it previously. In macro fractionation it is possible to set up a system whereby some of the material in the system is used to scrub out high-boiling material from the vapor, thus setting up an equilibrium and increasing the number of effective distillations in a single column.

However, in micro technique there is not enough material available to set up such a system. The only washing possible is between rising vapor in the tube and liquid returning down the sides of the tube. In a micro fractionation, the surface tension in a narrow tube does not allow of much backflow, so that separation must be obtained by a series of vaporizations, condensations on the side of the tube, and reevaporations from the tube without allowing any backflow. To obtain efficient fractionation from a micro tube requires a close temperature control and a very slow rate of distillation.

*The Emich Tube.* The Emich type tube[1] is the simplest and probably the only true micro fractionating tube. It consists of a 3 mm ID tube cut to any convenient length, usually 60-80 mm, and collapsed at a point part way to the top, as shown in Figure 113(a).

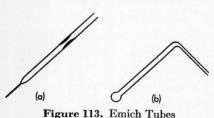

**Figure 113.** Emich Tubes

To use this tube a few small shreds of dry asbestos are pushed to the bottom of the tube by means of a thin wire. Several drops of the liquid to be distilled are forced into the tube either by centrifuging or by cooling the bottom of the tube in dry ice. The asbestos in the tube absorbs the liquid and aids smooth distillation. The tube is held at a 45-degree angle and heat is slowly applied by means of a bath. A free flame should not be used. A ring of distillate slowly ascends the tube. When it passes the constriction, the distillate is removed by means of a small capillary. The liquid remaining in the tube is forced back to the bottom again either by centrifuging or by cooling, and the process is repeated.

The same principle can be used with any type or shape of capillary tube. It is quite practical to use a tube of the shape shown in Figure 113(b). This tube is charged by first heating the bulb slightly, then dipping the open end below the surface of the material to be distilled, and cooling the bulb in a liquid air or dry ice bath, so that the charge is sucked back into the bulb The drops still clinging to the sides of the tube may be forced down into the bulb by shaking. The last traces of material still in the tube above the bulb are removed by gentle heating. The operation of this tube is the same as for the Emich tube described above, except that the fractions may be taken off the end directly into small containers. After each fraction is taken, the tube is cooled and the operation is repeated.

Gettler and Fine[2] use an Emich-type tube constructed as in Figure 114. The capillary shown in stage (a) is drawn from a piece of 8-mm tubing having a wall thickness of 1 mm. The bulb is formed by sealing both ends of the tube at the stage (b) in the construction, and then heating the larger end. The expanding air inside the tube blows out the bulb to the desired size. Asbestos is added to the tube at stage (b) before sealing off the large end. Charges of 0.02 to 0.1 cc may be distilled with a maximum of 50 per cent of the capacity

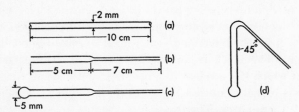

**Figure 114.** Construction of Micro-Distillation Tubes

of the bulb. The fractions taken usually amount to about 0.01 cc in volume. When 0.04 to 0.06 cc of charge comprising 50 per cent of each of two components was distilled in the above tube, these authors separated a number of binary mixtures. The products were obtained in such purity that identification was easy, and the boiling points of the fractions assumed pure corresponded to the boiling points of known pure materials. The following mixtures were separated: ethyl ether–acetone, methyl alcohol–methyl formate, ethyl ether–acetaldehyde, and propyl chloride–isopropyl chloride.

Morton and Mahoney[3] have introduced still further refinements into the art of capillary distillation. They use a 1.5–2 mm by 13 cm capillary packed with glass wool which has been ground fine in a mortar and pestle. The tube is made by sealing both ends of the thin-walled capillary, and heating one end until a bulb forms, as in the case of the tube in Figure 114. The top end of the tube is unsealed and the glass wool packing is inserted. A constriction is made about 13 cm from the bottom. This constriction is made as short as possible so as not to trap too large a volume of condensate. With this tube the authors report that in one instance 106 separate fractions were collected from a distillation of 23 mg of material. The usual number is about 30-35 fractions on 25 mg of charge over a period of four to five hours. The remarkable separations obtained in the above tube depend to a large extent on the ability of the operator. Efficient technique is developed only after considerable practice. A large part of the effectiveness of the distillation also is due to the manner of heating the tube. A copper block is used in which is inserted a glass jacket to hold the distilling tube. The effect is the heating of the distillation tube by means of an air jacket. A thermometer, also inserted in the block, indicates the temperature of the block, but not necessarily the temperature of the distilling vapor.

Morton and Mahoney recommend the following procedure for distillations in their tubes: The tube is weighed and a single drop of liquid is pipetted into it. The liquid is forced to the bottom of the tube by centrifuging. The tube is again weighed, and the weight of the charge is determined. A piece of wet filter paper is wrapped around the tube just above the constriction to act as a condenser. If low-boiling materials are being distilled, a dry-ice-cooled condenser can be used. The tube is placed vertically in the block and heating is started. When the first condensate appears above the constriction, the capillary is removed from the block and centrifuged to force the condensate back into the bottom. The block is cooled about four or five degrees below the temperature at which the condensate appeared, and heating is again started. This sequence is repeated until a temperature is found at which condensate appears after 1–1.5 minutes. The fraction of the desired size is removed from the condensing section by touching to it the tip of a smaller capillary tube. This latter tube will be used as a boiling point capillary to determine the property of the fraction. When the fraction has been removed, the distilling tube is centrifuged. The block is cooled to about 2 degrees below the temperature at which the previous fraction was collected, and the next distillation is started. A series of sequences as above completes the fractionation. Boiling points are taken in the capillaries in which the fractions are collected, and a boiling point-per cent distilled curve is drawn.

Correct boiling points for pure materials with remarkably small intermediate fractions were obtained for the following 50-50 volume per cent binary mixtures: benzene–xylene, benzene–toluene, ethyl alcohol–butyl alcohol, and acetone–ethyl alcohol. For a mixture of benzene–xylene–butyl benzene, correct boiling points of the benzene and xylene were obtained, and the boiling point of butyl benzene was reached, but no appreciable amount of pure sample was obtained.

*Semimicro Fractionation.* When larger amounts of material are available —amounts from 1 to 10 cc—the problem becomes somewhat simplified. The same technique used in macro distillation may be applied, that is, the jacket temperature and reflux can be controlled and the temperature of refluxing liquid can be observed.

*Empty Tube Columns.* Rose[4] has studied the separation obtained in 3 and 6 mm OD empty glass tubes, with the results shown in Table 59.

**TABLE 59**

| Diameter mm | Length cm | Throughput cc/min | Plates |
|---|---|---|---|
| 6 | 30.5 | 8 | 1 |
| 6 | 30.5 | 1 | 8 |
| 6* | 30.5 | 0.17 | 17.5 |
| 3 | 30.5 | 3 | 1 |
|  |  | 0.6 | 9 |

*Equipped with vacuum jacket around which is wound a heater kept at 5 degrees below the temperature of the liquid in the column.

A head such as is shown in Figure 50 is suitable for use with a micro column. The takeoff stopcock *B* is, of course, a capillary. A column of this type is operated in the same manner as that described for macro columns (Chapter XIII). It will be noticed that the efficiency increases tremendously as the throughput decreases. This is because of the fact that all contact between liquid and vapor takes place on the side of the tubes. If the velocity of distillation is too fast, the vapor simply passes up the middle of the tube without coming into contact to any great extent with the liquid reflux running down the tube.

*Vigreux Columns.* The Vigreux columns shown in Figure 115[5] and Figure 116,[6] the operating characteristics of which are described on page 62, may also be used for from 2 to 15 cc of material. The equivalent of 10 theoretical plates can be obtained when operating at a throughput of about 0.1 to 1.5 cc per minute.

Figure 115 is of the partial condensation type. The amount of distillation is determined by the temperature of the water in the condenser *A*, which is in turn determined by the rate at which the water passes through the condenser. This rate may be controlled by the stopcock *B* at the water outlet from the condenser.

The apparatus shown in Figure 117 was designed by Tiedcke[7] to meet the need for a small-scale distillation apparatus with minimum surface areas and

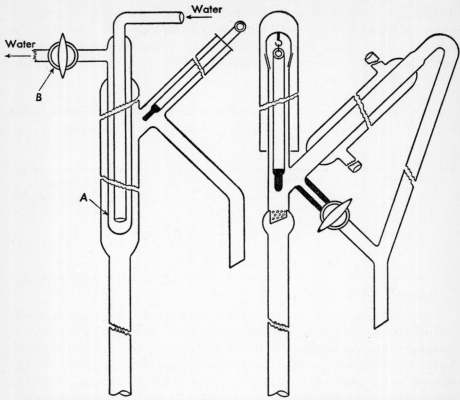

**Figure 115.** Partial Condensation-Partial Takeoff Vigreux Semimicro Column (Cooper-Fasce)

**Figure 116.** Total Condensation-Partial Takeoff Vigreux Semimicro Column (Weston)

minimum distance between the distilling flask and condenser in order to cut down on the system holdup. Continuous operation is made possible by the use of the *inside receiver A*, which consists of three cups of 1 ml capacity each, attached to each other and moved successively under the drip point $B$ by means of the glass rod $C$, which extends through the rubber stopper $D$.

When a 3-cc sample of 50-50 volume per cent of various mixtures was distilled, each distillation requiring 15 minutes, and three approximately 1-cc samples were collected, the following results were obtained: For ethyl alcohol and acetone, the first fraction was pure acetone, the third was pure alcohol; for benzaldehyde and benzoyl chloride (boiling points 179 C and 198 C) distilled at 15 mm pressure, the first and third fractions were practically pure; and for lauric acid and myristic acid (boiling points 225 C and 250 C) distilled at 0.1 mm, the first and third samples were almost pure, and on refractionation yielded pure samples.

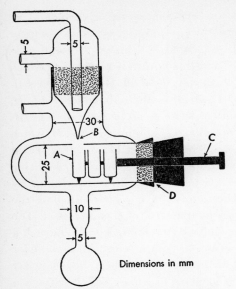

Figure 117.  Tiedcke Semimicro Column

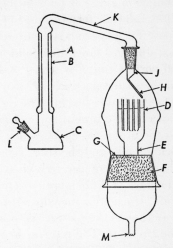

**Figure 118.**  Shrader and Ritzer Semimicro Column

Tiedcke does not recommend this apparatus for continuous distillation of mixtures the boiling points of which differ by more than 40 C. However, it can be used to distill such mixtures if each fraction is removed as it is collected. With a boiling point difference greater than about 40 degrees, the lower boiling fraction will boil from its receiver.

The apparatus as described will handle charges of 2 to 4 cc. By reducing the dimensions proportionately, apparatus capable of distilling a 0.5-cc charge can be made. In designing such equipment, Tiedcke states the following rule: "The volume of the distilling flask plus the volume of the condenser chamber and connections should be substantially less than the volume which the sample will occupy when transformed into vapor at its boiling point." Unless this principle is observed, reflux action will prevent distillation, especially with high boiling materials.

Figure 118 shows a column designed by Shrader and Ritzer[3] for distillation of volumes of materials from 0.5 to 2.0 cc under vacuum. The column proper *A* is of the Vigreux type, approximately 5 mm ID and 7 to 15 cm in length. The jacket *B* may be of the evacuated type as shown, or it may be of the wire wound type discussed previously (page 133). If this latter type is used, the temperature of the jacketed air space must be measured by a thermocouple since the spaces involved will not permit the entrance of a thermometer. The distilling flask *C* has a capacity of about 4 cc. The bottom is flattened to

permit the use of a layer of clean sea sand or 30-mesh silicon carbide as an
ebullition aid. The convenient receiver consists of a series of 4 mm diameter
glass tubes $D$, forming cups of about 0.10 cc capacity attached to 4 mm glass
rods. The cups and rods are sealed to $E$, and this in turn is sealed to $F$, which
is a standard taper male joint with the small end closed off. It is to this closed-
off portion that $E$ is sealed. A small hole $G$, about 6 mm in diameter, is blown
in the sealed portion of $F$ near $E$ so that the system can be evacuated at $M$.
The distillate is led into the receiving cups along a 1.0-mm glass rod $H$, which
tapers to 0.8 mm at the end near the cup. The rod must be smoothly sealed
to the 5 mm tubing $J$, which is ground to an angle as shown, the long side
being 9 mm and the short side 4 mm. The length of $H$ will be determined by
the position of the receiving cups. The number of cups is limited by the
diameter of $E$. If more cups are desired, the diameter of $E$ is increased. The
rods attached to the cups are sealed around the circumference of $E$ in such a
way that as the receiver is rotated at $F$, each succeeding cup will come under
the tip of $H$. The receiver is attached to the column through the 5 mm ID
condenser. This condenser may be water jacketed or it may be left without a
jacket so that it can accommodate a dry ice or wet paper cooling system. The
apparatus is charged at $L$. The temperature is raised slowly and distillation is
continued at such a rate that one drop is taken off every two or three minutes.

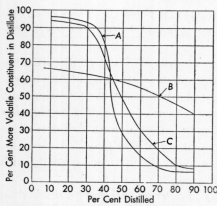

As an example of the performance
of this column, 1 gram of a 50-50
weight mixture of isoamyl salicylate
and caprylic acid was distilled at 1
mm. For comparison, curve $A$ of
Figure 119 is the same distillation
run in a Craig concentric tube column
(see page 175 and Figure 122, page
217), while curve $B$ was obtained in
a column without the jacket $B$ of
Figure 118. Curve $C$ is from the
column as described.

**Figure 119.** Distillation of Iso-Amyl
Salicylate-Caprylic Acid through Semimicro
Columns under Reduced Pressure

A rather complete study of several
types of small columns made by
winding glass yarn around a solid
rod and inserting it loosely into a
tube, has been made by Cheronis and Levin.[9] The most efficient of these is
made by winding 45 cm of 1.3-mm diameter glass yarn around a 160-mm
length of 4-mm glass rod, making 24 spirals around the length of the rod. The
ends of the yarn are cemented to the slightly tapered ends of the rod with

Sauereisen cement. The wound unit is inserted loosely into a 6.0–6.5 mm ID tube. Any packing support and low holdup head may be used. A study of this column is given in the graphs of Figure 120.

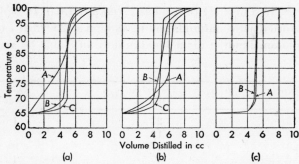

**Figure 120.** Characteristics of Glass Yarn Spiral Packing

All distillation mixtures consisted of 5 cc of methanol and 5 cc of water. Figure 120(a) shows the effect of throughput on efficiency. Curve *A* represents a throughput of 0.5 ml per minute; curve *B*, 0.3 ml per minute; and curve *C*, 0.2 ml per minute. As can be seen, the efficiency drops off considerably with increase in throughput. Figure 120(b) shows the effect of temperature control around the column. Curve *A* was determined for a column having no jacket, curve *B* shows the effect of a vacuum jacket, and curve *C* is for a column wrapped with asbestos. For the low-boiling materials used in these tests, the asbestos wrapped column is as good as the vacuum jacketed column. For higher boiling materials the addition of a suitable heating jacket might be required. Figure 120(c) gives a comparison between the spiral yarn packing (curve *A*) and a Podbielniak heli-grid type (curve *B*) of the same diameter and length. Distillation through both was at the same rate, 0.2 ml per minute. When tested under total reflux with *n*-heptane-methylcyclohexane, the heligrid column gave 14 theoretical plates while the glass yarn column gave 11 plates. Both columns required five to six hours to come to equilibrium.

Bowers and Cooke[10] have described in detail the

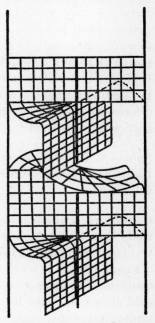

**Figure 121.** Wire Gauze Packing (Bowers-Cooke)

construction of a wire gauze packing somewhat similar to that of Lecky and Ewell, but simpler to construct and more applicable to small diameter columns. It consists of a strip of wire gauze twisted to produce a series of vertical plates at an angle of 90 degrees to each other, as shown in Figure 121. This type packing, inserted in 5 mm ID tubes, has given an *H.E.T.P.* of 1.88 cm, and works satisfactorily with materials boiling as high as 200 C at 1 mm pressure. On a 43-cm column, 5 mm in diameter, the data of Table 60 were obtained:

**TABLE 60**

| Throughput cc/hr | Theoretical plates | Operating holdup, cc |
|---|---|---|
| 38.5 | 23 | 1.035 |
| 63.0 | 19 | |
| 84.0 | 17 | |
| 110.0* | 15.5 | 1.23 |

*Slightly less than flood point.

A column of the same diameter and 90 cm long gave 45 theoretical plates. Thus, as in the case of the Fenske, Podbielniak, and other metal packings previously described (page 87), an increase in length gives substantially a proportional increase in plate value. This type of packing, as is true of most metal packings, works best when it has been preflooded. A most surprising characteristic, however, is the shortness of time required to bring the column to equilibrium, only 30 minutes being required at the lowest throughput reported in Table 60. With the partial condensation head used, distillation of 6 to 15 cc of material was accomplished with a takeoff of 100 to 200 mg per hour. For distilling smaller volumes of materials in the range of 1–5 cc, a shorter column must be used to reduce the holdup, since the holdup is directly proportional to the length.

*Spinning Band Columns.* The column of Lesesne and Lochne[11] shown in Figure 33 and characterized on page 82 has been used successfully for small volume work.

*Concentric Tube Columns.* A small column,[12] described by Craig, has already been discussed (Figure 95, page 176). The same author has described two other columns[13] of this type.

Figure 122 shows a column in which the concentric tubes are of very small diameter. The inner tube *A* acts also as an ebullition tube and consists of a solid glass rod, to the lower end of which is sealed about 1 mm of capillary tubing. The vapor condenses on the cold finger *B*, which is indented on the end in order that it may hold more liquid. When sufficient distillate to consti-

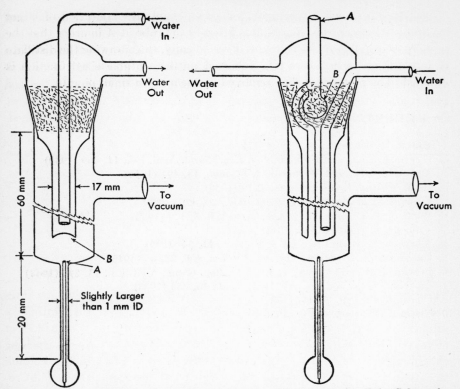

**Figure 122.** Craig Concentric-Tube Column Using Capillary Inner Tube

**Figure 123.** Craig Concentric-Tube Column for Collecting Larger Fractions

tute a fraction (about 0.2 cc) collects on the condenser, the distillation is stopped, the condenser is removed, and the condensate is taken as a fraction. Physical properties on each fraction may then be determined since the vapor temperature cannot be read during distillation.

The operation of this column is as follows. The bulb is immersed in an oil bath the temperature of which is carefully controlled. Heating is continued until bubbles rise from the end of the capillary. The temperature of the bath is recorded and held at that point while distillate collects. If vapor does not rise through the tubes at this point, the temperature is increased very slightly, or until condensate does appear on the tip of the condenser. The temperature of the oil bath at the time when ebullition first begins is usually about 3 degrees above the boiling point of the liquid. It should be noted that this is not necessarily the boiling point of the fraction since, unless the charge is a pure compound, the material constituting the vapor will have a lower boiling point than will the liquid.

The column shown in Figure 123 makes possible the collection of larger fractions. A mercury leveling bulb is fitted to the tube at $A$ in order that the pressure in chamber $B$ can be reduced periodically, thus drawing the distillate up into the chamber where it is collected until a suitable sized fraction is obtained. The material is then removed by means of a small pipette.

## REFERENCES

1. EMICH, F., *Monatsh.*, **38**, 219 (1917)
2. GETTLER, A. O., and FINE, J., *Ind. Eng. Chem.*, Anal. Ed., **11**, 469 (1939)
3. MORTON, A. A., and MAHONEY, J. F., *ibid.*, **13**, 494 (1941)
4. ROSE, A., *Ind. Eng. Chem.*, **28**, 1210 (1936)
5. COOPER, C. M., and FASCE, E. V., *ibid.*, **20**, 420 (1928)
6. WESTON, P. E., *Ind. Eng. Chem.*, Anal Ed., **5**, 179 (1933)
7. TIEDCKE, C., *ibid.*, **15**, 81 (1943)
8. SHRADER, S. A., and RITZER, J. E., *ibid.*, **11**, 54 (1939)
9. CHERONIS, N. D., and LEVIN, N., *J. Chem. Ed.*, **22**, 85 (1945)
10. BOWER, J. R., and COOKE, L. M., *Ind. Eng. Chem.*, Anal Ed., **15, 290 (1943)**
11. LESESNE, S. D., and LOCHTE, H. L., *ibid.*, **10**, 450 (1938)
12. CRAIG, L. C., *ibid.*, **9**, 441 (1937)
13. CRAIG, L. C., *ibid.*, **8**, 219 (1936)

# CHAPTER

# XXII

## *Molecular Distillation*

IN THE LABORATORY, it is frequently necessary to purify a high-boiling material, unstable at its boiling point, by some means other than extraction, recrystallization, or chromatographic absorption. In recent years the technique of molecular distillation has been developed to such a point that it has grown from a small-scale laboratory application to an industrial process, handling millions of pounds of distillate per year. It should be understood that molecular distillation is not a good method of separating materials. It gives a very poor separation. It is valuable, however, because it is a means of distilling a whole class of substances which cannot be readily purified in any other way.

Molecular distillation is the process of driving molecules from a layer of distilland to a cooled condenser, the condenser being placed in such a position that the distance from the surface of the distilland to the condenser is slightly less than the mean free path of the distilling molecules. The mean free path of the molecule is the average distance traveled by a molecule between collisions. At low pressure the order of magnitude of the mean free path is about $0.1/p$ mm where $p$ is in millimeters of mercury.

In every substance there is an equilibrium existing between the *vapor* above the substance and the substance itself. This *vapor* is caused by molecules of the parent material leaving the surface, returning to it to be replaced by other molecules. One of the factors affecting the number of molecules leaving a surface is the pressure of the atmosphere above the surface. A high pressure tends to keep the molecules in the original material, whereas a low pressure over the material encourages molecules to leave the surface. A second factor influencing the evaporation of molecules from a surface is temperature. A higher temperature increases the number of molecules leaving the surface by increasing the energy of the molecules, enabling them to push back the surrounding atmosphere. The third factor influencing the number of molecules escaping from a surface is the molecular weight of the compound. The higher the molecular weight, the less will be the escaping tendency.

Taking these factors into consideration, Langmuir[1] has derived an equation to predict the number of moles $n$ leaving a surface of area $A$ (sq cm) in one second:

$$n = p\, A\sqrt{\frac{1}{2\,\pi MRT}}$$

where $p$ is the vapor pressure (dynes per sq cm) at the evaporating surface at $T$ Kelvin, $M$ is the molecular weight, and $R$ is the gas constant.

For example, if we are to distill stearic acid at a pressure of 1 micron (0.001 mm) of mercury from a surface of 100 square centimeters, and at a temperature of 350 K, we have

$$n = (0.001)\,(1333)\,(100)\sqrt{\frac{1}{2\,\pi\,(284)\,(8.32\times10^7)\,(350)}}$$

$n = 18\times10^{-6}$

This means, then, that every second $18 \times 10^{-6}$ moles of stearic acid leave the surface of the distilland. It does not mean that there will be that much distillate. The actual rate of collection will be less, because some of the molecules will be returned to the distilland as a result of reflection from the condenser, and of collisions both with residual gas in the still and with like molecules. The rate of collection of distillate is equal to the rate of evaporation from the surface only when there are no residual molecules in the still, when the condensing surface is cold enough to condense all the molecules striking it, and when the condenser is quite close to the distilland surface.

Since molecular distillation takes place from a quiet surface, it is important to maintain the component to be fractionated at that surface. In ordinary fractionation or "equilibrant distillation," the surface of the distilland is in constant motion due either to artificial stirring or to agitation caused by boiling. However, in molecular distillation the process takes place at a rate much too low to cause agitation by ebullition. Usually the distilland is either a solid or a viscous liquid at the temperature of distillation. Therefore it takes a finite time for molecules at an appreciable distance below the surface to rise to the surface and evaporate. Now, if there are several components in the distilland, it is possible—and probable—that some slightly higher boiling material *at the surface* will evaporate before the desired lower boiling molecules can make their way up through the body of the viscous or solid distilland. Another factor then enters into the consideration of efficient molecular distillation. The surface must be as large as possible, and the depth of the layer of the distilland should be as small as possible. As a direct effect of decreasing the thickness of the layer, the time of exposure of any molecule to heat is greatly shortened.

A graphic illustration of the development of distillation practice in this field from the viewpoint of the thickness of the distilland, and of the time of exposure of any portion of the distilland to heat, has been given by Hickman,[2] as stated in Table 61.

**TABLE 61**

| Date | Stills | Thickness of distilland (approx) | Molecular thickness (approx) | Time of exposure (approx) |
|---|---|---|---|---|
| 1922 | Laboratory pot still | 1-5 cm | $5 \times 10^7$ | 1-5 hr |
| 1928 | Laboratory tray still | 0.1-1 cm | $5 \times 10^6$ | 5-60 min |
| 1935 | Industrial falling film still | 1-3 mm | $5 \times 10^5$ | 2-10 min |
| 1930 | Laboratory falling film still | 0.1-0.3 mm | $5 \times 10^4$ | 10-50 sec |
| 1940 | Industrial centrifugal still | 0.3-0.06 mm | $1 \times 10^4$ | 0.1-1 sec |
| 1936 | Laboratory centrifugal still | 0.01-0.02 mm | $3 \times 10^3$ | 0.04-0.08 sec |
| 1942 | High-speed centrifugal rim still | 0.001-0.005 mm | $4 \times 10^2$ | 0.001-0.005 sec |

*Uses of Molecular Distillation.* The principal use of molecular distillation is in the separation of substances the boiling points of which are too high for practical equilibrant fractionation, or which decompose at the boiling point necessary for equilibrant distillation. However, molecular distillation has another type of application, and that is in the separation of azeotropic mixtures, or in the separation of mixtures whose components have the same partial pressures.

In equilibrant fractionation we have seen earlier that the amount of separation is determined by the ratio of the partial pressures $P_1/P_2$, or the relative volatility of the components in the distilland. However, in molecular distillation the formula

$$n = P\,A\sqrt{\frac{1}{2\,\pi\,MRT}}$$

shows that the number of molecules of two components distilling depends not only on the partial pressure $P$, but also on the inverse square root of the molecular weight $\sqrt{1/M}$, since at any given temperature $A$ and $2\pi RT$ are constants. It immediately becomes apparent, then, that the relative quantities of the two components distilling are

$$\frac{P_1}{\sqrt{M_1}} \Big/ \frac{P_2}{\sqrt{M_2}}$$

Therefore two substances of different molecular weight can be separated by molecular distillation, even though the vapor pressures of the two are the same. An excellent example of this phenomenon is in the separation of two isotopes of mercury, both having the same vapor pressure but distilling at different rates because of the different molecular weights.

In equilibrant distillation, it sometimes becomes impossible to separate two components whose vapor pressures are different because an azeotrope is formed. In molecular distillation a somewhat similar situation arises when we have

$$\frac{P_1}{\sqrt{M_1}} = \frac{P_2}{\sqrt{M_2}}$$

Under these conditions we have the same number of molecules of each component distilling; so, of course, there is no separation.

It is sometimes possible to separate difficult mixtures by alternately using equilibrant and molecular distillation techniques, changing from azeotropic compositions by molecular distillation and then continuing by equilibrant fractionation.

**Interpretation of Results.**  In ordinary distillation, the curve of the operation can be followed fairly closely by observing the change in boiling point of the material distilling. In molecular distillation this is not possible since, in reality, there is no boiling point. The boiling point is defined as the temperature at which the vapor pressure of a material is equal to the pressure of gas other than the vapor above it. In molecular distillation there is by definition no residual gas; consequently, there is no boiling point.

In laboratory molecular distillation the fundamental process of analysis of results is somewhat simplified. The material is molecularly distilled and redistilled, and the fractions are collected and analyzed. Identification is made possible usually by chemical means. However, it is sometimes important to know the constitution of a mixture, rather than actually to separate it. Hickman has shown that, by drawing a curve of the concentration of the material under consideration in a given fraction against the temperature at which the fraction was collected, a definitive curve is obtained which yields much valuable information concerning the properties of the mixture.

**Elimination curve.**  The rate of elimination is defined as the rate at which the desired material appears in the receiver. Hickman[3] and Embree[4] have discussed a second kind of rate of evaporation, namely, "distillability." It is defined as the "ratio of the number of molecules of a given species leaving the distilling surface in any given interval compared with the number of similar molecules remaining undistilled in the surface layer during the same interval." If distillation takes place at a constant temperature, the ratio of the molecules distilling to the molecules remaining behind will remain constant. Therefore the distillability is constant. However, the number of molecules of the desired product distilling will decrease until after a long period practically all the desired product has been evaporated and the rate of elimination approaches zero. To shorten the time necessary to reduce the rate of elimination to zero, the temperature is increased during the distillation. If the temperature increments are constant, the distillability increases constantly, but the rate of elimination will first increase and then fall to zero when all the desired material has been distilled. The curve obtained by plotting the concentration of the desired material in the fraction against the temperature at which the fraction was collected is called the *elimination curve*. A typical elimination curve has the general shape shown in Figure 124. The form of the curve is independent of the kind of substance distilled. Each curve has a definite temperature maximum. Under standardized conditions the shape of the curve and the temperature maximum for a material can be duplicated with an accuracy of ± 1 C. The position of the maximum is dependent on the distillability and on the length of time that the distilland is exposed to the temperature between fractions. If the time intervals are increased, more product will distill per unit of time. The curve will be displaced (curve *B*, Figure 124) and the maximum will appear at a lower temperature.

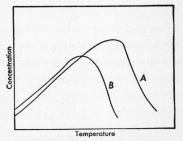

Figure 124.  Elimination Curve

Distillability in general varies with the inverse of the absolute temperature. However, it has been shown that, for a given temperature interval, the distillability of two materials varies as their latent heats of vaporization. Therefore a study of the elimination curves of two materials will give some indication of their vapor pressure curves. Substances with a high distillability increment will yield taller curves with narrower bases than will those with low increments.

Just as boiling points can be used to give an indication of the identity of a compound in ordinary distillation, so, too, can the elimination maxima be used in molecular distillation. The maxima of any group of materials for which curves have been determined under the same conditions may be compared. To further characterize the compound after its elimination curve has been found, another curve is run under the same conditions, this time using a *pilot dye* in the mixture also. The fractions are analyzed for dye concentration (usually colorimetrically) and for the product under consideration. The elimination curves are drawn for both, and the unknown is compared with the dye. In this way results of different workers may be correlated, taking into account differences in technique, rates of distillation, etc. For example, two workers might run elimination curves and get results for the maximum differing by 20 C. Now, a known pilot dye is run by each. Again, differences of 20 degrees are noted. However, the *difference* in maxima between the pilot dye and the unknown will be the same for both workers, even though the temperatures recorded by both are not the same.

When a material is to be identified rather than separated, it is dissolved in an oil and the distillation carried out so that both the material under consideration and the oil distill simultaneously. The oily distillate is analyzed and the elimination curve drawn. This necessitates an oil which gives a constant volume of distillate for each temperature increment used, and which will leave about half the original volume of oil as residue. Such oils are called "constant-yield" oil (C.Y.O.). Their preparation is completely described in the literature. [5]

***Types of Molecular Stills.***    From the above discussion on the theory of molecular distillation, it may be concluded that three factors are important in the design of a molecular still:

1. Pressure in the still
2. Position and temperature of the condenser
3. Depth of the distilland layer

A sufficiently low pressure can be obtained (1 to 10 microns) with any of the standard vacuum pumps. The same precautions concerning wide tubing and connections should be observed here as were discussed in Chapter XIV. All connections should be as large as possible to cut down pressure drop caused by friction.

The position of the condenser offers no difficulties. Usually, it is placed in the order of 1 cm from the distilland layer in laboratory stills. The selection of a condenser is somewhat important. If the condenser is not cool enough, some of the molecules striking it will not be condensed but will rebound to the distilland surface, thus cutting down on the efficiency of the process by increasing the reaction time. It is recommended, as an arbitrary estimation in case data are not available for calculation, that the temperature of the condenser be held 50 to 60 degrees below the temperature of the evaporating distilland.

There are four general types of stills in use:

1. The pot still          3. The falling film still
2. The tray still         4. The centrifugal still

The pot still (Figure 125) consists simply of a layer of distilland *A*, heated at *B*, with a condenser *C* placed close to the surface of the liquid. The large

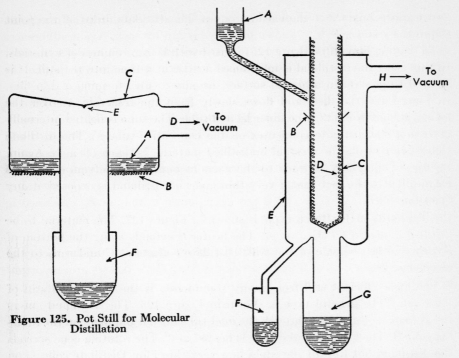

**Figure 125.** Pot Still for Molecular Distillation

**Figure 126.** Falling Film Molecular Still

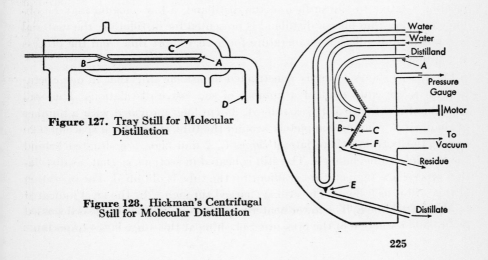

**Figure 127.** Tray Still for Molecular Distillation

**Figure 128.** Hickman's Centrifugal Still for Molecular Distillation

outlet $D$ is connected to the vacuum pump. The distillate drops off the point $E$ into the receiver $F$.

The falling film still (Figure 126) is used with larger volumes of materials. In this type, the distilland is introduced a little at a time into the still. It is allowed to flow down a heated surface, usually a tube, forming a thin film. In Figure 126 the distilland flows slowly from the reservoir $A$, over the trough $B$, and around $C$, the inner heated tube. The tube is heated internally at $D$ and the distillate condenses on the concentric tube $E$. The distillate collects in $F$ while the residual undistilled material is taken off at $G$. Again, the large connection $H$ leads to the vacuum pump. The advantage of this column lies in the fact that a very thin layer of distilland is exposed at any one time.

A tray still of the Burch type[6] is shown in Figure 127. The material to be distilled is placed on the tray $A$. The heater $B$ extends along the bottom of the tray to the outside of the still. Distillate collects at $C$ and runs to the receiver at $D$.

The most efficient still from many standpoints is the centrifugal still of Hickman.[2] The general type is shown in Figure 128. The distilland enters the system at $A$ and falls through the inlet tube until it impinges on the rotating cone $B$. The surface of the cone is heated at $C$. The rotating cone spreads the distilland out toward the edges in a very thin film. Distillate collects on the condenser $D$, and falls into the receiving tube at $E$, where it is removed from the system. The undistilled residue is forced to the edges of the cone, where it is collected and withdrawn from the system through $F$. Thus, this still possesses all the desirable features of a good molecular still. The condenser may be cooled conveniently to any desired temperature and placed in any position relative to the surface of the distilland, a low vacuum may be obtained, a very thin film of distilland is presented for distillation, the material is exposed to distillation temperature for a very short time, and the process is continuous.

Figure 129 shows a simply constructed molecular still[7] that in one operation gives the equivalent of a number of successive distillations. This still consists of a cylindrical Pyrex tube $A$, 38 cm long, provided with a number of channels $B$, running completely around the tube except for a space of 0.20 mm at the bottom, where lateral ridges $C$, 2 mm high, are situated behind the termini of the channels. The still is heated in sections so that, as distillation proceeds, a temperature gradient up the tube is obtained. The operation of this still is as follows: The still is charged through $F$ to the level indicated by the dotted line $E$. The lower heater is turned on and the charge is degassed by gradual reduction of the pressure. Splashing at this stage is not important.

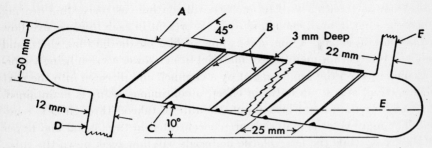

**Figure 129.** Multiple Stage Molecular Still (Wollner-Matchett-Levine)

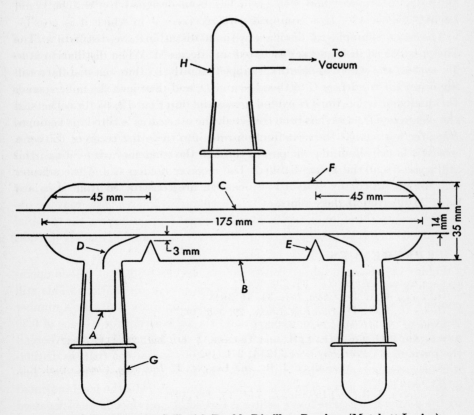

**Figure 130.** Molecular Still with Double Distillate Receiver (Matchett-Levine)

As the heat is increased on the bottom section, some material distills, condensing on the top of the tube. This distillate is transferred to the next higher heating area by means of the channel along which it flows. Transfer of materials from one heating area to another will continue as succeeding heating elements are cut in until enough material is present in each to cause overflow over the lateral ridges. A continuous flow of film on the bottom, sides, and top of the tube is thus maintained, material from a lower section being vaporized, condensed on the top, engaged by a channel, and directed into the next higher section, and so on until, in effect, a continuous reflux is maintained. By controlling the rate of heat input, the rate of takeoff through $D$ is regulated. The more volatile materials are concentrated in the takeoff and upper heating areas, while the less volatile materials will flow back down the tube. A source of vacuum is applied at $F$.

A molecular still capable of distilling 0.25 to 5 grams of material leaving a residue of not more than 0.15 gram has been designed by Matchett and Levine,[8] Figure 130. It is equipped with receivers $A$ in which it is possible to collect two samples of distillate without disturbing the distillation. The charge is placed in $B$ and is evacuated and degassed. When distillation is to be started, the whole apparatus is tipped slightly so that the distillate will run down the condenser $C$ to the glass rod $D$, and then into the first receiver $A$. The indented portions $E$ extend across the outer tube $F$ to form the still pot. When one fraction has been collected, the apparatus is tilted in the opposite direction so that the next fraction runs into the other receiver. Either a cool or a hot medium may be passed through the condenser, depending upon the type of material being distilled. The receiver holders $G$ and the adapter $H$, through which the system is evacuated, are constructed from standard taper 24/40 ground glass joints.

## REFERENCES

1. LANGMUIR, I., *Phys. Rev.*, **30**, 201 (1927)
2. HICKMAN, K. C. D., *Chem. Rev.*, **34**, 51 (1944)
3. HICKMAN, K. C. D., *Ind. Eng. Chem.*, **29**, 968 (1937)
4. EMBREE, N. D., *ibid.*, **29**, 975 (1937)
5. BAXTER, J. G., GRAY, E. LeB., and TISCHER, A. D., *ibid.*, **29**, 1112 (1937)
6. BURCH, C. R., *Proc. Roy. Soc.*, **123A**, 271 (1929)
7. WOLLNER, H. J., MATCHETT, J. R., and LEVINE, J., *Ind. Eng. Chem.*, Anal. Ed., **16**, 529 (1944)
8. MATCHETT, J. R., and LEVINE, J., *ibid.*, **15**, 296 (1943)

# General Bibliography

## CHAPTER I: THEORY

LEWIS, W. K.
*Ind. Eng. Chem.*, **1**, 522 (1909)
The Theory of Fractional Distillation.

GRABOWSKI, C.
*Prezemysl. Chem.*, **11**, 253 (1927)
Principles for Studying Rectification of Liquid Mixtures.

EGLOFF, G., and LOWRY, C. D.
*Ind. Eng. Chem.*, **21**, 920 (1929)
Distillation Methods, Ancient and Modern.

BURRELL, G. A., and TURNER, N. C.
*Nat. Petroleum News*, **25**, No. *12*, 26 (1929)
Principles of Rectification.

TREGUBOV, A. M.
*Aznefteiz dat.*, **15**, 159 (1932)
Basic Principles of Distillation and Rectification.

CAREY, J. S.
*Chem. Met. Eng.*, **41**, 248 (1934)
Distillation.

DOCKSEY, P.
*J. Inst. Petroleum Technol.*, **21**, 327 (1935)
Theory of Design of Distillation Equipment.

BALAREV, D., and KOLAROV, N.
*Z. anal. Chem.*, **107**, 30 (1936)
Mist Formation During Distillation.

BLOOMFIELD, A. L.
*Perfumery and Essential Oil Record*, **27**, 131, 177, 294 (1936)
Theory of Distillation as Applied to Essential Oils.

BROWN, G. G.
*Trans. Am. Inst. Chem. Engrs.*, **32**, 321 (1936)
Distillation.

KIRSCHBAUM, E.
*Chem. Eng. Cong. World Power Conf.*, **II**, 30 (1936)
Advances in Rectification Technology.

KEYES, D. B.
*Trans. Ill. State Acad. Sci.*, **30**, 195 (1937)
Fractional Distillation.

GUINOT, H. M.
*Tech. ind. chim.*, No. *277*, 151 (1938)
Distillation and Rectification. Importance of These Operations in the Manufacture of Chemical Products by Modern Methods.

OTHMER, D. F.
*Chem. Met. Eng.*, **49**, 84 (1942)
Distillation Practice and Methods of Calculation.

BLANC, J.
*Bull. assoc. chim.*, **63**, 397 (1946)
The Theory of Distilling Columns.

BENEDICT, M.
*Trans. Am. Inst. Chem. Engrs.*, **43**, 41 (1947)
Multistage Separation Processes.

LITWIN, H.
*Oil Gas J.*, **45**, 237 (1947)
Cascade-Type Tray Introduces New Fractionating Principle.

# CHAPTER II: MATHEMATICAL TREATMENT

LEWIS, W. K.
*Ind. Eng. Chem.*, 14, 492 (1922)
The Efficiency and Design of Rectifying Columns for Binary Mixtures.

MURPHREE, E. V.
*ibid.*, 17, 960 (1925)
Graphical Rectifying Column Calculations.

SHIRK, L. H., and MONTANNA, R. E.
*ibid.*, 19, 907 (1927)
A Critical Analysis of Equations for the Design of Fractionating Columns.

KEYES, D. B., SOUKOR, R., and NICHOLS, W. A., JR.
*ibid.*, 20, 464 (1928)
Design of Fractionating Column.

GAY, L.
*Chimie et industrie*, 22, 3 (1929)
Distillation and Rectification of Complex Mixtures.

CHILLAS, R. B., and WEIR, H. M.
*Trans. Am. Inst. Chem. Engrs.*, 22, 79 (1929)
The Design of Fractionating Columns with Particular Reference to Petroleum Distillation.

BAKER, E. M., and PETTIBONE, E. E.
*Ind. Eng. Chem.*, 21, 562 (1929)
Rapid Graphical Method for Calculation of Steam Distillation Problems.

LIBINSON, S. L.
*J. Chem. Ind.* (U.S.S.R.), 7, 765 (1930)
Graphical Calculations of Rectifying Columns.

BEALL, I. N.
*Ref. Nat. Gas Mfgr.*, 9, No. 6, 86 (1930)
Design and Operation of Fractionating Columns.

BAKER, T., and STOCKHARDT, J. S.
*Ind. Eng. Chem.*, 22, 376 (1930)
Graphical Rectifying Column Calculations.

TREGUBOV, A. M.
*Neftyanoe-Khozyaistvo*, 24, 287 (1932)
Calculation of the Elements of Distillation.

ELLIOT, W. R.
*Can. Chem. Met.*, 16, 83 (1932)
Industrial Distillation.

COPE, J. Q., and LEWIS, W. K.
*Ind. Eng. Chem.*, 24, 498 (1932)
Graphical Method of Computation for Rectifying Complex Hydrocarbon Mixtures.

TREGUBOV, A. M.
*Neftyanoe-Khozyaistvo*, 25, 33 (1933)
Calculation of the Elements of Distillation.

KIRSCHBAUM, E.
*Chem. Fabrik*, 6, 431 (1933)
The Efficiency of Rectification Columns.

BROWN, G. G., and SOUDERS, M., JR.
*Trans. Am. Inst. Chem. Engrs.*, 30, 438 (1933)
Methods for Determining the Number of Equilibrium Plates.

MASAKICHI, K.
*J. Soc. Chem. Ind.* (Japan), 37, 540, 769 (1934)
Calculations for Discontinuous Fractionating Column.

KALITOV, J. P.
*Khiimstroi*, 7, 402 (1935)
Theory and Calculation of the Two-Phase Process.

DOCKSEY, P.
*J. Inst. Petroleum Technol.*, 21, 327 (1935)
Theory of Design of Distillation Equipment.

GILLILAND, E. R.
*Ind. Eng. Chem.*, 27, 260 (1935)
New Design Calculation for Multicomponent Rectification.

EDGEWORTH-JOHNSTONE, R.
*Trans. Inst. Chem. Engrs.* (London), 14, 107 (1936)
Nomograph for Fractionating Columns.

BROWN, G. G.
*Trans. Am. Inst. Chem. Engrs.*, 32, 321 (1936)
Distillation.

LEWIS, W. K. JR.
*Ind. Eng. Chem.*, 28, 399 (1936)
Rectification of Binary Mixtures. Plate Efficiency of Bubble-Cap Columns.

KIRSCHBAUM, E.
*Chem. Eng. Cong. World Power Conf.*, II, 30 (1936)
Advances in Rectification Technology.

AREFIV, A. D.
*J. Chem. Ind.*, 13, 1235 (1936)
Method of Calculations for Rectifying Columns.

BOGART, M. J. P.
*Trans. Am. Inst. Chem. Engrs.*, 33, 139 (1937)
Design of Equipment for Fractional Batch Distillation.

MEYER, P.
*Trans. Inst. Chem. Engrs.* (London), 15, 209 (1937)
Graphical Computation for Complex Distillation Systems.

BEWSHER, J. N.
*Chem. Ind.*, 13, 424, 432 (1937)
Fractionating Columns for Batch Stills.

HAUSEN, H.
*A. ges. Kalte Ind.*, 44, 59 (1937)
Graphic Method for Calculating Rectification Plate Efficiency.

RANDALL, M., and LONGTIN, B.
*Ind. Eng. Chem.*, 30, 1063 (1938)
Separation Processes. General Method of Analysis.

BAKER, E. M.
*Ind. Eng. Chem.*, 31, 717 (1939)
Entrainment in Plate Columns.
Graphical method for determining plates where entrainment is a factor.

RANDALL, M., and LONGTIN, B.
*ibid.*, 31, 908 (1939)
Separation Processes. Point Transformation of y vs. x Diagrams.

KOWALCZYK, L.
*Przeglad Chem.*, 3, 514 (1939)
Calculation and Design of Rectification Apparatus.

JENNY, F. J.
*Trans. Am. Inst. Chem. Engrs.*, 35, 635 (1939)
Graphical Solution of Problems in Multicomponent Fractionation.

KARAVAEAR, N. M.
*Bull. Acad. Sci. U.S.S.R. Classe Sci. Tech. No. 9*, 79 (1940)
Batch Rectification and the Theory and Layout of the Process.

BROWN, G. G., and HOLCOMB, D. E.
*Petroleum Eng.*, 11, 31 (1940)
Calculating the Minimum Number of Plates.

BROWN, G. G.
*ibid.*, 11, 55 (1940)
Calculations Involved in the Design of Fractionating Columns.

GILLILAND, E. R.
*Ind. Eng. Chem.*, 32, 918 (1940)
Multicomponent Rectification. Optimum Feed-Plate Composition.

HIBSHMAN, H. J.
*ibid.*, 32, 988 (1940)
Multicomponent Distillation Problems.

GILLILAND, E. R.
*ibid.*, 32, 1101 (1940)
Multicomponent Rectification. Minimum Reflux Ratio.

GILLILAND, E. R.
ibid., 32, 1220 (1940)
Multicomponent Rectification. Estimation of the Number of Theoretical Plates as a Function of the Reflux Ratio.

SMITH, R. L.
Trans. Am. Inst. Chem. Engrs., 37, 333 (1941)
Design of Fractionating Columns for Multicomponent Mixtures.

BONILLA, C. P.
ibid., 37, 669 (1941)
Graphical Design of Continuous Distillation Columns for Ternary Mixtures.

COLBURN, A. P.
Ind. Eng. Chem., 33, 459 (1941)
Simplified Calculations of Diffusional Processes. Number of Transfer Units or Theoretical Plates.

HOGAN, J. J.
ibid., 33, 1132 (1941)
Multicomponent Fractionation. Distribution of Three Components.

GILLILAND, E. R., and REED, C. E.
ibid., 34, 551 (1942)
Degrees of Freedom in Multicomponent Adsorption and Rectification Columns.

KARNOFSKY, G.
ibid., 34, 839 (1942)
Rapid Solution of Multicomponent Distillation Problems.

THOMSON, G. W., and BEATTY, H. A.
ibid., 34, 1124 (1942)
A Simplified Calculation of Theoretical Plates. Fractionation of a Binary Mixture in Which Concentration of One Component Is Small.

UNDERWOOD, A. J. V.
J. Inst. Petroleum, 29, 147 (1943)
Fractional Distillation of Binary Mixtures. Number of Theoretical Plates and Transfer Units.

KIRSCHBAUM, E.
Z. Ver. deut. Ing. Verf. No. 1, 15 (1943)
Determination of the Height of Packed Columns in Distillation and Rectification Practice.

GERSTER, J. A., KOFFOLT, J. H., and WITHROW, J. R.
Trans. Am. Inst. Chem. Engrs., 39, 37 (1943)
Extension of H.T.U. Method of Plate Column Distillation.

BAKER, E. M., and LINDSAY, R. A.
Ind. Eng. Chem., 35, 418 (1943)
Design Calculations for Plate Columns.

CORN, L. H.
ibid., 36, 378 (1944)
Graphical Solution of Ternary Distillation Problems.

HUMMEL, H. H.
Trans. Am. Inst. Chem. Engrs., 40, 445 (1944)
Multicomponent Fractionation: A Simplified Approach to Plate-to-Plate Calculations.

UNDERWOOD, A. J. V.
J. Inst. Petroleum, 30, 225 (1944)
Fractional Distillation of Binary Mixtures.

KIRKBRIDE, C. G.
Petroleum Refiner, 23, 321 (1944)
Process Design Procedure for Multicomponent Fractionators.

MILLER, O.
Bull. soc. chim. Belg., 53, 97 (1944)
Distillation of Non-Ideal Binary Mixtures.

WHITE, R. R.
ibid., 24, 299, 357 (1945)
Calculation of Plate Columns for Binary Distillation.

JENNY, F. J., and CICALESE, M. J.
Ind. Eng. Chem., 37, 956 (1945)
Two-Component Equilibrium Curves for Multicomponent Fractionation.

HARBERT, W. D.
ibid., **37**, 1162 (1945)
System of Distillation Equations.

CLARK, A. M.
Trans. Faraday Soc., **41**, 738 (1945)
Equation for the Liquid-Vapor Relations
of Binary Systems. Application to the
Theory of Practical Distillation.

UNDERWOOD, A. J. V.
J. Inst. Petroleum, **31**, 111 (1945)
Fractional Distillation of Ternary Mixtures.

HARBERT, W. D.
Ind. Eng. Chem., **37**, 1162 (1945)
System of Distillation Equations.
Equations relating liquid composition and
plate number for both binary and multicomponent distillation at total reflux and
at any reflux ratio.

SIMON, J.
Current Sci., **14**, 20 (1945)
New Method of Designing Packed
Columns.

UNDERWOOD, A. J. V.
J. Inst. Petroleum, **32**, 598 (1946)
Fractional Distillation of Ternary Mixtures.

UNDERWOOD, A. J. V.
ibid., **32**, 614 (1946)
Fractional Distillation of Multicomponent Mixtures. Calculation of Minimum
Reflux Ratio.

SCHEIBEL, E. G.
Ind. Eng. Chem., **38**, 397 (1946)
Multicomponent-Tray Calculations Based
on Equilibrium Curve of Key Components.

STOPPEL, A. E.
ibid., **38**, 1271 (1946)
Calculation of Number of Theoretical
Plates for Rectifying Column.

EDMISTER, W. C.
Trans. Am. Inst. Chem. Engrs., **42**, 15
(1946)
Multicomponent Fractionation Design
Method.

GEDDES, R. L.
ibid., **42**, 79 (1946)
Local Efficiencies of Bubble Plate Fractionators.

WOHL, KURT
ibid., **42**, 215 (1946)
Thermodynamic Evaluation of Binary
and Ternary Liquid Systems.

HENGSTEBECK, R. J.
ibid., **42**, 309 (1946)
A Simplified Method for Solving Multicomponent Distillation Problems.

NORD, M.
ibid., **42**, 863 (1946)
Plate Efficiencies of Benzene-Toluene-
Xylene Systems in Distillation.

KUHN, W.
Helv. Chim. Acta, **29**, 26 (1946)
Instantaneous Values of the Composition
of the Distillate and Residue in the Course
of a Distillation.

KUHN, W.
ibid., **29**, 329 (1946)
The Separation Effect in a Distillation of
Mixtures Containing Any Number of
Components.

PLANOVSKIĬ, A. N., and KAFAROV, V. V.
Khimicheskaya Prom. No. 3, 16 (1945),
(C. A. **40**, 2037[5] (1946))
Calculation of Packed Rectification
Columns.

NELSEN, J. M., BROOKS, F. R., and
ZOHN, V.
Anal. Chem., **19**, 814 (1947)
Nomographs for Distillation of Low Boiling Hydrocarbons.

NORD, M.
*Ind. Eng. Chem.*, **39**, 232 (1947)
Batch Distillation Nomograph.

STANTON, W. H.
*ibid.*, **39**, 1042 (1947)
Batch Distillation Nomograph for Binary
or Multicomponent Mixtures.

UNDERWOOD, A. J. V.
*Chem. Eng. Progress*, **44**, 603 (1948)
Fractional Distillation of Multicompo-
nent Mixtures.

SMITH, R. B., and DRESSER, T.
*ibid.*, **44**, 789 (1948)
Distillation Calculations in Ideal and
Non-Ideal Systems.

YU, K. T., and COULL, J.
*ibid.*, **44**, 795 (1948)
Application of Zygograph to Distillation
of Binary Mixtures.

MURDOCH, P. G.
*ibid.*, **44**, 855 (1948)
Multicomponent Distillation. Constant
Volatility Ratio and Constant Reflux.
Derivation and Application of Basic Alge-
braic Equations to Three- and Four-
Component Systems.

NICHOLLS, C. M.
*Natl. Research Council Can., At. Energy
Project, N.R.C. No.* **1679**, 1947.
The H.T.U. Concept in Column Calcula-
tions.

KOHRT, H. U.
*Angew. Chem.*, **B20**, 117 (1948)
Minimum Reflux Ratio in the Fractionation of Quaternary and Ternary Substances.

SIMON, M. J., and GOVINDA RAU, M. A.
*Ind. Eng. Chem.*, **40**, 93 (1948)
Method for Designing Packed Columns.

## CHAPTER IV: THEORETICAL PLATES AND REFLUX RATIO REQUIRED FOR A GIVEN SEPARATION

RODEBUSH, W. H.
*Ind. Eng. Chem.*, **14**, 1036 (1922)
A Simple Graphical Method of Calculat-
ing the Number of Plates Required for a
Distilling Column.

KEYES, D. B., SOUKOR, R., and
NICHOLS, W. A. JR.
*ibid.*, **20**, 464 (1928)
Design of Fractionating Column.

BROWN, G. G., and SOUDERS, M. JR.
*Trans. Am. Inst. Chem. Engrs.*, **30**, 438
(1933)
Methods for Determining the Number of
Equilibrium Plates.

BROWN, G. G.
*Ind. Eng. Chem.*, **27**, 383 (1935)
Number of Plates for Gas and Gasoline
Fractionators.

CHARNOBAEV, D. A.
*J. Chem. Ind.* (U.S.S.R.), **13**, 1283 (1936)
Calculation of Theoretical Number of
Plates.

DODGE, B. F., and HUFFMAN, J. R.
*Ind. Eng. Chem.*, **29**, 1434 (1937)
Calculation of Number of Theoretical
Plates for a Rectifying Column.

BOGART, M. J. P.
*Trans. Am. Inst. Chem. Engrs.*, **33**, 139
(1937)
Design of Equipment for Fractional
Batch Distillation.
Plates required for three-component
systems.

MEYER, P.
*Trans. Inst. Chem. Engrs.* (London), **15**,
209 (1937)
Graphical Computation for Complex
Distillation Systems.

RANDALL, M., and LONGTIN, B.
*Ind. Eng. Chem.*, **30**, 1063 (1938)
Separation Processes. General Method of
Analysis.


BAKER, E. M.
*ibid.*, **31**, 717 (1939)
Entrainment in Plate Column.
Calculation of Plates Where Entrainment
Is An Important Factor.


RANDALL, M., and LONGTIN, B.
*ibid.*, **31**, 908 (1939)
Separation Processes.
Point Transformation of y vs. x Diagrams.
Special Diagram of McCabe-Thiele Type.


HIBSHMAN, H. J.
*ibid.*, **32**, 988 (1940)
Multicomponent Distillation Problems.


GILLILAND, E. R.
*ibid.*, **32**, 1101 (1940)
Multicomponent Rectification. Optimum
Feed Plate Composition.


GILLILAND, E. R.
*ibid.*, **32**, 1220 (1940)
Multicomponent Rectification. Estimation of the Number of Theoretical Plates
as a Function of the Reflux Ratio.


BROWN, G. G., and HOLCOMB, D. E.
*Petroleum Eng.*, **11**, 31 (1940)
Calculating the Minimum Number of
Plates.


COLBURN, A. P.
*Ind. Eng. Chem.*, **33**, 459 (1941)
Simplified Calculation of Diffusional Proc-
esses. Number of Transfer Units or
Theoretical Plates.


HOGAN, J. J.
*ibid.*, **33**, 1132 (1941)
Multicomponent Fractionation. Distribution of Three Components.


BONILLA, C. P.
*Trans. Am. Inst. Pet. Engrs.*, **37**, 669
(1941)
Graphical Design of Continuous Distillation Columns for Ternary Mixtures.


COLBURN, A. P.
*ibid.*, **37**, 805 (1941)
The Calculation of Minimum Reflux
Ratio in the Distillation of Multicomponent Mixtures.


SMOKER, E. H.
*Ind. Eng. Chem.*, **34**, 509 (1942)
Nomographs for Minimum Reflux Ratio
and Theoretical Plates for Separation of
Binary Mixtures.


THOMPSON, G. W., and BEATTY, H. A.
*ibid.*, **34**, 1124 (1942)
Simplified Calculation of Theoretical
Plates. Fractionation of a Binary Mixture
in Which Concentration of One Component Is Small.


UNDERWOOD, A. J. V.
*J. Inst. Petroleum*, **29**, 147 (1943)
Fractional Distillation of Binary Mix-
tures. Number of Theoretical Plates and
Transfer Units.


FAASSEN, J. W.
*Ind. Eng. Chem.*, **36**, 248 (1944)
Chart for Distillation of Binary Mixtures.
Gives number of theoretical plates and
corresponding reflux ratios.


SCHEIBEL, E. G., and MONTROSS, C. F.
*ibid.*, **38**, 268 (1946)
Empirical Equation for Theoretical Minimum Reflux.


STANTON, W. H.
*Chem. Eng.*, **55**, 124 (1948)
Nomograph Gives Number of Theoretical
Contacts.

# CHAPTER V: SEPARATION TO BE EXPECTED

BORRMANN, C. H.
*Oel u. Kohle, Petroleum*, **35**, 784 (1939)
Recent Distillation Apparatus.

EDGEWORTH-JOHNSTONE, R.
*Ind. Eng. Chem.*, **35**, 407 (1943)
　　　　　　　　**36**, 482 (1944)
Batch Rectification. Effect of Fractionation and Column Holdup.

EDGEWORTH-JOHNSTONE, R.
*ibid.*, **36**, 1068 (1944)
Batch Rectification Yield at Finite Reflux Ratios.

HEPP, H. J., and SMITH, D. E.
*Ind. Eng. Chem.*, Anal. Ed., **17**, 579 (1945)
Laboratory Distillation of Normally Liquid Hydrocarbons.
A discussion of the variables involved in separating the components.

# CHAPTER VII: BUBBLE PLATE COLUMNS

CHILLAS, R. B., and WEIR, H. M.
*Trans. Am. Inst. Chem. Eng.*, **22**, 79 (1929)
The Design of Fractionating Columns with Particular Reference to Petroleum Distillation.

BACKHAUS, A. A.
*Chem. Met. Eng.*, **36**, 429 (1929)
Glass Plates Prolong Life of Distilling Columns.

CHILLAS, R. B., and WEIR, H. M.
*Ind. Eng. Chem.*, **22**, 206 (1930)
The Design of Fractionating Columns with Particular Reference to Petroleum Distillation.

CAREY, J. S., GRISWOLD, J., LEWIS, W. K., and McADAMS, W. H.
*Trans. Am. Inst. Chem. Engrs.*, **30**, 504 (1933)
Plate Efficiency in Rectification of Binary Mixtures.

HOLBROOK, G. E., and BAKER, E. M.
*Ind. Eng. Chem.*, **26**, 1063 (1934)
Entrainment in a Bubble-Cap Distillation Column.

DANES, V. Z.
*Chem. Listy.*, **33**, 153 (1939)
Laboratory Column with Fifty Fractionation Cups.

CAMPBELL, J. A.
*Petroleum World* (Los Angeles), **33**, 2, 55 (1936)
A New Design of Fractionating Plate.

BROWN, G. G.
*Trans. Am. Inst. Chem. Engrs.*, **32**, 321 (1936)
Distillation.
Discussion of commercial equipment.

CANZLER, H.
*Z. Ver. deut. Ing. Beiheft Folge No. 6*, 187 (1937)
Factors in the Design and Construction of Rectifying Equipment.

DEPONTE, G.
*Int. Congr. Mond. Petrole*, **2**, 8103 (1937)
Continuous Laboratory Distillation Apparatus.

SIEGEL, C. L.
*Chem. Met. Eng.*, **44**, 493 (1937)
Design of Bubble-Cap Columns for Fractional Distillation.

PEAVY, C. C., and BAKER, E. M.
*Trans. Am. Inst. Chem. Engrs.*, **33**, 315 (1937)
Efficiency and Capacity of a Bubble-Plate Column.

PEAVY, C. C., and BAKER, E. M.
*Ind. Eng. Chem.*, **29**, 1056 (1937)
Efficiency and Capacity of a Bubble-Plate Fractionating Column.

BEWSHER, J. N.
*Chem. Ind.*, **13**, 424, 432 (1937)
            **14**, 54, 76, 157 (1938)
Fractionating Columns for Batch Stills.

CAREY, J. S.
*Chem. Met. Eng.*, **46**, 314 (1939)
Plate Type Distilling Columns.

STABNIKOV, V. N.
*Khim. Referat. Zhur.*, **10**, *No. 7*, 123 (1940)
The Performance of Perforated Plates in Rectification Columns.

STABNIKOV, V. N.
*Khim. Mashinostroenie*, **9**, *No. 2*, 9 (1940)
Rectification Columns with Perforated Plates.

GOOD, A. J., HUTCHINSON, M. H., and ROUSSEAU, W. C.
*Ind. Eng. Chem.*, **34**, 1445 (1942)
Liquid Capacity of Bubble-Cap Plates.

BOWER, J. R., and COOKE, L. M.
*Ind. Eng. Chem.*, Anal. Ed., **15**, 290 (1943)
An Efficient Low-Holdup Laboratory Column.

MENUCCI, A., and AUBONE, E.
*Bol. Uniform, petrol.* (Buenos Aires), **21**, *No. 235*, 3 (1944)
Comparative Distillation with Bruun and Podbielniak Fractionating Columns.

GRISWOLD, J.
*Ind. Eng. Chem.*, **36**, 1119 (1944)
Development of Laboratory Pilot-Plant Screen-Plate Fractionating Columns.

LANGDON, W. M., and TOBIN, D. J.
*Ind. Eng. Chem.*, Anal. Ed., **17**, 801 (1945)
Glass Perforated Plate Distillation Column.

# CHAPTER IX: PACKED COLUMNS

LESLIE, E. H., and GENIESSE, J. C.
*Ind. Eng. Chem.*, **18**, 590 (1926)
Distillation Studies.

JAULMES, P.
*Chimie et industrie*, **33**, 1045 (1935)
Distillation and Rectification of Dilute Solutions.

ROPER, E. E., WRIGHT, G. F., RUHOFF, J. R., and SMITH, W. R.
*J. Am. Chem. Soc.*, **57**, 954 (1935)
Glass Helices for Fractionating Column Packing.

MENUCCI, A., and AUBONE, E.
*Bol. Uniform, petrol.* (Buenos Aires), **21**, *No. 235*, 3 (1944)
Comparative Distillation with Bruun and Podbielniak Fractionating Columns.

BRAGG, L. B., and LEWIS, J. W. JR.
*World Petroleum*, **14**, *No. 13*, 61 (1945)
100-Plate Pilot Fractionating Unit.

ABEGG, H.
*Chimia* (Switz.), **2**, 133 (1948)
The Application of High-Efficiency Rectifying Columns in the Laboratory.

# CHAPTER X: MISCELLANEOUS PACKING

GROSS, P., and WRIGHT, A. H.
*Ind. Eng. Chem.*, **13**, 701 (1921)
Distillation Apparatus.

MARSHALL, M. J., and SUTHERLAND, B. P.
*ibid.*, **19**, 735 (1927)
Effectiveness of Laboratory Distillation
Columns.

NOYES, W. A.
*ibid.*, **20**, 1190 (1928)
Dufton Distilling Column for Preparation
of Absolute Alcohol.

EVANS, H. M., CORNISH, R. E., LEP-
KOVSKY, S., ARCHIBALD, R. C., and
FESKOV, G.
*Ind. Eng. Chem.*, Anal. Ed., **2**, 339 (1930)
Construction and Use of Raschig's
Laboratory Fractionating Column.

HALL, H. J., and BACHMAN, G. B.
*ibid.*, **10**, 548 (1938)
Laboratory Columns Packed with Silicon
Carbide.

VILBRANDT, F. C., SCHUFFLE, E., JR.,
and Row, S. B.
*Trans. Am. Inst. Chem. Engrs.*, **34**, 51
(1938)
Metal Knit-Cloth Tower Packing and Its
Use in Plate Columns.

SNYDER, H. R., and SHRINER, R. L.
*J. Chem. Education*, **17**, 588 (1940)
Efficient Fractional Distillation Column.

HUFFERD, R. W., and KRANTZ, H. A.
*Ind. Eng. Chem.*, **33**, 1453 (1941)
Laboratory-Size Continuous Distillation
Unit.

MINARD, G. W., KOFFOLT, J. H., and
WITHROW, J. R.
*Trans. Am. Inst. Chem. Engrs.*, **39**, 813
(1943)
Fibrous Glass as a Packing Material for
Packed Column Distillation.

HERMAN, A., and KAISER, R. R.
*ibid.*, **40**, 487 (1944)
Distillation of Ethanol in a Fiberglas
Packed Column.

KIRSCHBAUM, E.
*Angew. Chem.*, **B20**, 197 (1948)
New Types of Tower Packing and Their
Evaluation.

MITCHELL, F. W. JR., and O'GORMAN,
J. M.
*Anal. Chem.*, **20**, 315 (1948)
Helical Packing for Small Laboratory
Distilling Columns.

# CHAPTER XI: ROTARY DISTILLATION COLUMNS

KEYES, D. B.
*Nat. Petroleum News*, **22**, 22 (1932)
New Rotary Type Plates Improve Vac-
uum Fractionating Column.

PIAZZA, J.
*Ind. y quim.*, **1**, 151 (1936)
Fractional Distillation.
Rotary column.

PIAZZA, J.
*Anales inst. invest. cient. tecnol.*, **8-9**, 78
(1938-39)
Fractional Distillation in Spirals with an
Oscillating and Eccentric Movement.
Uses oscillating glass and copper spirals.

PIAZZA, J.
*Ind. y quim.*, **3**, 22 (1940)
Spiral Fractional Distillation with Oscil-
lating and Eccentric Motion.
Glass spirals.

PIAZZA, J.
*Anales inst. invest. cient. tecnol.*, **10-11**, 5 (1940-41)
Fractional Distillation with Intensive Countercurrent Apparatus.
Liquid and vapor mixed by screw rotating at 3000 R.P.M.

ROUZANT, R.
*ibid.*, **10-11**, 115 (1940-41)
Laboratory Applications of the Piazza Distilling Apparatus.

PIAZZA, J.
*ibid.*, **12-13**, 187 (1942-43)
Fractional Distillation in Concentric Rings with Temperature Jumps.

KOCH, H., HILBERATH, F., and WEINROTTER, F. A.
*Chem. Fabrik*, **14**, 387 (1944)
A Column with Rotating Metal Band for the Fractional Distillation of Small Amounts of Substances.
Uses rotating metal band. Obtains 15 theoretical plates in 60 mm length.

BIRCH, S. F., GRIPP, V., and NATHAN, W. S.
*J. Soc. Chem. Ind.*, **66**, 33 (1947)
Spinning Band Column for High Vacuum Fractionation.

JOST, W.
*Angew. Chem.*, **B20**, 231 (1948)
Fractionating Column with Rotating Band Inserts.

## CHAPTER XII: EFFECT OF VARIABLES ON COLUMN CHARACTERISTICS

HOLBROOK, G. E., and BAKER, E. M.
*Trans. Am. Inst. Chem. Engrs.*, **30**, 543 (1934)
Entrainment in a Bubble-Cap Distillation Column.
Effect of surface tension, plate design, etc., on entrainment in an experimental laboratory column.

HOLBROOK, G. E., and BAKER, E. M.
*Ind. Eng. Chem.*, **26**, 1063 (1934)
Entrainment in a Bubble-Cap Distillation Column.

COLBURN, A. P.
*ibid.*, **28**, 526 (1936)
Effect of Entrainment on Plate Efficiency in Distillation.

TONGBERG, C. O.
*ibid.*, **29**, 571 (1937)
Equipment.
Study of operating variables.

COWEN, W.
*J. Inst. Fuel*, **12**, 28 (1938)
Distillation. Some Present-Day Problems.
Study of entrainment, reflux ratio, vapor-velocity, and mechanical design of plates.

KEYES, D. B.
*Univ. Ill. Engr. Exp. Sta. Cir.*, **35**, 3 (1938)
Factors Involved in Plate Efficiencies.

DALLA VALLE, J. M.
*Chem. Met. Eng.*, **45**, 688 (1938)
Surface Area in Packed Columns.
Gives relation of total surface of packing to pressure drop.

BJÖRKMAN, A., and OLAVI, S.
*Svensk. Kem. Tids.*, **58**, 145 (1946) (C.A. **40**, 5962[4] (1946) )
Fractionation of Small Amounts of Liquid in Vacuum by Using an Improved Spinning Band Column.

Fuchs, O., and Roth, F. H.
*Chem. Fabrik*, 11, 401 (1938)
Influence of the Packing in Distillation
Columns on the Separation of the Liquid
Mixtures.

Furnas, C. C., and Taylor, M. L.
*Trans. Am. Inst. Chem. Engrs.*, 36, 135
(1940)
Distillation in Packed Towers.
Study of size and type of packing, and
the concentration and rate of flow of the
distilling materials.

Colburn, A. P., and Stearns, R. F.
*ibid.*, 37, 291 (1941)
The Effect of Column Holdup on Batch
Distillation.

Byman, L., and Keyes, D. B.
*Chem. Met. Eng.*, 48, 85 (1941)
Plate Efficiency Study in Ethyl Alcohol
Distillation.

Kuhn, W.
*Helv. Chim. Acta*, 25, 252 (1942)
Distillation.
Consideration of ideal column at total
reflux.

Duncan, D. W., Koffolt, J. H., and
Withrow, J. R.
*Trans. Am. Inst. Chem. Engrs.*, 38, 259
(1942)
The Effect of Operating Variables on the
Performance of a Packed Column Still.

Langdon, W. M., and Keyes, D. B.
*Ind. Eng. Chem.*, 35, 464 (1943)
Plate Factors in Fractional Distillation
of Isopropyl Alcohol-Water System.
Effect of operating variables and physi-
cal properties.

Brown, G. G., and Lockhardt, F. J.
*Trans. Am. Inst. Chem. Engrs.*, 39, 63
(1943)
The Effect of Vapor Load on Plate Efficiency in Fractionating Columns.

Mariller, C.
*Bull. assoc. chim.*, 59, 445 (1942)
61, 3 (1944)
The Operation of Distilling and Rectifying Columns. Study of Factors Which Influence Efficiency.

Pérard, J.
*ibid.*, 60, 121 (1943)
Consideration of Plate Efficiency and Determination of Elements of Distillation
and Rectification Columns.

Perry, C. W.
*Chem. Met. Eng.*, 52, 108 (1945)
Analysis Determines Control Variables
for Distillation Systems.

Brandt, P. L., Perkins, R. B., Jr.,
and Halverson, L. K.
*Oil Gas J.*, 45, 86 (1946)
Operating Characteristics of Hypercal
Fractionating Columns.

Kirschbaum, E.
*Angew. Chem.*, B19, 13 (1947)
Packed Columns with Varying Packing
Height.

Griswold, J., and Stewart, P. B.
*Ind. Eng. Chem.*, 39, 752 (1947)
Rectification of Benzene-Toluene. Effect
of Operating Variables on Plate Efficiency.

Robu, I. V.
*Chimie et industrie*, 57, 562 (1947)
Problem Relative to the Design of Frac-
tionating Columns.

Weintraub, M., and Leva, M.
*Chem. Eng. Progress*, 44, 801 (1948)
Pressure Drop in Packed Tubes. A Nomo-
gram.

# CHAPTER XIII: OPERATION OF THE COLUMN

CICALESE, M. J., DAVIES, J. A., HARRINGTON, P. J., HOUGHLANG, G. S., HUTCHINSON, A. J. L., and WALSH, T. J.
*Petroleum Processing*, 1, 296 (1946)
Miscellaneous Fractionating Techniques.

BOYD, D. M., JR.
*Petroleum Refiner*, 25, 187 (1946)
Control of Fractionation Columns.

GALLAGHER, G. G.
*Instruments*, 20, 1004 (1947)
The Control of Narrow-Boiling-Range Fractionating Columns.

# CHAPTER XIV: VACUUM FRACTIONATION

MORRELL, J. C., and EGLOFF, G.
*Ind. Eng. Chem.*, 19, 1292 (1927)
Apparatus for Fractional Distillation under Reduced Pressure.

FICHOUX, A.
*Chimie et industrie*, 21, Special No. 292 (1928)
Distillation and Rectification under Reduced Pressure.

NAUMANN, H. N.
*Chem. Fabrik*, 505 (1930)
The Technique of Vacuum Evaporation and Distillation.

MOORE, F.
*J. Inst. Petroleum Technol.*, 21, 993 (1935)
Vacuum Distillation Unit.

MAYOR, Y.
*Industrie chimique*, 22, 329 (1935)
Distillation under Reduced Pressure.

KEFFLER, L.
*Bull. soc. chim. Belg.*, 44, 425 (1935)
Fractional Distillation in Vacuo.

BRADFIELD, A. E.
*J. Soc. Chem. Ind.* (Trans.), 54, 6 (1935)
Fractional Distillation under Reduced Pressure.

VIGREUX, H.
*Ana. Fals.*, 31, 26 (1938)
Distillation Columns for Fractionations at Atmospheric Pressure and under Reduced Pressure.
Glass plate columns.

LEVIN, I.
*Chemist Analyst*, 29, 89 (1940)
Foam Preventative in Vacuum Distillation.
Uses an electric current.

BURGER, W.
*J. Lab. Clin. Med.*, 25, 1221 (1940)
Continuous Vacuum Distillation.

DEWITT, C. B.
*Chemist Analyst*, 30, 40 (1941)
Apparatus for Vacuum Distillation.

REXFORD, D. R.
*Ind. Eng. Chem.*, Anal. Ed., 13, 95 (1941)
Distillation of Foaming Solutions under Vacuum.

KIRSCHBAUM, E.
*Z. Ver. deut. Ing. Verf.*, 140, 60 (1942)
Behavior of Rectifying Plates at Subatmospheric Pressures.

LANGLAIS, P., and MARCHÈSE, J.
*Ind. Parfumerie*, 1, 299 (1946)
Continuous Fractional Distillation under Reduced Pressure.

# CHAPTER XV: CONSTRUCTION OF COLUMNS

GRIMAUD, G.
*Bull. assoc. chim.*, **54**, 506 (1937)
Automatic Control of Rectifying Columns.

BELSEN, J. H.
*Oel u. Kohle*, **15**, 363 (1939)
Fractionating Apparatus of Light Construction.
Uses aluminum or enameled iron.

TODD, F.
*Ind. Eng. Chem.*, Anal. Ed., **17**, 175 (1945)
Efficient and Versatile Laboratory Fractionation Column Assembly.

KIESELBACK, R.
*ibid.*, **19**, 815 (1947)
Still Head with Automatic Control of Reflux Ratio.

GROSSBERG, A. L., and ROEBUCK, J. M.
*Chem. Eng.*, **54**, 132 (1947)
Automatic Reflux Control and Timer for Pilot-Plant Distillations.

DOSTROVSKY, I., and JACOBS, T. R.
*Chemistry and Industry*, (1947) 627
Efficient Sleeve Type Vacuum Jackets for Fractionating Columns.

WILKINSON, W. R., and BEATTY, H. A.
*ibid.*, **18**, 725 (1946)
Proportional Flow Controller for Liquids.

TAFT, R. W., JR., and VANDER WERF, C. A.
*J. Chem. Ed.*, **23**, 82 (1946)
Construction of a Fractionating Column.

WILLINGHAM, C. B., and ROSSINI, F. D.
*Proc. Am. Petroleum Inst.*, **26**, 63 (1946)
Laboratory Distilling Columns of High Efficiency Used in the Work of the A.P.I. Research Project 6.

THACKER, G. O., and WALKER, B. Y.
*J. Soc. Chem. Ind.*, **66**, 32 (1947)
Electronic Timing Device and Reflux-Ratio Controller.

BAKER, A. W., and DIXON, O. G.
*ibid.*, **66**, 189 (1947)
An Automatic Take-off for Fractionating Columns.

The following references are to a variety of column still heads:

PETERS, W. A., and BAKER, T.
*Ind. Eng. Chem.*, **18**, 69 (1926)

LESLIE, E. H., and GENIESSE, J. C.
*ibid.*, **18**, 591 (1926)

LOVELESS, A. W. T.
*ibid.*, **18**, 826 (1926)

CLARKE, H. T., and ROHRS, E. J.
*ibid.*, **18**, 1092 (1926)

HILL, J. B., and FERRIS, S. W.
*ibid.*, **19**, 379 (1927)

MARSHALL, M J., and SUTHERLAND, B.P.
*ibid.*, **19**, 735 (1927)

MARSHALL, M. J.
*ibid.*, **20**, 1379 (1928)

MAINTZ, H.
*Chem. Ztg.*, **54**, 422 (1930)

HICKMAN, K. C. D., and WEYERTS, W.
*J. Am. Chem. Soc.*, **52**, 4714 (1930)

LESLIE, R. T., and SCHICKTANZ, S. T.
*J. Research Nat. Bur. Standards*, **6**, 379 (1931)

SCHWARTZ, A. M., and BUSH, M. T.
*Ind. Eng. Chem.*, Anal. Ed., **3**, 138 (1931)

KESTER, E. B., and ANDREWS, R.
*ibid.*, **3**, 373 (1931)

EDDY, C. W.
*ibid.*, **4**, 198 (1932)

FENSKE, M. R., QUIGGLE, D., and TONGBERG, C. O.
*Ind. Eng. Chem.*, **24**, 411 (1932)

WAGNER, E. C., and SIMONS, J. K.
*Ind. Eng. Chem.*, Anal. Ed., **5**, 183 (1933)

ROTHMAN, S. C.
*ibid.*, **5**, 338 (1933)

VICKBERY, H. B., and PUCHER, G. W.
*ibid.*, **6**, 372 (1934)

MEANS, E. A., and NEWMAN, E. L.
*ibid.*, **8**, 231 (1936)

SMITH, C. L.
*Chem. Ind.*, **55**, 93 (1936)

TOOKE, J. W.
*Ind. Eng. Chem.*, Anal. Ed., **10**, 214 (1938)

GIBSON, G. P.
*J. Soc. Chem. Ind.*, **58**, 317 (1939)

GANSHIN, A. A.
*Khim. Mashinostroenie*, **8**, 8 (1939)

EWELL, R. E., and HARDY, P. E.
*J. Am. Chem. Soc.*, **63**, 3460 (1941)

SUEN, TZENG-JIUEQ
*Ind. Eng. Chem.*, Anal. Ed., **13**, 519 (1941)

BAILEY, A. J.
*ibid.*, **14**, 177 (1942)

PALKIN, S., and HALL, S. A.
*ibid.*, **14**, 901 (1942)

RICHARDS, A. R.
*ibid.*, **14**, 649 (1942)

BARTHEL, W. J.
*ibid.*, **16**, 374 (1944)

TOWNE, R. S.
*ibid.*, **16**, 584 (1944)

PATRICK, G.
*Chem. Ind.*, **56**, 74 (1945)

ZIMMERMAN, B. G.
*Ind. Eng. Chem.*, Anal. Ed., **17**, 815 (1945)

LLOYD, L. E., and HORNBACHER, H. G.
*Anal. Chem.*, **19**, 120 (1947)

HOWARD, F. L.
*ibid.*, **19**, 144 (1947)

RUSSELL, R. R., and VANDER WERF, C. A.
*ibid.*, **19**, 698 (1947)

# CHAPTER XVI: TESTING THE COLUMN

CALINGAERT, G., and HUGGINS, F. E.
*Ind. Eng. Chem.*, **16**, 584 (1924)
The Efficiency of Fractionating Columns.

GOODLIFFE, A. H.
*Trans. Inst. Chem. Engrs.* (London), **12**, 107 (1934)
The Practical Testing of a Continuous Petroleum Still.

BUCK, A. C.
*J. Chem. Education*, **31**, 476 (1944)
Efficiency of Fractional Distillation Column.

STAGE, H., and SCHULTZE, G. R.
*Oel u. Kohle*, **40**, 905 (1944)
General Method for the Determination in Series of the Number of Theoretical Plates at Total Reflux.

BARTKY, W., and DEMPSTER, A. J.
*Revs. Modern Phys.*, **20**, 123 (1948)
The Approach to Equilibrium in Fractionation.

# CHAPTER XVII: ACCESSORY EQUIPMENT

HEISEG, G. B.
*Ind. Eng. Chem.*, **20**, 382 (1928)
A Simplified Manometer for Vacuum Distillation.

RICHTER, G. H.
*ibid.*, **20**, 682 (1928)
Pressure Regulation in Vacuum Distillations.

PALKIN, S., and NELSON, O. A.
*Ind. Eng. Chem.*, *Anal. Ed.*, **6**, 386 (1934)
Differential Pressure Control Mechanism for Vacuum Distillation.

JACOBS, G. W.
*ibid.*, **7**, 70 (1935)
Apparatus for Control of Pressure in Distillation.

SCHIERHOLTZ, O. J.
*ibid.*, **7**, 284 (1935)
A Pressure Regulator for Vacuum Distillation.

NOONAN, E.
*ibid.*, **10**, 34 (1938)
Fractionating Device for Vacuum Distillation.
One stopcock fraction cutter.

FERRY, C. W.
*ibid.*, **10**, 647 (1938)
Improved Vacuum Regulator.

DOUSLIN, D. R., and WALLS, W. S.
*ibid.*, **16**, 40 (1944)
Semi-Automatic Pressure Control in Low-Pressure, Low-Temperature Laboratory Fractionation.

COULSON, E. A., and WARNE, A. J.
*J. Sci. Instruments*, **21**, 122 (1944)
Automatic Pressure Regulation in Vacuum Distillation.

LECOQ, H.
*Bull. soc. chim. Belg.*, **53**, 107 (1944)
Boiling-Point Apparatus.

RUNCKEL, W. J., and OLDROYD, D. M.
*Ind. Eng. Chem.*, *Anal. Ed.*, **18**, 80 (1946)
Di- and Triethylene Glycols as Manostat Fluids.
Describes manostat.

DONAHOE, H. B., RUSSELL, R. R., and VANDER WERF, C. A.
*ibid.*, 156 (1946)
A Variable Pressure Manostat.

BROWN, T. F., and COLES, K. F.
*Anal. Chem.*, **19**, 935 (1947)
Automatic Vacuum Take-off Arrangement for Fractional Distillation.

DUSHMAN, SAUL
*Instruments*, **20**, 234 (1947)
Manometers for Low Pressures. A Review.

SIMMONS, L. M.
*Australian Chem. Inst. J. and Proc.*, **14**, 51 (1947)
An Apparatus for the Measurement and Comparison of Boiling Points and Vapor Pressures.

BOYD, D. M., JR.
*Petroleum Refiner*, **26**, 83 (1947)
Fractionator Pressure Control (for Atmospheric, Vacuum, and Pressure Distillations).

GOODWIN, R. D.
*J. Chem. Education*, **24**, 511 (1947)
A Simple Manostat of Constant Sensitivity.

# CHAPTER XVIII: SPECIAL COLUMNS

OBERFELL, G. G., ALDEN, R. C., and HEPP, H.
*Oil Gas J.*, **27**, 22, 251, 281 (1928)
High Pressure Fractionation Method.

OBERFELL, G. G., and ALDEN, R. C.
*ibid.*, **27**, 142 (1928)
Fractionation at Low Temperature.

CUMMINGS, L. W. T.
*Ind. Eng. Chem.*, **23**, 900 (1931)
High Pressure Rectification.

CUMMINGS, L. W. T.
*ibid.*, **25**, 728 (1933)
High Pressure Rectification. n-Pentane-n-Heptane System.

BEALL, F. N.
*Refiner and Natural Gasoline Mfr.*, **13**, 62, 69 (1934)
Design of High Pressure Rectifiers.

CAMP, H. R., and HENRY, R.
*Chem. Met. Eng.*, **44**, 380 (1937)
Inspecting and Testing Pressure Still Equipment.

LAIRD, F. N.
*Oil and Gas J.*, **36**, 58, 62 (1937)
Rapid Method for Low-Temperature Fractionation of Gases, Vapors and Liquids.

FISCHER, V.
*Z. Ver. deut. Ing. Beiheft Verfohrensteck*, 118 (1937)
Separation of an Ethane-Ethylene Mixture by Means of Rectification.

GUNNESS, R. C.
*Ind. Eng. Chem.*, **29**, 1092 (1937)
Column Performance in the Rectification of Petroleum.
High pressure distillation.

JANTZEN, E., and HAKER, W.
*Chem. Fabrik*, **12**, 329 (1939)
High Efficiency Distillation Column for the Laboratory.
Describes use of three-tandem column.

KOCH, H., and HILBERATH, F.
*Brennstoff-Chem.*, **21**, 197 (1940)
Suitable Apparatus for Fractional Distillation at Low Temperatures.

KLEIN, K., STAGE, H., and SCHULTZE, G. H.
*Z. physik. Chem.*, **A. 189**, 163 (1941)
Fine-Fractionating Column Constructed of Glass and Employing Multi-Chamber Tubes.

BORRMANN, C. H.
*Oel u. Kohle*, **1**, 26 (1941)
Spray Columns for Distilling and Condensing.

BORRMANN, C. H.
*ibid.*, **37**, 26 (1941)
Spray Columns for Distillation and Condensation.

BAILEY, A. J.
*Ind. Eng. Chem.*, Anal. Ed., **14**, 177 (1942)
Immersion Still Head for Low Pressure Distillation of Organic Mixtures.

FOWLER, F. C., and BROWN, G. G.
*Trans. Am. Inst. Chem. Engrs.*, **39**, 241 (1943)
Cost of Pressure Vessels and Pressure Fractionating Columns.

SMOKER, E. H.
*ibid.*, **40**, 105 (1944)
A High Efficiency Multi-Tubular Packed Column.

BOOTHE, H. S., and McNABNEY, R.
*Ind. Eng. Chem.*, Anal. Ed., **16**, 131 (1944)
Improved Fractionating Column for Gases.

ASKEVOLD, R. J., and AGRUSS, M. S.
*ibid.*, **17**, 241 (1945)
Light Constituents in Crude Petroleum
by Low Temperature Fractional Distillation.

LANGDON, W. M.
*ibid.*, **17**, 590 (1945)
Backward-Feed Distillation Column.

LANGDON, W. M., and TOBIN, D. J.
*Ind. Eng. Chem.*, Anal. Ed., **17**, 801 (1945)
Glass Perforated Plate Distillation Column.

NARAGON, E. A., and LEWIS, C. J.
*ibid.*, **18**, 448 (1946)
Small Glass Center-Tube Fractionating
Column.

STARR, C. E., JR., ANDERSON, J. S., and
DAVIDSON, V. M.
*Anal. Chem.*, **19**, 409 (1947)
Laboratory Low Temperature Fractional
Distillation. Optimum Charging Rates.

NANDI, S. K., and KARIM, B.
*J. Indian Chem. Soc.*, Ind. and News Ed.,
**11**, 3 (1948)
Performance of Sieve Plate Fractionating
Columns.

# CHAPTER XIX: VAPOR-LIQUID EQUILIBRIUM DETERMINATIONS

BROWN, A. C.
*Trans. Am. Inst. Chem. Engrs.*, **21**, 87
(1928)
Vapor-Liquid Equilibria in Complex
Hydrocarbon Mixtures.

CORNELL, L. W., and MONTONNA, R. E.
*Ind. Eng. Chem.*, **25**, 1331 (1933)
Studies in Distillation. Liquid-Vapor
Equilibria in Systems Ethanol-Water,
Methanol-Water, Acetic Acid-Water.

BRUNJES, A. S., and FURNAS, C. C.
*ibid.*, **27**, 396 (1935)
Vapor-Liquid Equilibrium Data for Commercially Important Systems of Organic
Solvents. Binary Systems *n*-Butanol–*n*-Butyl Acetate and *n*-Butanol–Acetone.

SCHEELINE, H. W., and GILLILAND, E. R.
*ibid.*, **31**, 1050 (1939)
Vapor-Liquid Equilibrium in the System
Propane-Isobutylene.

BAKER, E. M., and HUBBARD, R. O. H.
*ibid.*, **31**, 1260 (1939)
Equilibria in the Systems Ethanol-Water,
Ethanol-Cellusolve, and Cellusolve-Water.

BAKER, E. M., CHADDOCK, R. E.,
LINDSAY, R. A., and WERNER, R. C.
*ibid.*, **31**, 1263 (1939)
Equilibria Between Liquid and Vapor in
the System Ethanol-Cellusolve-Water.

BRAGG, L. B., and RICHARDS, A. R.
*ibid.*, **34**, 1088 (1942)
Binary Mixtures for Testing Fractionating Columns at Atmospheric and Reduced Pressures.

OTHMER, D. F.
*ibid.*, **36**, 669 (1944)
Correlating Vapor Pressures and Equilibrium Constant Data.

BENEDICT, M., JOHNSON, C. A.,
SOLOMON, E. S., and RUBIN, L. G.
*ibid.*, **37**, 55 (1945)
Liquid-Vapor Equilibrium in Methane-Ethylene-Isobutane System.

OTHMER, D. F., and BENENATI, R. F.
*ibid.*, **37**, 299 (1945)
Composition of Vapors from Boiling
Binary Solution.

BLOM, R. H., REED, D. L., EFROM, A., and MASTAKAS, G. C.
*ibid.*, **37**, 870 (1945)
Liquid-Vapor Equilibria in Mixture of 2,3-Butylene Glycol and Water.

HANSON, G. H., and BROWN, G. G.
*ibid.*, **37**, 821 (1945)
Vapor-Liquid Equilibrium in Mixtures of Volatile Paraffins.

OTHMER, D. F.
*ibid.*, **37**, 895 (1945)
Composition of Vapors from Boiling Mercury Solutions. System Used in Butadiene Manufacture from Butylene Glycol.

BLOM, R. H., and EFROM, A.
*ibid.*, **37**, 1237 (1945)
Liquid-Vapor Equilibria in Acetyl Methyl Carbinol-Water System.

ROGERS, J. W., KNIGHT, J. W., and CHOPPIN, A. R.
*J. Chem. Education*, **24**, 491 (1947)
An Improved Apparatus for Determining Vapor-Liquid Equilibrium.

# CHAPTER XX: AZEOTROPIC AND EXTRACTIVE DISTILLATION

SWIETOSLAWSKI, W.
*J. Chem. Phys.*, **32**, 393 (1935)
A Study of the Distillation of Azeotropic Mixtures.

OTHMER, D. F.
*Ind. Eng. Chem.*, **27**, 250 (1935)
Separation of Water from Acetic Acid.

BRATTON, A. C., FELSING, W. A., and BAILEY, J. R.
*ibid.*, **28**, 424 (1936)
Amplified Distillation.

GUINOT, H. M., and CLARK, F. W.
*Trans. Inst. Chem. Engrs.* (London), **16**, 189 (1938)
Azeotropic Distillation in Industry.

DUBOIS, G.
*Bull. Fed. Ind. Chim. Belg.*, **7**, 501 (1938)
Industrial Distillation of Azeotropic Substances.

FESTER, G. A.
*Rev. centio estua. ind. quim. univ. Natl. litoral* (Santo Fe, Argentina), **8-9**, 137 (1938-39)
Co-Distillation-Distillation by Means of Carriers.

RANDALL, M., and LONGTIN, B.
*Ind. Eng. Chem.*, **31**, 1181 (1939)
Fractionation of Partially Miscible Liquids.

OTHMER, D. F.
*Chem. Met. Eng.*, **48**, 91 (1941)
Azeotropic Distillation for Dehydrating Acetic Acid.

KEYES, D. B.
*Ind. Eng. Chem.*, **33**, 1019 (1941)
Binary Liquid Mixtures. Use of Third Component to Improve Fractional Distillation.

OTHMER, D. F.
*ibid.*, **33**, 1106 (1941)
Partial Pressure Processes.

FESTER, G. A., and COLLADOS, A. R.
*Anales. Assoc. quim. Argentina*, **30**, 36 (1942)
Entrainment Distillation in an Anhydrous Medium.

SMITHHUYSEN, W. C. B.
*Chem. Weekblad*, **39**, 57, 145 (1942)
Azeotropic Distillation and Rectification.

PRIGOGINE, I.
*Bull. soc. chim. Belg.*, **52**, 95 (1943)
The Variation of Azeotropic Temperature
under the Influence of Pressure.

WHITE, R. R.
*Nat. Pet. News*, 36, R731 (1944)
Azeotropic Distillation.

COULSON, E. A., and HOLT, E. C.
*J. Soc. Chem. Ind.* (Trans.), **63**, 329 (1944)
The Use of Azeotropes in the Separation
of the Aromatic, Saturated, and Unsaturated Constituents of Hydrocarbon Fractions from the Carbonization of Coal.

COULSON, E. A., HOLT, E. C., and
SLEVEN, A.
*ibid.*, **63**, 333 (1944)
The Use of Azeotropic-Forming Substances in the Separation of Light Hydrocarbon Fractions from the Carbonization
of Coal into Aromatic, Saturated, and
Unsaturated Constituents.

COLBURN, A. P., and PHILLIPS, J. C.
*Trans. Am. Inst. Chem. Engrs.*, **40**, 333
(1944)
Experimental Study of Azeotropic Distillation. Use of Trichloroethylene in Dehydration of Ethanol.

LAKE, G. R.
*ibid.*, **41**, 327 (1945)
Recovery of Toluene from Petroleum by
Azeotropic Fractionation.

BENEDICT, M., and RUBIN, L. C.
*ibid.*, **41**, 353 (1945)
Extractive and Azeotropic Distillation.
Theoretical Aspects.

BENEDICT, M., JOHNSON, C. A., SOLO-
MON, E., and RUBIN, L. C.
*ibid.*, **41**, 371 (1945)
Extractive and Azeotropic Distillation.
Separation of Toluene from Paraffins by
Azeotropic Distillation with Methanol.

COLBURN, A. P., and SCHOENBORN,
E. M.
*ibid.*, **41**, 421 (1945)
The Selection of "Separating Agents" for
Azeotropic and Extractive Distillation
and for Liquid-Liquid Extraction.

DUNN, C. L., MILLER, R. W., PIER-
OTTI, G. J., SHIRAS, R. N., and SOUDERS,
M. JR.
*ibid.*, **41**, 631 (1945)
Toluene Recovery by Extractive Distilla-
tion.

BERG, L.
*Ind. Eng. Chem.*, **37**, 585 (1945)
Azeotropic Dehydration of Pyridine and
Its Homologues.

DICKS, R. S., and CARLSON, C. S.
*Trans. Am. Inst. Chem. Engrs.*, **41**, 789
(1945)
Extractive Distillation of Hydrocarbon
Mixtures in a Packed Column.

EWELL, R. H., and WELCH, L. M.
*Ind. Eng. Chem.*, **37**, 1224 (1945)
Rectification in Ternary Systems Con-
taining Binary Azeotropes.

FLEER, K. B.
*J. Chem. Education*, **22**, 588 (1945)
Azeotropism: A Useful Tool Clarified.

BENEDICT, M., and RUBIN, L. C.
*Can. Chem. Process Inds.*, **29**, 746, 756
(1945)
Theory of Extractive and Azeotropic Distillation.

JOST, W.
*Z. Naturforsch*, **1**, 576 (1946)
Boiling Behavior of Multicomponent Sys-
tems.

HÄHNEL, S.
*Tek. Tid.*, **76**, 1307 (1946)
Azeotropic Distillation. General Review
of Theory and Industrial Applications.

COULSON, E. A., and HERRINGTON, E. F. G.
*Nature*, **158**, 198 (1946)
Theory of Binary Azeotropes.

LECAT, M.
*Compt. rend.*, **222**, 733 (1946)
Some Orthobaric Azeotropes.

LECAT, M.
*ibid.*, **222**, 1488 (1946)
The Behavior of Binary Azeotropes with One Bifunctional Constituent.

SIMMONS, L. M.
*J. Proc. Roy. Soc. N. S. Wales*, **80**, 196 (1947)
The Mechanism Underlying the Formation of Aqueous Negative Binary Azeotropes.

FENSKE, M. R., CARLSON, C. S., and QUIGGLE, D.
*Ind. Eng. Chem.*, **39**, 1322 (1947)
Solvent Separation of Hydrocarbon Mixtures by Vapor-Liquid Extraction.

COULSON, E. A., and HERRINGTON, E. F. G.
*J. Chem. Soc.*, 597, (1947)
Composition, Pressure, and Temperature Relationships in Binary Azeotropic Systems.

HORSLEY, L. H.
*Anal. Chem.*, **19**, 508 (1947)
Table of Azeotropes and Nonazeotropes.

NUTTING, H. S., and HORSLEY, L. H.
*ibid.*, **19**, 602 (1947)
Graphical Method for Predicting Effect of Pressure on Azeotropic Systems.

HORSLEY, L. H.
*ibid.*, **19**, 603 (1947)
Graphical Method for Predicting Azeotropism and Effect of Pressure on Azeotropic Constants.

MEISSNER, H. P., and GREENFIELD, S. H.
*Ind. Eng. Chem.*, **40**, 438 (1948)
Composition and Boiling Points of Binary Azeotropes.

SKOLNIK, H.
*ibid.*, **40**, 442 (1948)
Correlation of Azeotropic Data.

LICHT, W., JR., and DENZLER, C. G.
*Chem. Eng. Progress*, 44, 627 (1948)
Azeotropic Mixtures. Variation of Boiling Point and Latent Heat with Pressure.

# CHAPTER XXI: MICRO AND SEMIMICRO FRACTIONATION

BOIVIN, M.
*Mém. services chim. état* (Paris), **31**, 29 (1944)
A Semimicro Distillation Column. Extension of Lesesne and Lochte Column.

GOULD, C. W., JR., HOLZMAN, G., and NIEMANN, C.
*Anal. Chem.*, **20**, 361 (1948)
Distillation Equipment Suitable for Centigram and Decigram Quantities.

HAENDLER, H. M.
*ibid.*, **20**, 596 (1948)
Semimicro Distilling Head.

# CHAPTER XXII: MOLECULAR DISTILLATION

WEST, J. H.
*J. Am. Chem. Soc.*, **49**, 2118 (1927)
High Vacuum Distillation.

LEVIN, F.
*J. Prakt. Chem.*, **126**, 217 (1930)
High Vacuum Distillation by the Use of Liquid Air.

BLASCO, E.
*Oil and Gas J.*, **32**, No. 2, 753 (1932)
Molecular Distillation.

HOLLAND-MERTEN, E. L.
*Tek. Tid. Uppl. C. Kemi.*, **65**, 1 (1935)
Innovations in the Field of Vacuum Apparatus.

BLADE, O. C.
*Oil and Gas J.*, **33**, No. 45, 25, 133 (1935)
High-Vacuum Distillation Apparatus for Testing Heavy Oils.

BROWN, O. A., and TANNICH, R. A.
*ibid.*, **36**, No. 46, 80 (1936)
Distillation of Lubricating Oils in a Laboratory Still.

KILLEFFER, D. H.
*Ind. Eng. Chem.*, **29**, 966 (1937)
Molecular Distillation. Useful Capacity.

HICKMAN, K. C. D.
*ibid.*, **29**, 1107 (1937)
Molecular Distillation. State of Vitamins in Certain Fish Liver Oils.

HICKMAN, K. C. D.
*ibid.*, **29**, 1108 (1937)
Molecular Distillation. Apparatus and Methods.

BAXTER, J. G., GRAY, E. L., and TISCHER, A. O.
*ibid.*, **29**, 1112 (1937)
Molecular Distillation. Synthetic Constant Yield Mixtures.

FAWCETT, E. W.
*Chem. Age* (London), **39**, 371 (1938)
Characteristics and Scope of Molecular Distillation.

LESLIE, R. T., and HEUER, W. W.
*J. Research Nat. Bur. Standards*, **21**, 515 (1938)
Continuous High-Vacuum Still.

HICKMAN, K. C. D., and GRAY, E. L.
*Ind. Eng. Chem.*, **30**, 796 (1938)
Molecular Distillation. Examination of Natural Vitamin D.

FARMER, E. H., and VAN DE HEUVEL, F. A.
*J. Soc. Chem. Ind.*, **57**, 24-T (1938)
Separation of Highly Unsaturated Acids. Uses vacuum distillation.

BURCH, C. R., and VAN DIJCK, W. J. D.
*ibid.*, **58**, 39 (1939)
Theory and Development of High Vacuum Distillation.

FURTER, M.
*Mit. Lebensm. Hyg.*, **30**, 200 (1939)
New Problems in Distillation. Molecular Distillation.

FAWCETT, E. W., and BURROWS, G.
*J. Soc. Chem. Ind.*, **58**, 45 (1939)
General Technique of Molecular Distillation.

DETWILER, S. B., JR., and MARKLEY, K. S.
*Oil and Soap*, **16**, 2 (1939)
Bibliography on Molecular or Short Path Distillation.

DETWILER, S. B., JR.
*ibid.*, **17**, 241 (1940)
Supplement to Bibliography on Molecular or Short Path Distillation.

Morse, R. S.
*Ind. Eng. Chem.*, **33**, 1039 (1941)
Molecular Distillation of Polymerized Drying Oils.

Kabias, J.
*Chem. Zentr.*, **113**, I, 1912 (1942)
Molecular Distillation.

Howat, O. D.
*Chem. Age* (London), **45**, 309, 323 (1941)
Molecular Distillation.

Howat, O. D.
*ibid.*, **46**, 3 (1942)
Molecular Distillation.

Withers, W. F.
*Chem. Met. Eng.*, **49**, 174 (1942)
Molecular Distillation.

Bailey, A. J.
*Ind. Eng. Chem.*, Anal. Ed., **14**, 177 (1942)
Molecular Still Heads.

Hickman, K. C. D.
*ibid.*, **14**, 250 (1942)
The High Vacuum Still in Medicine.

Utzinger, G. E.
*Die Chemie*, **56**, 130 (1943)
New Molecular Distillation Apparatus and Film Distillation.

Todd, S. S.
*Oil and Soap*, **20**, 205 (1943)
Supplement to Bibliography on Molecular or Short Path Distillation.

Riegel, B.
*Ind. Eng. Chem.*, Anal. Ed., **15**, 417 (1943)
A Vacuum Sublimation and Molecular Distillation Apparatus.

Quackenbush, F. W., and Steenbock, H.
*ibid.*, **15**, 468 (1943)
A Molecular Still of New Design.

Hickman, K. C. D.
*Chem. Rev.*, **34**, 51 (1944)
High-Vacuum Short Path Distillation.

Kurt, N. H.
*Rev. Brasil quim.* (Sao Paulo), **17**, 189 (1944)
Distillation in High Vacuum.

Olive, T. R.
*Chem. Met. Eng.*, **51**, 100 (1944)
Molecular Distillation—A New Path to the Separation of Chemicals.

Raoul, Y., and Meunier, P.
*Bull. soc. chim.*, **11**, 368 (1944)
An Apparatus for Molecular Distillation in the Laboratory.

Utzinger, G. E.
*Chem. Tech.*, **16**, 61 (1945)
New Molecular Distillation and Thin Layer Distillation.

Farmer, E. H., and Sutton, D. A.
*J. Soc. Chem. Ind.*, **65**, 164 (1946)
A Simple Laboratory Falling-Film Molecular Still.

Taylor, J. K.
*J. Research Nat. Bur. Standards*, **37**, 173 (1946)
A Simple Cyclic Falling-Film Molecular Still.

Hickman, K. C. D., and Mees, G. C.
*Ind. Eng. Chem.*, **38**, 28 (1946)
Molecular Distillation. A Review.

Hickman, K. C. D.
*Chem. Products*, **9**, 25 (1946)
The Molecular Still in America.

Seymour, H.
*Ind. Chemist*, **22**, 265 (1946)
Technical Advances in Molecular Distillation.

# Index